CANBERRA
THE GREAT WHITE WHALE

CANBERRA
THE GREAT WHITE WHALE

Based on a facsimile reprint of the original Souvenir Number of the
SHIPBUILDER AND MARINE ENGINE BUILDER
published in 1961 to commemorate the building of the great ship with an
EPILOGUE by Neil McCart
describing and illustrating her history up to her participation in the battle for the Falkland Islands

 Patrick Stephens, Cambridge

First published in 1983

British Library Cataloguing in Publication Data

Canberra.
1.Canberra. *Ship*—History
I. McCart, Neil
387.2'43   VM383.C/

ISBN 0-85059-636-X

Additional material photoset in 9 on 10 pt Times by
Manuset Ltd, Baldock Herts. Printed in Great Britain
on 135 gsm Fineblade coated cartridge, and bound, by
The Garden City Press, Letchworth, Herts, for the
publishers, Patrick Stephens Limited, Bar Hill,
Cambridge, CB3 8EL, England.

CONTENTS

———

INTRODUCTION

—

IT is hard to believe now, when looking back, that the *Canberra* was a product of the 1950s. This lovely ship was so well ahead of her time that even in the 1980s her design still holds its own, even when compared with the streamlined cruise liners which have been built in the last few years.

Her story goes back to 1954 when the P&O and the Orient lines were considering how best to replace their pre-war ships. It was in this year that the Orient Line had extended their Australian voyages across the Pacific Ocean, calling at new ports such as Suva, Honolulu and the West Coast of North America. The potentialities of this new route were enormous, and so in order to gain a foothold in the area, P&O and the Orient Line formed the Orient & Pacific Lines. The idea of this new service was to provide three new routes which would cover the Pacific Ocean. The first would extend the traditional Australian voyages beyond Sydney to create a new service linking Australia, New Zealand and the west coast of North America. The second would extend P&O's Far East voyages, so that Hong Kong and Japan would also be linked with North America's west coast. The third route was a triangular voyage linking Australia, Asia and the United States, then returning to Australia.

Having worked out these completely new routes (and all of them meant much longer voyages), the next thing was to try to shorten the sailing times by means of greater speeds. If the pre-war ships were replaced by similar vessels to the *'Himalaya'/ 'Orcades'* Class, or *'Arcadia'/'Orsova'* Class, it was very doubtful whether they could achieve the speeds required and, with the increased building costs, it would have been impossible to make them them pay. So the technical requirements for the new service entailed larger and faster ships, but at the same time vessels which could negotiate the Suez Canal, and could be handled at the major ports en route. The outcome of all these plans was, of course, *Oriana* for the Orient Line, and for the P&O the even larger and more revolutionary *Canberra*.

On December 20 1956, the P&O company placed the order with Harland & Wolff, Belfast, for yard number 1621, (it was to be another 15 months before her name was announced). In January 1957 the news was announced to the Press, and a model of the proposed new vessel was unveiled. Her unusual design was certainly a surprise to the shipping world. On September 23 1957, the keel was laid on slipway 14 of the Musgrave Yard and in March of the following year Sir Donald Anderson, who was then P&O's deputy chairman, announced that the new ship would be named *Canberra*. The name was chosen because it symbolised the part played by P&O in Australian trade and commerce. There has been much argument about the origin of the name, but it is now generally accepted that it comes from the Aboriginal, and means 'meeting place by the water'. Of course, the name was known throughout the world as the capital city of Australia and was first officially bestowed on the new city in March 1913 by Lady Denman, wife of the Governor General of Australia. The creation of the city in an area of 940 square miles known as the Federal Capital Territory was a direct result of the formation of the Commonwealth of Australia in 1901. It was almost inevitable that so distinguished a name should already have been given to a ship, and so it was, as for four years a small cargo ship, employed on the Australian coastal trade, had borne the name. Fortunately her owners, the Australasian United Steam Navigation Co Ltd made it available to P&O for the new liner. The name *Canberra* was also a very honourable one in Australian maritime history, having been given to a RAN *'Kent'* Class cruiser built in 1927. She was torpedoed and sunk by Japanese ships in the Pacific in August 1942, and the US Navy had in fact perpetuated the name when they called a heavy cruiser USS *Canberra* as a tribute to the Australian warship.

Given this background it was only fitting that *Canberra*'s sponsor for the launching ceremony should be Dame Pattie Menzies. The launching took place on Wednesday March 16 1960, as has been described elsewhere. It was a cloudy day, and this made it necessary to cancel a fly past which had been planned by an RAF Canberra bomber, but fortunately the rain held off for the ceremony itself. In reply to a telegram from the P&O chairman, Her Majesty the Queen sent the following message, 'Please convey to all assembled in Belfast for the launching of *Canberra* by Dame Pattie Menzies my warm thanks for their kind and loyal message of greetings. I send my very best wishes for the future of this fine ship as a link between the countries of the Commonwealth, and for the good fortune of all who sail in her'. Twenty-two years later the whole nation would echo the words of the last sentence, as *Canberra* sailed to war.

In May 1960, whilst the ship was at her fitting out berth, P&O and the Orient Line were merged and the company called P&O-Orient Lines (Passenger Services) Ltd was formed to manage the combined fleets. At the same time the Orient & Pacific Line was dropped, as it had not proved a great success, but the company still kept its Pacific routes. So the stage was set for the arrival on to the scene of *Canberra*, and the P&O-Orient Line possessed one of the most modern and formidable passenger fleets in the world.

THE
SHIPBUILDER
AND
MARINE ENGINE-BUILDER

CANBERRA
SOUVENIR NUMBER

BOC electric arc welding equipment and materials were used exclusively for the welding of the aluminium superstructure, and the steel hull of the Canberra at Harland and Wolff's Belfast Yard.

WELDED · GOOD VOYAGE CANBERRA · BOC WELDED · GOOD VOY

THE BRITISH OXYGEN COMPANY LTD
ELECTRIC WELDING DEPARTMENT

QUASI-ARC WORKS · BILSTON · STAFFORDSHIRE · TELEPHONE: BILSTON 41191

The most notable advance in Passenger Liner Construction

"Canberra" fitting out at Belfast with Oiler in attendance

HARLAND & WOLFF
LIMITED

BELFAST   GLASGOW   LONDON   LIVERPOOL   SOUTHAMPTON

M1025

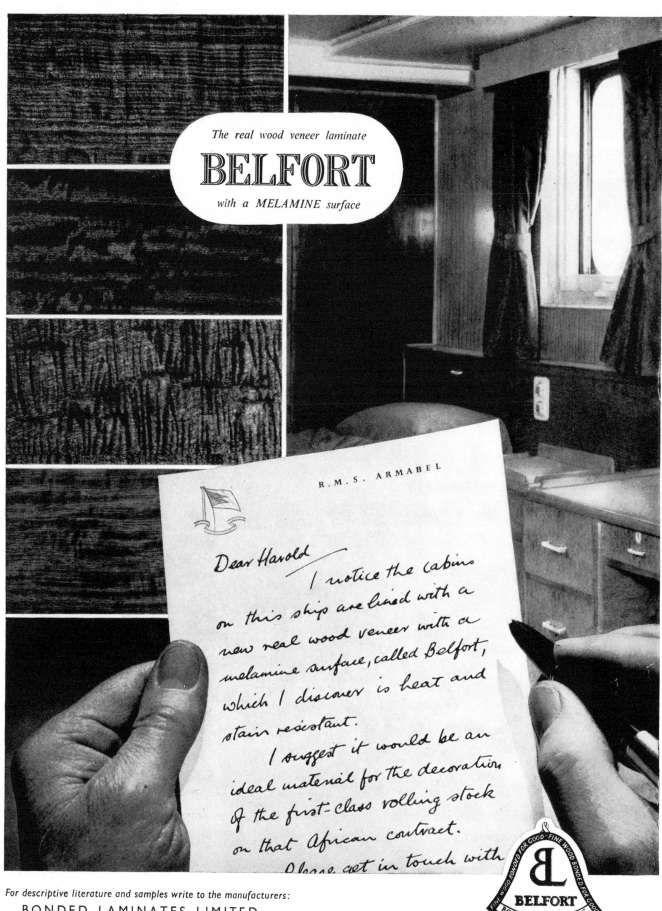

The real wood veneer laminate

BELFORT

with a MELAMINE surface

R.M.S. ARMABEL

Dear Harold

I notice the cabins on this ship are lined with a new real wood veneer with a melamine surface, called Belfort, which I discover is heat and stain resistant.

I suggest it would be an ideal material for the decoration of the first-class rolling stock on that African contract.

Please get in touch with

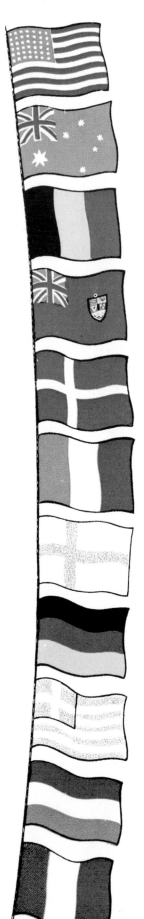

and the S.S. "Canberra"

We have been privileged for many years to supply our Machine Tools to Messrs. Harland and Wolff Ltd. for use in their various yards and we were very pleased to learn that our plant has been used extensively in the construction of the S.S. "Canberra". In particular, we understand that all the plate straightening has been carried out with our Rolls and that all the frames have been bent and bevelled in our Cold Frame Bender.

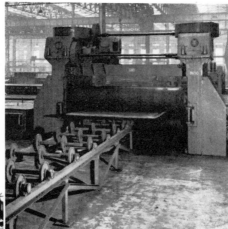

The illustrations show two of our Straightening Rolls recently supplied to Messrs. Harland and Wolff Ltd., the larger having a capacity of 11ft. × 2in., whilst the smaller will deal with plates up to 1½in. thick

× 11ft. wide. The views shown were taken at the Belfast Yard and show the heavy construction of the machines. The controls for the roll drive and all roll adjustments are centralised at the electric control desks and our Clients have so arranged these desks that the operators have a very good view of the work, considerably facilitating fast and accurate output.

We also include a photograph of one of our Cold Frame Bending Machines, which machine is rapidly becoming an indispensable tool for the accurate, speedy and economical bending and bevelling of ships' frames. Furnace charges are drastically reduced and the manpower available is employed to the best advantage. Frames cold bent and bevelled on our machines are acceptable to all the leading Classification Societies.

We should like to thank Messrs. Harland and Wolff Ltd. for giving us the above information and for permission to publish it and the two photographs taken in their Yard.

SCOTTISH
MACHINE TOOL
CORPORATION LTD.
17 Lynedoch Crescent
Glasgow, C.3
———————DOUGLAS 6586/9———————
Lion House, Red Lion St., Richmond, Surrey
RICHMOND 7667/9
256 Moseley Road, Birmingham, 12
CALTHORPE 2541
The Building Centre, Brunswick Ter., Leeds, 2
LEEDS 25250

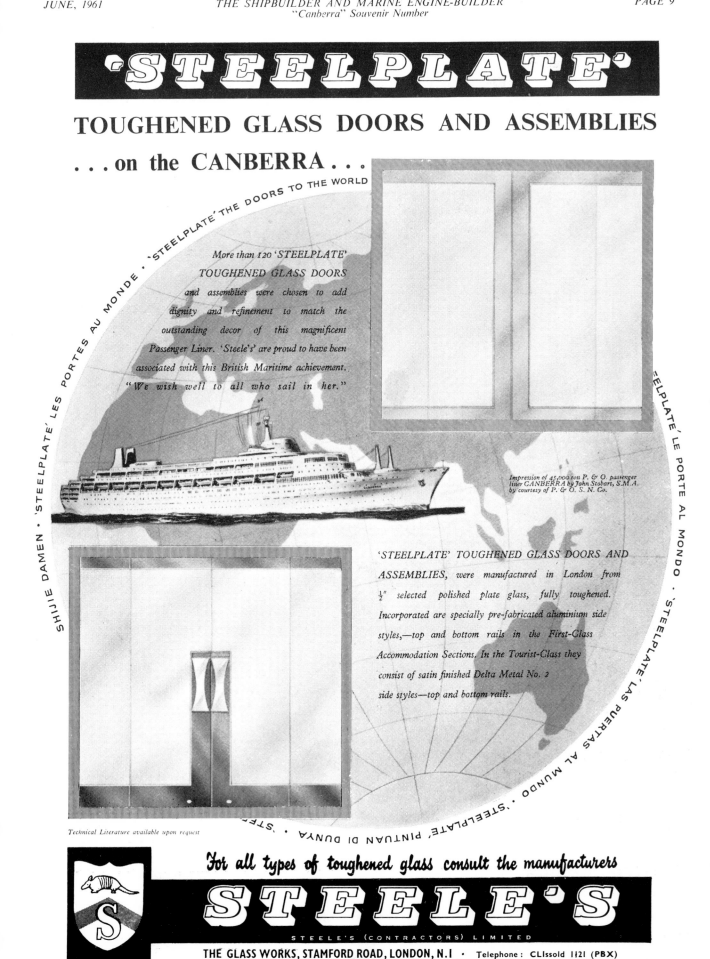

Above: photograph by Skyfotos Ltd.

Signal Mast
for "Canberra"

The new P & O Liner S.S. "Canberra" built by Harland & Wolff Limited, Belfast, will be the latest ship to be equipped with a signal mast built by our Company. Our masts are constructed from high quality and salt-water-resistant aluminium, and their modern design and low weight have made them the natural choice for leading shipbuilders all over the World.

The signal mast for "Canberra" weighs only 4,100 kg.—
(9,000 lb.) approx. and has been supplied by—

JOHN BURNHAM LIMITED
ESSEX HALL
STRAND, LONDON, W.C.2

Manufacturers:

FRED OLSEN AVIATION MAINTENANCE
(NORSK FLYINDUSTRI A/S)
FORNEBU, OSLO, NORWAY

NORSK FLYINDUSTRI A.S.

LEADING MANUFACTURERS OF
MARITIME ALUMINIUM PRODUCTS

For the

Ship that shapes the future

Starters that stand the test

CANBERRA

Allen West and Co. Ltd. have been privileged

to provide starters for a whole range of

CANBERRA motors—from the $\frac{1}{2}$ H.P. ventilating fans

to the 800 H.P. bow thrust propeller unit.

ALLEN WEST

For every electric motor,
whatever the application,
there is an Allen West starter

ALLEN WEST & CO LTD BRIGHTON ENGLAND · Telephone: Brighton 66666 · Telegrams: Control, Brighton
Engineers and Manufacturers of Electric Motor Control Gear and Switchgear
SUBSIDIARY COMPANIES IN CANADA, SOUTH AFRICA AND RHODESIA · AGENCIES THROUGHOUT THE WORLD

B

throughout the length and breadth of

BRITAIN'S largest post-war liner

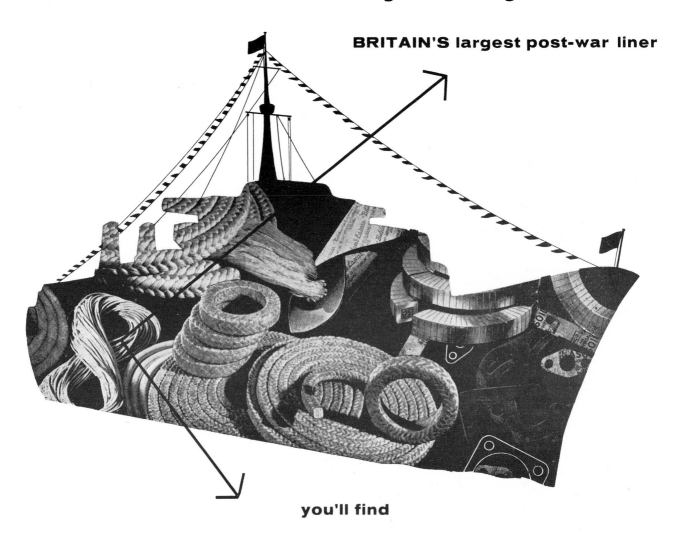

you'll find

BELDAM Lascar joints and packings

Almost every type of jointing and packing material produced by Beldam's has eventually found its way to the huge new P. & O. liner, S.S. Canberra – as an integral part of one important component or other. Beldam's are proud to be associated with this fine British shipbuilding project.

To know the differences between one Beldam material and another, you would need to have our manual close at hand. May we send it to you?

 **BELDAM'S** *LASCAR PRECISION PACKINGS*

BELDAM ASBESTOS COMPANY LIMITED

Lascar Works, Hounslow, Middlesex. Telephone: HOUnslow 7722 (10 lines)

Helping to Safeguard Britain's Newest Liner

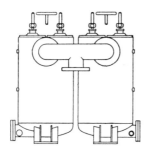

—at 27,600 gallons per hour

Helping to protect the twin A.E.I. turbo-alternators of P & O's new liner, S.S. *Canberra*, are four AUTO-KLEAN Duplex Twin filters. Operating on the discharge side of the main lubrication oil systems, these handle a total of 27,600 gallons per hour at 115 lb. p.s.i. Another small but still important contribution to recent British engineering achievements.

Photo (courtesy of A.E.I. (Rugby) Ltd.) shows assembly of one of the vast turbo-alternators which relies on AUTO-KLEAN filtration.

AUTO-KLEAN FILTRATION
CHOSEN FOR S.S. *CANBERRA*

AUTO-KLEAN STRAINERS LTD · LASCAR WORKS · HOUNSLOW · MIDDX.

Telephone: Hounslow 7722

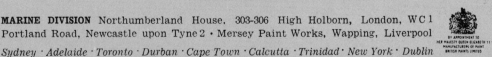

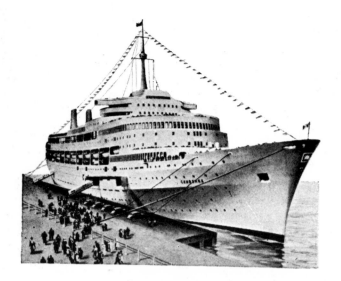

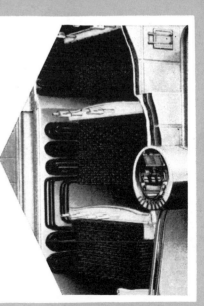

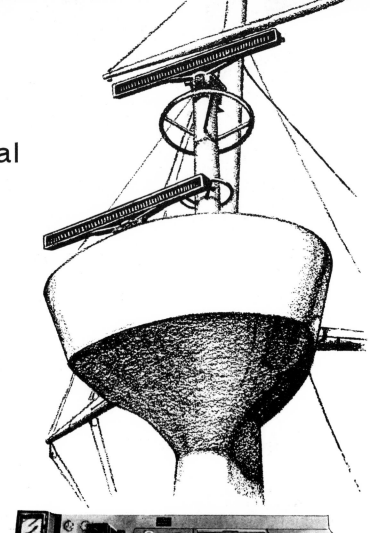

For the 'Canberra'

The most comprehensive and versatile of all navigational radar systems

Such is the installation which Kelvin Hughes have supplied for this great ship. Her Navigational Console includes every modern aid to navigation and incorporates two complete and entirely separate master radar systems. One of these is an adaptation of the Kelvin Hughes Type 14/16P equipment providing relative motion or true motion presentation on a 16″ display with built-in reflection plotter. The other is a 24″ relative motion or true motion optically projected bright display, with direct plotting facilities now made possible through the Rapid Photographic Processing System produced exclusively by Kelvin Hughes. The aerial system comprises two 10′ Slotted Waveguide Scanners on the mainmast. Each Scanner can be switched to operate with either display independently or with both displays together. An additional Slave display can be brought into operation when required. On her maiden voyage the 'Canberra' can truly claim to have a navigational radar system which is unique in merchant shipping practice.

 KELVIN HUGHES

KELVIN & HUGHES [MARINE] LIMITED, ST CLARE HOUSE, MINORIES, LONDON EC3
M003

Bon Voyage to s.s. 'CANBERRA'

fitted with
Britain's largest
a.c. marine switchboard

'ENGLISH ELECTRIC' are proud to be associated with this outstanding marine engineering achievement and wish 'Canberra' a long and active service.

The entire auxiliaries' electrical system of this unique ship which was built for P. & O.–Orient Lines by Harland and Wolff, Belfast, is controlled and protected by 'ENGLISH ELECTRIC' Class 'M' Switchgear.

This modern medium-voltage switchgear controls the electrical supplies to the steering gear, navigation equipment, galleys, laundries, cinema – in fact, to every electricity consuming device aboard; helping to ensure the safety and comfort of passengers and crew.

This a.c. main distribution switchboard, over 70 feet long, is the largest of its kind ever built in the United Kingdom for a passenger or merchant vessel.

'ENGLISH ELECTRIC' Switchgear has been specified for other passenger vessels and also merchantmen and tankers.

'ENGLISH ELECTRIC'
switchgear

A revised and enlarged second edition of this widely circulated publication "A.C. Electrical Distribution for Ships' Auxiliaries" is available on request. Ask for Publication SG/350.

SWITCHGEAR DEPARTMENT, EAST LANCASHIRE ROAD, LIVERPOOL, 10
The English Electric Company Limited, English Electric House, Strand, London, W.C.2

SGL.51

GKN

wish the Canberra

a long and successful life

at sea. She carries with her

not only our good wishes

but an enormous variety

of our products in the structure

of her hull and fittings.

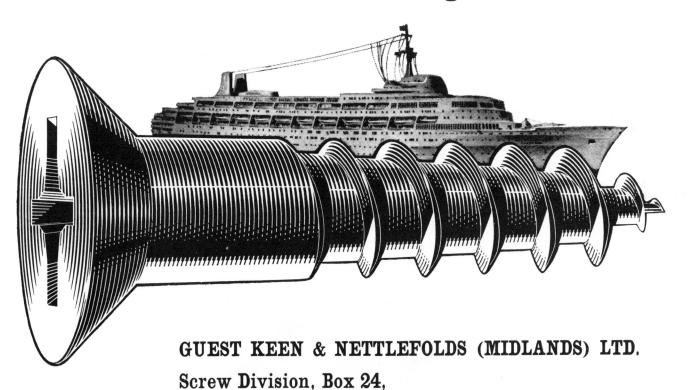

GUEST KEEN & NETTLEFOLDS (MIDLANDS) LTD.

Screw Division, Box 24,

Heath Street, Birmingham 18.

Tel: Smethwick 1441. Telex: 33-239.

S/GF/2520

Original ideas and advantageous materials combine to make Canberra unequalled for years to come. High on the list of materials used in her interior is Swedish Perstorp, the original plastic laminate. Giving a splendid glow of colour and freshness to Canberra's public rooms and alleyways, her 1st class courts, her tourist cabins, public bathrooms and toilets is Swedish Perstorp, a total of 1,250,000 square feet.

Perstorp economy pushes maintenance cost down and decorative standards up, enhances every surface, vertical, horizontal, curved or flat. Swedish Perstorp has also been chosen for use in ORIANA and many other vessels in the P. & O. Company's group building programme as well as for CANBERRA herself. Long-lasting and beautifully colourful Swedish Perstorp enhances decor and design; advances maintenance saving of great ships throughout the world.

Skånska Ättikfabriken AB, of Perstorp, Sweden, have been manufacturing plastic laminates for the markets of the world for over 35 years.

built for P & O—Orient Line by Harland and Wolff Limited, Belfast

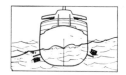

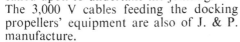

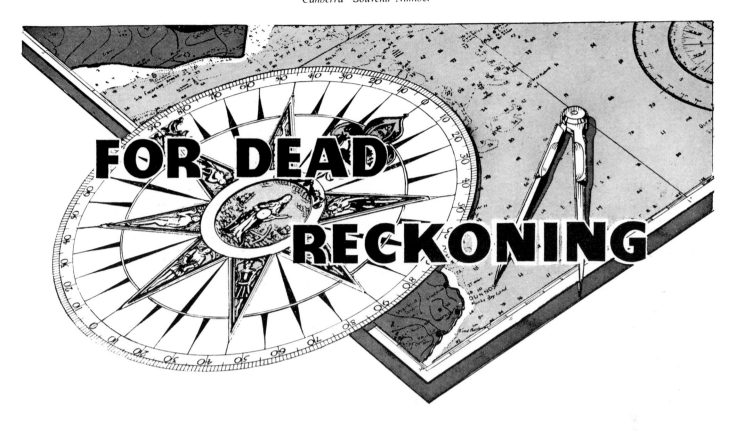

FOR DEAD RECKONING

S.S. "CANBERRA"

is equipped with

Walker's
'COMMODORE' LOG

DISTANCE RUN

SPEED FEED FOR RADAR

ACCURATE and RELIABLE

THOMAS WALKER & SON LTD.
58 OXFORD STREET, BIRMINGHAM 5

Telegrams : Shiplog Birmingham   Telephone : Birmingham MIDland 5474

T.W

Extra Holes!

...With the compliments of

Exceptional performances from an odd drill in a batch are of little value to the regular user of Twist Drills. Multiple drilling, repetitive drilling, production drilling, demand consistency in the working life of each tool, therefore the capability of obtaining extra holes from **every** drill is an obvious advantage. The manufacture of DORMER Drills is keyed to this very principle.

THE SHEFFIELD TWIST DRILL & STEEL CO. LTD

DORMER

MAKERS OF THE FINEST TWIST DRILLS
— BY ANY STANDARD

THE SHEFFIELD TWIST DRILL AND STEEL COMPANY LIMITED
SHEFFIELD **ENGLAND**

DORMER TOOLS ARE OBTAINABLE FROM YOUR USUAL ENGINEERS' MERCHANTS

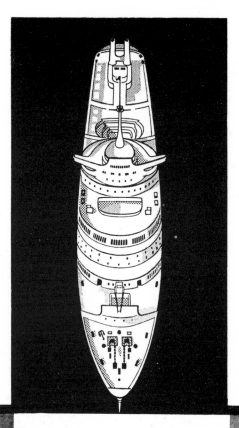

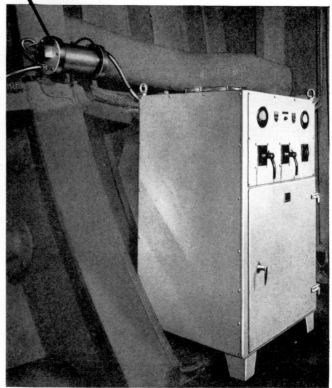

CANBERRA

Built by Harland & Wolff for P & O-Orient Lines

and AEI

POWER FOR A MODERN CITY AFLOAT

The aim of her owners and designers has been to make this ship the last word in marine comfort, efficiency, and reliability. With every luxury on board and many new design innovations, electric power was needed and AEI equipment was the choice . . . Electric power for lighting, heating, cooking and all other ship's hotel and auxiliary services, is provided by AEI equipment and over 90 miles of AEI cables are used in the distribution system. AEI turbo-compressors contribute to efficient cooling for air-conditioning in warmer weather. Powerful, smooth-running AEI propulsion turbines and electric drives silently give this 'ship of tomorrow' a service speed of $27\frac{1}{2}$ knots! Here is sea travel with new and exciting standards of speed and comfort.

POWER FOR A 'SHIP OF TOMORROW'

 **Associated Electrical Industries Limited**

A5585

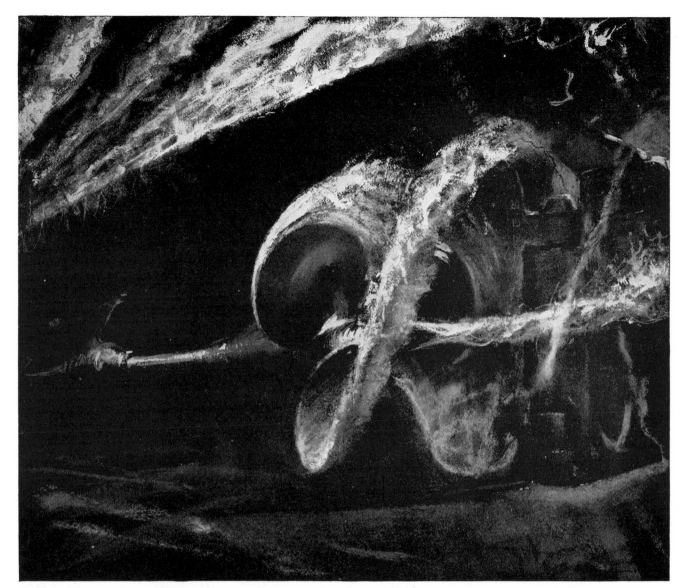

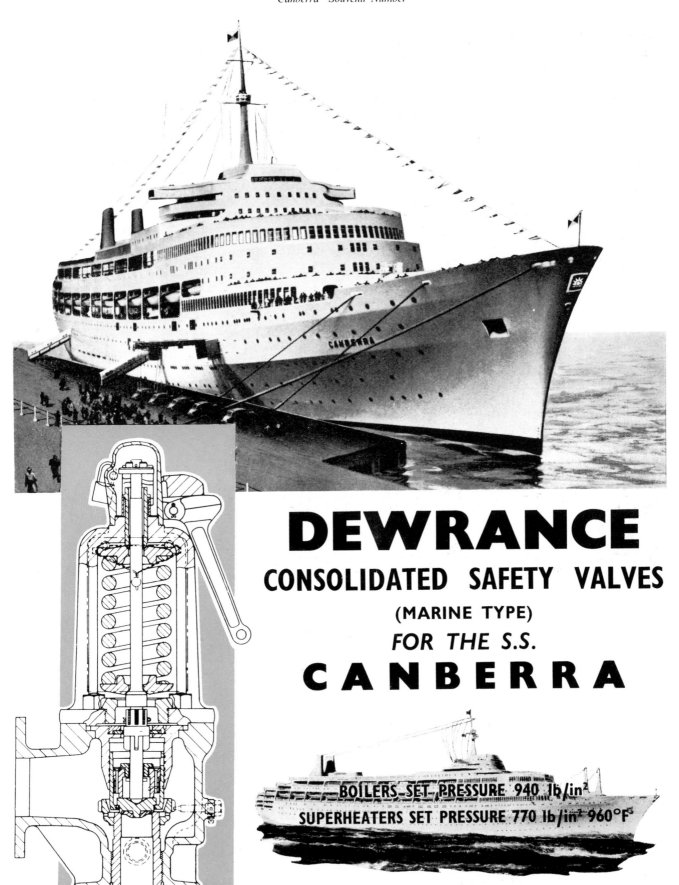

DEWRANCE
CONSOLIDATED SAFETY VALVES
(MARINE TYPE)
FOR THE S.S.
CANBERRA

BOILERS SET PRESSURE 940 lb/in²
SUPERHEATERS SET PRESSURE 770 lb/in² 960°F

Standardised by many Shipping Companies and installed in over 150 ships, including liners, tankers and cargo vessels.

DEWRANCE AND COMPANY LIMITED
GREAT DOVER STREET   LONDON S.E.1   ·   Telephone: HOP. 3100 (12 lines)

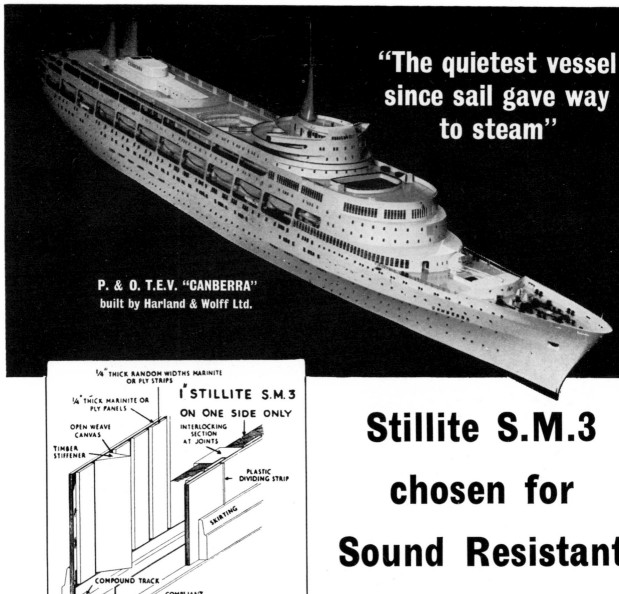

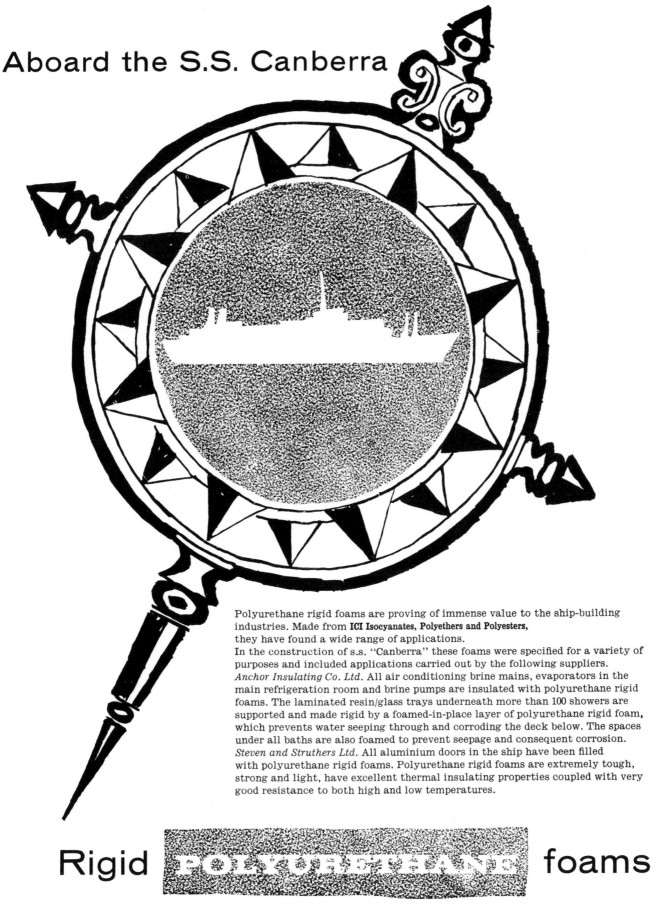

There are no finer springs

than Springs by **Riley**

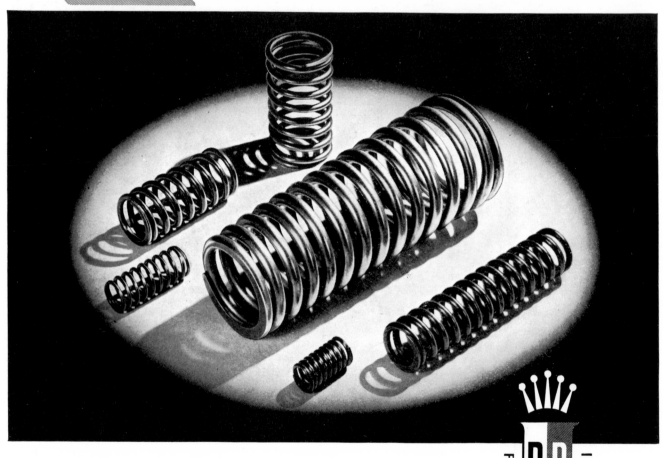

Robert Riley Ltd. of Rochdale are proud of the position they hold as makers of the finest precision springs known today. Continuous research and the constant development of fresh uses for Springs during the past 140 years have consolidated Riley's position as technical leaders in the manufacture of compression springs, extension springs and torsion springs, spiral springs and flat springs—indeed every type of spring.   Small wonder then that the country's leading companies in the Shipbuilding, Aircraft, Electrical, Nuclear and Light and Heavy Engineering industries invariably specify Springs by Riley.   Contractors to H.M. Government, the Admiralty, the War Office and the Air Ministry.

RR FAMOUS FOR SPRINGS SINCE 1821

ROBERT RILEY LTD., MILKSTONE SPRING WORKS, ROCHDALE. *Tel.*: ROCHDALE 2237 (5 lines).
Grams: 'RILOSPRING' ROCHDALE.   *Telex*: 63–151.

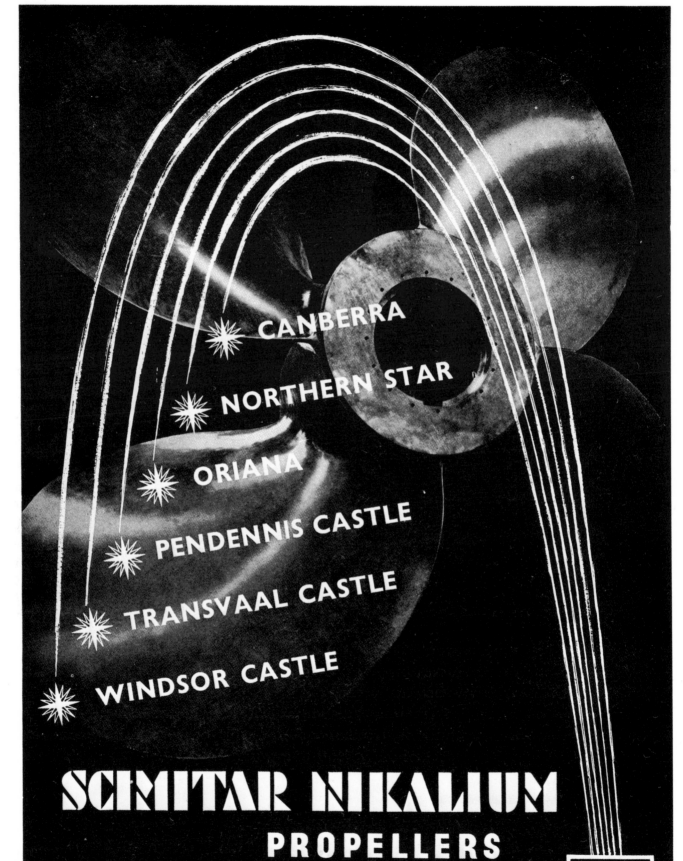

CANBERRA

NORTHERN STAR

ORIANA

PENDENNIS CASTLE

TRANSVAAL CASTLE

WINDSOR CASTLE

SCIMITAR NIKALIUM
PROPELLERS

THE MANGANESE BRONZE & BRASS CO. LTD., DOCK ROAD, BIRKENHEAD, ENGLAND.

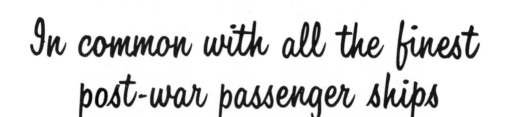

S.S. CANBERRA

Mural 'Vynide'

completes the setting

for good living

on the Canberra

Top P. & O. passengers expect their cocktails and haute cuisine in superlative surroundings. That's why the walls of the first class restaurant and verandah lounge on the Canberra are discreetly, yet impressively covered with Mural 'Vynide'. The choice is doubly wise from the P. & O. point of view, because Mural 'Vynide' is as hard wearing and easy to clean as it is good looking. 15,000 yards of this material have been used in the Canberra, plus 12,000 yards of 'Vynalast', a P.V.C. decorative foil, which is laminated to marine plywood on the deckheads.

Mural 'Vynide'

registered trade mark

FROM **ICI**

I.C.I. (HYDE) LIMITED · HYDE · CHESHIRE

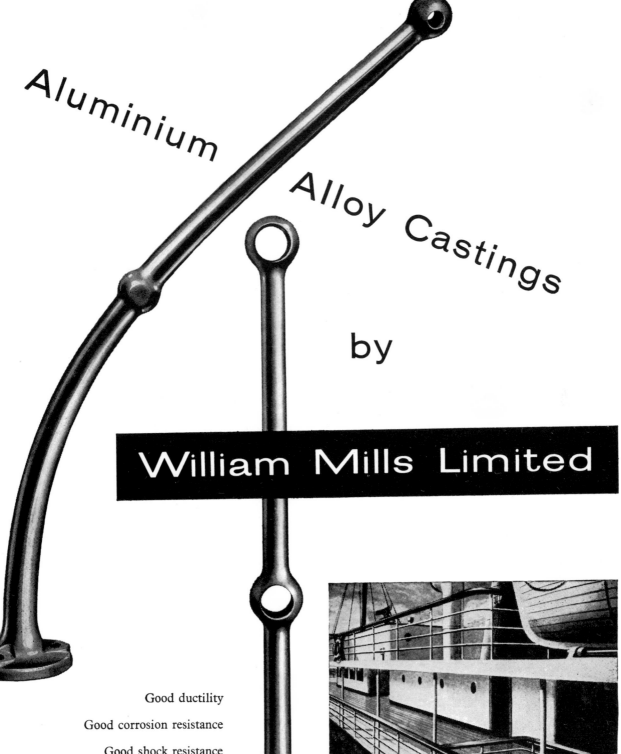

E

ORIANA
AND NOW
CANBERRA!

S.S. Canberra
COMPLETE HULL PROTECTION

using HANGERS *New* MARINE PAINTS

Following its successful use on S.S. ORIANA, HANGERS EPOXIDE PAINT SYSTEM, giving a hard, smooth, underwater surface, was again chosen by the P. & O. Orient Lines Management to provide complete protection to the hull of S.S. CANBERRA.

EPISOLVE—The REVOLUTIONARY SOLVENTLESS EPOXIDE. Bare patches produced by late engineering work were effectively brought forward with EPISOLVE, which gives an equivalent film thickness of 4 or 5 coats of normal paint in ONE APPLICATION—a valuable product for all marine work, particularly TANK LINING.

Hangers technical specialists are available to discuss your problems. Write to:—

HANGERS PAINTS LTD.,
MARINE DIVISION and WEBSTERS LTD.,
STONEFERRY WORKS, HULL
Telephone: 42111

GIANT S&L DERRICK ON

Carrying a test load of 181·5 tons which induced an angle of heel of 10·5 degrees, this derrick is the largest so far supplied by a British manufacturer for a merchant vessel and will operate up to 165 tons safe working load. It was recently installed by the Greenock Dockyard Company Limited aboard the 'Clan Sutherland'.

The derrick was made of S&L steel tube and assembled at one of the Company's works at Coatbridge, where it is shown before being transported to Greenock. The ball-joint heel piece and headpiece carrying pulleys and pulley

S&L **STEWARTS AND**

Tubemakers for a Century

THE 'CLAN SUTHERLAND'

attachments, shown in the small illustrations, were cast in the Company's steel foundry at Tollcross near Glasgow. The derrick has a working length of 68 ft. 6 in. and an overall length of approximately 71 ft.

With improved derrick facilities, such as this, on the ship itself, there is less dependence on the lifting tackle at ports, which is so frequently inadequate.

S & L engineers will be pleased to assist in the design of derricks for installation in vessels in any part of the world.

LLOYDS LIMITED

GLASGOW · BIRMINGHAM · LONDON

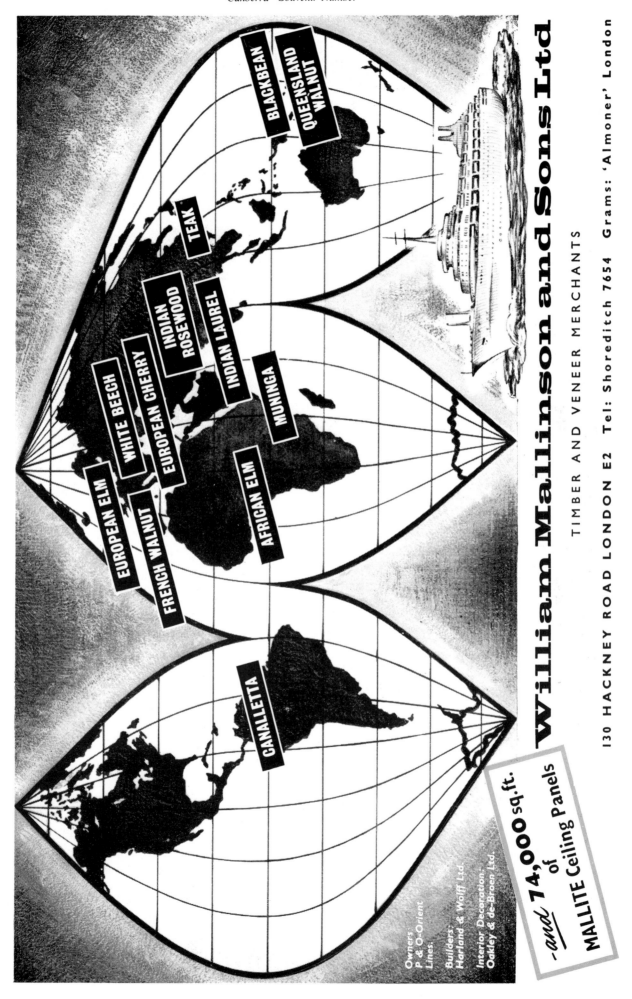

BP ENERGOL Marine Lubricants have been selected for exclusive use in the new 45,000 ton P & O passenger liner 'Canberra' built at Belfast by Harland and Wolff Ltd. The Power Petroleum Company are sole distributors in Gt. Britain of BP ENERGOL Marine, Industrial and Commercial Transport Lubricants, products of The British Petroleum Company Ltd.

THE POWER PETROLEUM COMPANY LTD
76-86 STRAND LONDON WC2 TEMple Bar 3535

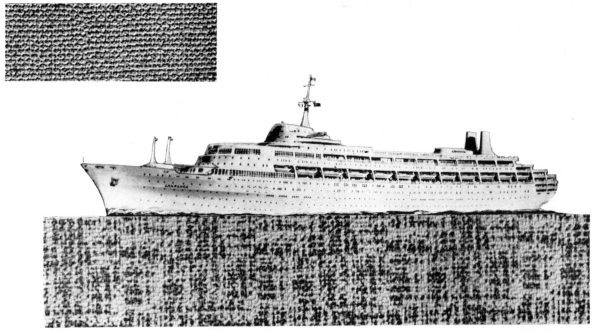

Mural Texturide in the "CANBERRA"

Arlington Plastics Development Ltd., are proud that Mural Texturide vinyl wall covering was among the materials specified for the internal decoration of the 'Canberra'. Mural Texturide was used for wall covering in the Senior Officers cabins and for ceiling covering in the first class bathrooms.

Mural Texturide found its sea legs a long time ago, and many miles have now been specified by marine architects and designers for ships large and small, from P. & O. Orient Line's 'Canberra', Canadian Pacific's Flagship 'Empress of Canada', Royal Mail Line's 'Amazon', 'Aragon' and 'Arlanza' down to cross-channel packets and private cruisers.

No other surface covering offers such beauty of texture, colour and design allied to great durability, for Mural Texturide's vinyl surface resists dirt, stains, burns, scuffing, ozone, and is completely washable. Maintenance is simple and there is no need for frequent re-decoration.

There is a wide range of colours and designs to suit almost any decor.

Mural Texturide
VINYL COATED FABRIC

Please write for full details to:—
ARLINGTON PLASTICS DEVELOPMENT LIMITED
Eastern Industrial Estate, Harlow, Essex.
Telephone: HARLOW 24611.

F

FIROLA

FIRE - RESISTING STEEL ROLLING SHUTTERS

as approved by M.O.T., L.C.C., L.F.B. & F.O.C.

PREVENTION OF FIRE SPREAD AT SEA

Firola is the only fire-resisting rolling shutter approved by the Ministry of Transport under CLASS A risk for ships at sea.

T.E.V. CANBERRA

is equipped with

Haskins (Approved) **FIROLA**

FIRE-RESISTING SHUTTERS

Haskins single Firola fire-resisting steel rolling shutters are judiciously placed about the ship. These shutters are capable of normal operation, but are also fitted with an automatic fusible link release, which causes the shutter to descend slowly in the event of fire, the melting point of the fuse for release being 155 deg. F.

For detailed information write for booklet No. 520/60

Other ships fitted with
FIROLA fire-resisting shutters include
the **EMPRESS OF CANADA**, the **CAESAREA**,
the **ORIANA**, the **EMPRESS OF ENGLAND**,
the **IBERIA**, the **ARCADIA**, the **CORINTHIA**,
the **SYLVANIA**, the **QUEEN ELIZABETH**,
the **QUEEN MARY**, etc.

Haskins

Gnome House, Blackhorse Lane, London, E.17
Telephone: LARkswood 2622

FIROLA
FIRE-RESISTING ROLLING SHUTTERS

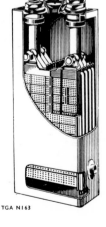

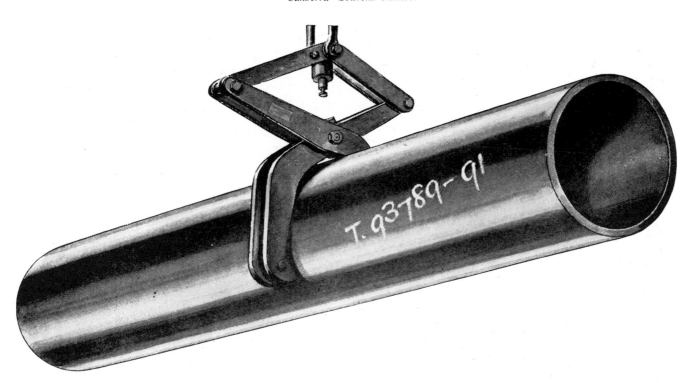

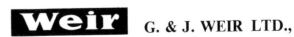

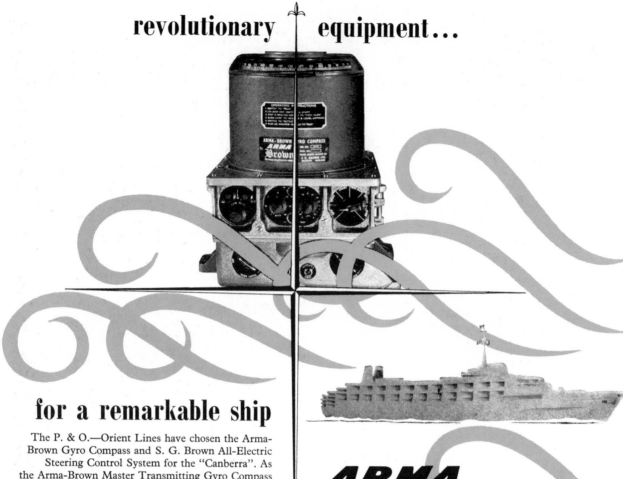

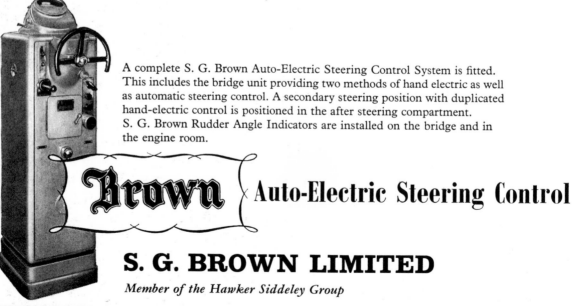

S.S. Canberra

THE
TURBO-ELECTRIC VESSEL

"*Canberra*"

BUILT
BY

HARLAND AND
WOLFF LIMITED

FOR

P&O-ORIENT LINES

SOUVENIR NUMBER OF

THE SHIPBUILDER AND MARINE ENGINE-BUILDER

JUNE, 1961

CONTENTS

PUBLISHERS

THE SHIPBUILDER PRESS, LIMITED

39, VICTORIA STREET, LONDON, S.W.1.

Telegrams: "AFLOSHIPYA, SOWEST"   *Telephone:* ABBEY 6577

Head Office and Editorial Department:

TOWNSVILLE HOUSE, 274, HEATON ROAD, NEWCASTLE-ON-TYNE, 6

Telegrams: "AMIDSHIPS"   *Telephone:* NEWCASTLE 659086

INDEX TO ADVERTISERS FACES INSIDE BACK COVER

Pattie Menzies

Sir Donald Forsyth Anderson, Chairman,
P & O - Orient Lines.

OWNERS

P & O – ORIENT LINES

THE tiny wooden paddle steamer *William Fawcett*, of some 206 tons measurement, was the first in a series of noble ships which has culminated in the construction of the finest of them all, the *Canberra*. The history of the Peninsular and Oriental Steam Navigation Company began early in the nineteenth century when two partners, Brodie McGhie Willcox and Arthur Anderson, chartered ships to trade with the Iberian Peninsular. They were able to offer valuable support to the Royal houses of Portugal and Spain and this was rewarded by trading facilities and the right to use the colours which to-day form the quarterings of the present company's house flag, the blue and white of Portugal and the red and yellow of Spain.

In 1837, the two partners succeeded in breaking the monopoly of the Falmouth packets and obtained a contract to carry Her Majesty's Mails to the Peninsular. On the strength of this contract the Peninsular Steam Navigation Company was formed. Two years later it was arranged to extend the mail contract to Egypt.

In 1840, the name was changed to the Peninsular and Oriental Steam Navigation Company on being granted a Royal Charter for the purpose of carrying the Mails to India. This extension to India commenced in 1842 and was by means of the existing service from Southampton to Alexandria, thence by overland route to Suez, and from Suez *via* Ceylon and Madras to Calcutta. By 1844 an additional service to Penang, Singapore, Hong Kong and Shanghai was operating from Ceylon, connecting with the Calcutta service at Galle.

During these formative years, the founder partners were still in control, but the former died in 1862 and the latter in 1868. The next year, 1869, was to be a critical one for the Company. It was to see the opening of the Suez Canal. The fleet, constituted as it was, half for operation in temperate and half in tropical climates, became much less suitable for a through voyage. Fortunately, from the organisation came a worthy successor to the early pioneers, a young man, Thomas Sutherland, who became managing director in 1872.

New ships were built—bigger, faster, and more comfortable, and trade flourished. With the turn of the century, however, competition began to develop from foreign shipowners—in a very small way at first but enough to warn the Board of directors of what lay ahead. Therefore, in 1914, the P. & O. Company acquired the equity of the British India Steam Navigation Co., Ltd., which brought 1¼ million tons of shipping under one Board.

In 1916 the New Zealand Shipping Company and the Federal Steam Navigation Company were added to the fold. Next year followed the acquisition of the Hain and Nourse Companies, both owning cargo ships, and the Union Steamship Company of New Zealand operating services in Pacific and Australasian waters. In 1919 an interest in the Orient Line was purchased and another in the General Steam Navigation Company the following year.

The P. & O. Company earned a proud record in the grim days of the Second World War. One half its ships were sunk, and the Group lost a total of 182 ships; one company, the Hain Line, losing its entire fleet. These losses were to have their effect on the fortunes of the post-war years. If the trades of the Group were to be re-opened, services had to be restored and new ships had to be built. Soon the great task of reconstruction was put in hand, financed out of the Group's resources and monies from war risks insurance.

Prices were already far higher than pre-war days, and rising fast. For instance, the difference in the cost of one of a group of similar passenger ships between the first laid down in April, 1946, and the last delivered in September, 1954, was over £3,000,000. Nevertheless rehabilitation of the fleet had to go on.

In May, 1960, the Orient Line merged with the P. & O. Company and the combined service became known as P. & O.-Orient Lines.

Now, the Company under the most able leadership of the chairman, Sir Donald Forsyth Anderson, who succeeded Sir William Currie in 1960, have a fine fleet of modern ships plying both traditional and new routes.

The *Oriana* joined the fleet in December, 1960, and she has now been followed by her consort, the *Canberra*, both of which will serve Australia, the Pacific and the West Coast of North America. This service is relatively new and exploits the tourist potential in the Pacific, which is the last great frontier of tourism.

Foresight and courage were evident qualities when Wilcox and Anderson chartered their tiny ships to establish regular sailings to Spain and Portugal, whatever the state of the weather. That similar foresight and courage are qualities possessed in full by the present directors of the Peninsular and Oriental Steam Navigation Company is evident from the vast amount of money which they have poured into the construction of fine vessels at a time when critics decry the future of British shipping.

BUILDERS

HARLAND & WOLFF LTD.

Sir Frederick E. Rebbeck, K.B.E., D.Sc., D.L., J.P., Chairman and Managing Director, Harland & Wolff, Ltd.

BORN in 1831, the founder of Messrs. Harland & Wolff, Ltd., Mr. E. J. Harland (later Sir Edward Harland, Bart.), served an apprenticeship in Scotland and later, in 1854, attained the position of manager of Robert Hickson's shipyard, a small shipbuilding concern in Belfast. Four years later he purchased the interest, goodwill and property at Queen's Island and his dynamic energy, coupled with a genius for the design of revolutionary and successful vessels, plus the excellent quality of their workmanship, quickly made the new concern famous.

The business rapidly expanded, and in 1861 Mr. E. J. Harland entered into partnership with Gustaf Wilhelm Wolff, an able engineer of considerable experience, and the firm of Messrs. Harland & Wolff was born.

Manufacture of the machinery required for the many and varied vessels built at the Queen's Island was commenced in 1880, and the steady expansion of the company continued up to the present time and included the acquisition and establishment of shipbuilding, ship-repairing, and engineering branches in other parts of Britain. During the First World War the shipbuilding potential of Messrs. Harland & Wolff at Belfast was augmented by the new and extensive Musgrave Yard with building facilities for vessels of over 1,000ft. in length. The acquisition, in 1935, of the shipyard of Messrs. Workman Clark & Company provided further extensive capacity.

Heavy bombing during the Second World War caused immense damage at the Belfast shipyards, and during the subsequent rebuilding opportunity was taken to replan the works, grouping the fitting-out shops to ensure economic handling of material and equipping them with up-to-date machinery.

To-day the immense shipbuilding and engineering works in Belfast is the largest single unit of its kind in the world, employing over 20,000 persons and extending over 300 acres (including dry-docks). These shipyards are equipped for the construction of ships of all classes and particularly for the building of large ocean-going passenger liners. Ships completed in recent years have included aircraft-carriers, cruisers, passenger vessels, cargo ships, oil-tankers, whale factory ships, cross-Channel vessels, etc.

The Belfast establishment embraces four shipyards, as well as a large engineering works. The shipyards are the Musgrave Yard and the Queen's Yard, in which are built aircraft-carriers, large passenger vessels, and oil-tankers; the Abercorn Yard, where moderate-sized passenger ships, cargo liners, and smaller warships are built; and the Victoria Yard, which is devoted mainly to the construction of dry-cargo vessels.

Each yard is arranged on up-to-date lines, and all adopt modern prefabrication and welding techniques. Among the many new facilities now provided are a shot-blasting plant, pickling bath, cold-bending machines, and all the latest equipment for processing the heaviest plates used in shipbuilding. Complete radiographic equipment for the examination of welds in ships' hulls is available, and there is a large radiographic laboratory.

Construction of marine propelling engines, both steam and Diesel, up to the largest size required, is the main activity of the engineering works. In addition, however, there are manufactured in the department watertube boilers, Diesel engines for industrial and rail traction purposes, and compressors of both horizontal and centrifugal types. A considerable volume of general engineering work is also undertaken. Among the many and varied tools installed in the machine and erecting shops are a lathe, capable of taking a 98ft. by 8ft. diameter shaft, a spindle boring and milling machine, weighing 70 tons, and a gear-cutting machine for dealing with gear wheels up to 15ft. in diameter. Two stress-relieving furnaces and a large modern shot-blasting plant are also installed.

Pioneers in the development of marine electrical equipment, Messrs. Harland & Wolff, Ltd., have had an electrical division for 40 years. The manufacturing facilities include D.C. and A.C. shops where D.C. generators, alternators, motor generators, D.C. and A.C. motors, together with their control gear, are produced. The electrical department is also responsible for the electrical equipment throughout the works and has in its care arrangements for the distribution of electrical power through 11 substations with a maximum demand of 20,000 kW.

Messrs. Harland & Wolff, Ltd., have extensive establishments in Great Britain, including a large shipyard on the Clyde; engineering works at Finniston and Scotstoun, Glasgow; the largest iron foundry in Europe, at Govan; and well-equipped ship-repairing works in London, Liverpool, and Southampton.

The company owes its success and prosperity largely to the energy, foresight and leadership of its present chairman and managing director, Sir Frederick E. Rebbeck, K.B.E., D.Sc., D.L., J.P., who has occupied his present position since 1930.

DESIGN FEATURES

By J. West, B.Sc., A.M.R.I.N.A., A.M.I.Mar.E.

(Assistant Manager P & O – Orient Lines)

FOUR fundamental objectives have dominated the design of the *Canberra*. They are:—

(1) In a passenger ship, passengers must be given priority.

(2) As the ship would be sailing on her maiden voyage in 1961, there should be abundant evidence of progressive thought and good design.

(3) The ship must be economically successful, both in these difficult days of depression as well as times of prosperity, and also be able to compete with subsidised ships of other nations. The greatest possible efficiency is required in operation, while economy in building costs is also of prime importance.

(4) One of the biggest drains of a ship's earnings is the constant need for repairs, and special thought had to be given to this during the design and building.

The company felt that there were advantages to be gained in having the machinery aft, so it was decided to adopt this arrangement in the *Canberra*, care being taken to ensure that the underwater form would not be hydrodynamically unsuitable and that there would not be any insoluble problems of trim, stability and subdivision.

Before finally deciding on the hull form many models of various shapes were tested and modifications made. There was little basic data for high speed ships having a speed/length ratio of unity, so it was necessary to amass this data by performing many experiments. From the outset we were determined to produce the most efficient ship possible and, therefore, many other investigations were carried out. One idea was to fit a twin skeg stern. Another was to fit a ram-bulb bow, while a third was to employ novel designs of appendages, such as open shaft brackets, as opposed to bossings. The skeg stern was rejected, but the large bulbous bow and the exposed or naked shafts, supported by specially designed and angled "A" brackets, were both favoured. These features, together with a very good hull form, showed that if 85,000 H.P. were put into the ship, there would be an adequate margin of speed to cope with delays due to bad weather and fog, etc.

The entire middle portion of the ship has been reserved for passenger accommodation and to preserve this "hotel block," the officers have their rooms above the passenger spaces, while the crew are accommodated forward, above the cargo spaces. In this way the ship has actually been designed round the passenger accommodation.

It was quickly realised that by using aluminium for the superstructure another deck could be incorporated, and the additional accommodation provided completely off-set the additional costs involved. The final design covered a fully-welded aluminium superstructure weighing more than 1,000 tons.

With increased ship's speed and large areas of sports decks the shaping of the superstructure and selective placing of screens to give sheltered decks has proved to be most difficult. With the assistance of wind-tunnel experiments, however, the problems have been solved without marring the appearance of the ship, or cluttering up the open decks, and passengers will be able to relax comfortably in the sun even when travelling at $27\frac{1}{2}$ knots into a 30-knot wind.

With fully air-conditioned ships and particularly where machinery is placed aft, there is a definite tendency for the more usual ship noises to become less, and irregular disturbing noises to become irritatingly loud. Undesirable noises come from the auxiliary machinery and various other sources, and in the *Canberra* every effort has been made to diminish these, but the greatest problem is that of living-in noise caused by the passengers themselves. This problem has been fully investigated on ships actually at sea, and as a result a specially-designed sound-proofed bulkhead has been produced which considerably reduces noise transmission. Although acoustically efficient the bulkhead is light in weight.

In developing the design of the *Canberra* it has been possible to introduce many new and exciting features.

For example, the main feature in the first-class accommodation is the fact that many of the cabins have been planned on the air/light principle, in which courts or verandas, with several windows looking out to sea, are surrounded by cabins, each of which has a window looking into the veranda.

Many new ideas have been introduced into the cabins themselves and plastics have been cleverly used to produce restful atmospheres. Other new features for the passengers' benefit include a special two-programme radio in each cabin, iced-water led to each cabin and the substitution, wherever possible, of windows for sidelights.

In two of the cargo holds it seemed both impractical and undesirable to have an orthodox cargo trunk passing up through all the accommodation and surmounted with derricks and winches. Side loading has been adopted, therefore, and a device has been specially designed which raises the cargo or cars on a pallet, through a central trunk, to a convenient height and then traverses it across the ship, through shell doors, to a point over the quay where it is lowered.

An elaborate system of conveyors and elevators has also been developed to handle the passengers' baggage.

ENGINEERING FEATURES

By T. W. Bunyan, B.Sc., M.I.Mech.E., M.I.Mar.E.

(Engineering Adviser P & O – Orient Lines)

FOR the *Canberra's* main propulsion machinery, design studies were undertaken, on behalf of the P. and O. Company, by the Yarrow-Admiralty Research Department. The final selection of a turbo-electric installation developing 85,000 S.H.P. was made for twin-screw drive.

Steam conditions of 750 lb per sq. in. at the stop valve and a temperature of 960 deg. F. were chosen, as these were considered to be the limit for satisfactory superheater operation with commercially available fuels.

Although turbo-electric drive has meant a small penalty in additional weight, space and cost, it is interesting to note that there is no penalty on fuel consumption as there are certain advantageous turbine design features with this arrangement over the direct geared drive. One singular advantage is the ability to run the propellers locked together in any given relative phase relationship to produce minimum effective vibratory force which could excite principal or local modes of vibration of the hull. The most careful theoretical investigations have been made with the co-operation of engineers of the B.T.H. Company and their mathematics division, equipped with a digital computer. All shafting modes were investigated, as well as the possible propeller excited resonances of the "A" bracket supports.

Probably the largest steam-raising units to be fitted in a British ship to date are the Foster Wheeler E.S.D. type boilers chosen for the *Canberra*. Three units, each with an evaporation of 260,000 lb per hour are installed in the after part of the ship and one of 50,000 lb per hour. The latest "suspended-flame" type oil burners are arranged for either straight pressure-jet or steam-assisted atomisation at will—an arrangement designed to give impeccable burning with wide turn-down and having compact flames even when burning the 6,500 second Redwood fuel for which the pumping and heating units, as well as the fuel-oil handling equipment, have been designed.

With very few exceptions, all bolted flanges in the boiler integral main and auxiliary steam piping have been eliminated, but adequate provision has been made for survey requirements of inspection and testing. Whenever possible all-welded construction has been adopted, and the entire operation is an outstanding example of teamwork producing the most helpful co-operation of the Ministry of Transport, Lloyd's Register of Shipping, the shipbuilders and subcontractors.

An attempt has been made to eliminate entirely, or at most to reduce to trimming proportions only, the chemical treatment of boiler water. An ion-exchange technique is employed using water obtained from a single distillation of sea water. For regeneration, the ion-exchange equipment uses a cheap and safe alkaline re-agent and sea water which is plentiful. This is an important new development as it has the most desirable feature that CO_2 and all mineral salts will be absent from the distillate, there remaining a small oxygen trace which will be removed in the de-aerator and condensate distiller. One fruitful source of fresh-water is the collection of part of the condensed moisture from the coolers of the air-conditioning plant, amounting to some 60—120 tons per day, depending on atmosphere conditions. This water is processed through the ion-exchange plant and is piped to the reserve tanks for the boilers.

With the International Convention requirements for damage stability in passenger ships, we were presented with the difficult problem of discharging about 2,000 tons of oil contaminated water ballast from double bottom tanks and simultaneously taking on board about 7,000 tons of fuel oil, the whole operation to be completed in a matter of hours. This called for an entirely new approach as the conventional methods were quite out of court. All tank valves are pneumatically controlled from a single control console having the necessary interlocks, depth gauges and warning devices which would enable high-speed control to be achieved without confusion. Two king-size oily-water separators are built into two of the ship's deep tanks to deal with the contaminated ballast at approximately 1,500 tons an hour.

A further interesting development is the docking propeller, which is mounted in an open transverse tunnel near the bows of the ship. The thrust of this propeller can be controlled from ten tons down to about two tons, and is also rapidly reversible. A simple controller is situated on the bridge for this purpose.

The use of an oil gland bearing with a view to eliminating the heavy cost of re-wooding the tail-end bearings is another interesting development. Bare 30-in. diameter steel shafts run in white-metal bearings with oil seals at each end of the "A" brackets and hull bossing bearings. The oil is circulated by a small pump, and a modified form of rope guard acts as an oil seepage collector which is self-purging only when the vessel is under way. The seepage collector is another safeguard against oil pollution of harbours.

BUILDING "CANBERRA"

By Denis Rebbeck, C.B.E., D.L., M.A.(Cantab.), M.A. (Dublin), Ph.D. (Belfast), J.P.

(Deputy Managing Director, Harland and Wolff, Ltd.)

IT was not without a certain feeling of nostalgia that I stood on the bridge of the *Canberra* as she slowly pulled away from her fitting-out berth on Saturday, the 29th April, and I watched the faces of the hundreds of workmen who were saying their final farewell to a ship that had become a part of themselves over the last four and a half years. Queen's Island and, synonymously, the City of Belfast had taken a real pride in the construction of this the largest passenger ship built in the United Kingdom since the days of the *Queens*, and those of us most intimately connected with the challenging task of building this wonderful liner felt that the task had been faithfully carried out in the spirit of fullest co-operation which had been urged upon us all.

The services of experts in all fields had been sought and it had not proved to be the easiest of tasks to co-ordinate the many facets of expert opinion to produce a ship which for comfort, amenities and service aimed to set the new pattern in ocean travel.

With a gross tonnage of over 45,000 the *Canberra* is the largest passenger ship built at the Queen's Island since the First World War and although some 3,000 tons less than the first *Britannic*, completed as a hospital ship in 1915, it is a significant commentary on the development of the modern passenger liner that although *Britannic* was docked in Belfast, as were *Olympic* and *Titanic*, the dry-dock which accommodated these three ships was just short of the necessary width to take the *Canberra*.

The choice of turbo-electric machinery of 85,000 S.H.P. to be manufactured by Associated Electrical Industries, Ltd., was made after an exhaustive analysis of different types of installation had been carried out and carefully studied. Having decided on the type of installation, further detailed investigation had then to be made concerning vibration characteristics of the propulsion motor, shafting and propeller systems, and in this instance the British Thomson-Houston Mathematics Division carried out a careful theoretical investigation based on stiffness readings obtained from the ship by means of straining rigs developed by us and built into the ship on the slip for this purpose.

The use of aluminium for the superstructure had always been an integral part of the design and the incorporation of over 1,000 tons of this material in welded form raised many problems and led to the development of many new techniques. In this enterprise Lloyd's Register of Shipping, the Ministry of Transport and the aluminium manufacturers co-operated fully, and it was not until a complete test rig had been set up and scores of welding samples had been exhaustively tested that the final method of assembly was decided upon.

It is only when walking round the ship that one realises that here indeed is a vessel that embodies a more than usual combination of new features and there is evidence that down to the smallest detail, optimum advantage has been taken of the latest developments in each particular field. From the roomy, well-equipped galley to the stores conveyors; from the wide-view cinema screen to the automatic selective baggage-handling equipment; from cargo transporters to the bow propeller—there is ample evidence of the forward thinking policy enunciated by the P. & O. Company in the early days of the ship's conception.

A new note has also been struck on the decorative side and without doubt the whole treatment is arresting and challenging. The decorative contracts were placed by P. & O. with various subcontractors and the theme was supervised by Sir Hugh Casson and his partners. Ship decoration, as such, is essentially a matter of individual opinion and there is no doubt that the *Canberra's* public rooms will stimulate widespread interest and comment from the travelling public This is just as it should be in an age of progressive thinking.

For the comfort of the passengers it was decided to fit two pairs of stabilisers of Denny-Brown type and this installation, together with the electric propulsion situated towards the after end of the vessel, should ensure the greatest possible comfort. One further advantage of electric propulsion is the ability to lock the propellers in a given relative phase relationship, in order to keep disturbing vibratory forces to a minimum. The advantage of phasing had already been demonstrated in two cross-Channel vessels built by us in Belfast in 1949, which have been operating ever since with a synchronising gear of our own manufacture. Already the effect of varying phase relationship has been investigated on the *Canberra* and the optimum phase setting determined.

It goes without saying that an extensive series of tank tests had to be carried out before the final hull form was determined. These tests were undertaken by Messrs. William Denny & Brothers, Ltd., and by the National Physical Laboratory and the form selected incorporates a bulbous bow in order to give the most economical performance at service speeds.

Speaking for the Queen's Island, I now wish the *Canberra* God speed. The many hundreds of our workpeople who helped to fashion this wonderful liner will follow with interest her future career in the service of the great P. & O. Company.

Fig. 1.—Aerial View of Part of the Harland & Wolff Works at Belfast with "Canberra" Dominating the Musgrave Shipyard.

GENERAL ARRANGEMENT

THE *Canberra* is a twin-screw turbo-electrically propelled passenger and cargo liner and has been built in accordance with the requirements of Lloyd's Register of Shipping for the classification ✠ 100 A.1, and under the special survey of officers of that Society. The construction and outfit of the vessel also comply in every respect with the recommendations of the Ministry of Transport. The principal particulars of the vessel are given in Table I.

Very finely modelled, the vessel has a curved rounded stem and modern cruiser stern. The underwater portion of the bow is of bulbous form designed to give the best possible speed performance. Photographs of the vessel under construction and reproduced in Figs. 1 to 8 inclusive.

As shown on the general-arrangement drawing, the machinery spaces, *i.e.* generator-room, engine-room, propulsion motor-room and boiler-room, are all located at the after end of the vessel and also located aft are thin funnels of distinctive design.

The superstructure erections are well-proportioned and stream-lined, the height from the load line to the navigating bridge being about 108ft. Just abaft the navigating bridge is a well-raked stream-lined signal mast.

In all, there are 14 decks and a Navigating Bridge deck. Five of the levels are complete decks, *i.e.* the Promenade, *C*, *D*, *E* and *F* decks, the partial lower decks being *G*, *H* and *J* decks while the superstructure levels are the Captain's deck, Officers' deck, Sun deck, Games deck, *A* and *B* decks.

The hull is divided into 16 main compartments by 15 transverse watertight bulkheads extending up to *E* deck. There is also a continuous double bottom suitably subdivided into separate compartments for the carriage of fuel oil, water ballast and fresh water. Arrangements are also made for the carriage of fresh water in the forward and after peak tanks, and deep tanks are also located forward of, and below,

H

No. 1 cargo hold. Further deep tanks immediately forward of the machinery spaces provide additional capacity for fuel oil.

Spaces allocated to the carriage of cargo are Nos. 1, 2 and 3 holds and their associated lower 'tween deck spaces, with special lock-up spaces in No. 1 'tween decks.

Aluminium has been used almost exclusively in place of steel above the main hull structure, thus effecting a valuable saving in weight and as the saving is largely restricted to the upper works it provides a valuable contribution to the stability.

Fig. 2.—An Impressive View of the Bulbous Bow.

Fig. 3.—First Keel Plate being Laid.

Fig. 4.—Centre Girder Erected.

Fig. 5 (Left).—Tank Top in Position.

TABLE I.—PRINCIPAL DIMENSIONS AND OTHER LEADING CHARACTERISTICS OF THE "CANBERRA"

Length overall	820ft. 0in.
Length B.P.	740ft. 0in.
Breadth	102ft. 0in.
Gross tonnage	45,000
Passengers:—	
First-class	548
Tourist-class	1,690
Crew	960
Total complement....................	3,198
Cargo capacity cu. ft.	150,000
S.H.P.	85,000
Service speed, knots	27½

Accommodation for some 548 first-class passengers is arranged in cabins on A, B, C and D decks, a large number of the rooms being single berth with the provision of a folding upper berth, which can be used if required. Similarly many of the two-berth rooms have a folding upper berth.

A large number of the cabins are arranged in blocks of "courts" so designed that each of the inboard cabins receives daylight through specially arranged windows in the stepped bulkheads of the "courts." A number of suites are also provided, and all cabins have a private bathroom or toilet.

The first-class public rooms include an observation lounge, ballroom, lido café and nursery on the Games deck, lounge, golden bar and writing room on the Promenade deck and dining saloon on E deck.

Tourist-class passengers are accommodated in two and four-berth rooms on A, B, C, D, E, F and G decks. A certain number of the two-berth rooms can alternatively be arranged as four-berth rooms. A good proportion of the remaining rooms have private toilets.

Public rooms for the tourist-class passengers include a ballroom, nursery and children's playground on the Games deck, pool café on B deck, lounge, long bar, teenagers' room, smoking room and card room and reading and writing rooms on the Promenade deck, and a large dining saloon on E deck.

A number of cabins are arranged and positioned so that they can be allocated to first-class or tourist-class accommodation, increasing the first-class total by 50 or the tourist-class by 100.

Centrally arranged on A deck is a large cinema which can be used for first or tourist-class passengers as required.

Extensive games and promenade areas are provided for both first-class and tourist-class passengers, while a swimming pool with terraced surround is centrally situated for first-class passengers and two swimming pools are provided for the tourist-class. Both the first and tourist-class games areas on the Sun deck are enclosed with glazed screens.

Suitable shopping areas and hairdressing saloons are provided for both classes of passengers.

For the captain, officers and engineers, accommodation is arranged in stream-lined deckhouses on the Captain's deck, Officers' deck and Sun deck. Rooms for the petty officers are on C deck forward of the first-class accommodation while cabins for the crew are on D, E, F and G decks forward.

A large galley and pantry area, equipped with modern electrical cooking appliances is situated centrally for serving the first and tourist-class dining saloons, and these are amply refrigerated and dry storerooms are conveniently arranged on the decks below.

Electric lifts serve all decks for passenger use, while a staff lift serves all decks from the Captain's deck to the tank top, and stores and baggage lifts are also arranged, in addition to which specially designed store and baggage conveyors are also provided.

A fully-equipped laundry is arranged aft for general use, while separate launderettes are conveniently placed for passengers' personal convenience.

Cargo handling equipment includes two electric cargo transporters which handle cargo for Nos. 2 and 3 holds through ship's side doors, while derrick posts and derricks with electric winches are provided for dealing with cargo at No. 1 hatchway.

The vessel is fitted with electro-hydraulic steering and powerful electric anchor and warping capstans forward and aft. Two pairs of stabilisers are fitted and a bow propeller is installed to assist in manoeuvring the vessel in harbour.

The lighting installation is extensive and the public rooms are equipped with modern design lighting schemes which make full use of fluorescent tubes. Special floodlighting is installed for the Sun deck, swimming pool, etc. Illuminated signs at lavatories, lifts, etc., are fitted throughout the ship.

The generating plant comprises four 1,500-kW. 440-volts, three-phase, 60-cycle turbo alternators and there are also two 200-kW. 440-volts three-phase, 60-cycle Diesel-driven emergency alternators. A 230-volts battery comes into circuit automatically in the event of power failure to supply lights and communications until the emergency generators are started.

The 300-kW. direct-current generators which supply excitation power for the main propulsion motors are coupled in tandem with the 1,500-kW. alternators and they are driven by the same turbine. Two large turbo-alternators supply power to the propulsion motors.

Electric power is distributed from the main switchboard to masterboards which are positioned throughout the ship, and an interconnector is fitted between the main and emergency switchboards. Auxiliary motors in the machinery spaces are controlled from five group starter switchboards situated in the engine-room, boiler room and auxiliary machinery rooms.

Power is supplied for engine and deck auxiliaries, steering gear, refrigerating plant, galley and pantry equipment, air-conditioning plant, ventilating fans, lifts and lighting.

Two 24-volt batteries supply the low power system and they are arranged so that, while one battery is supplying power the other is being charged. Manual fire alarms are supplied from this source.

The main propelling machinery consists of a turbo-electric two-shaft installation. The two turbines, of all-impulse design, are each directly coupled to an alternator, and each propulsion motor is of the double unit type.

Exhaust from the turbines is collected in regenerative type condensers.

One small and three large oil-fired watertube boilers of the two-drum single-furnace E.S.D. type are fitted. The large boilers supply steam at a pressure of 750 lb per sq. in. and a temperature of 960 deg. F. at the superheater outlet, while the small boiler supplies steam at a pressure of 750 lb per sq. in. and a temperature of 900 deg. F. at the superheater outlet.

A Weldex bled-steam air pre-heater and a Foster Wheeler gilled-tube economiser are incorporated in each boiler. The boilers work under the Howden system of forced draught, in conjunction with automatic combustion control.

Steam for hotel services, tank heating, etc., is supplied from the auxiliary turbo-alternator pass-out steam range.

Before entering the boilers the condensate from the main propelling units passes through a system of regenerative feed heating.

Cooling water for the main condensers is supplied by means of scoop circulation with four motor-driven axial-flow circulating pumps. Fresh-water for the main boilers and ship's use is supplied by a Weir double-effect evaporating

Fig. 8 (Right).—Bulbous Bow under Construction.

Fig. 6.—Main Frames Practically Complete.

Fig. 7.—Aluminium Superstructure.

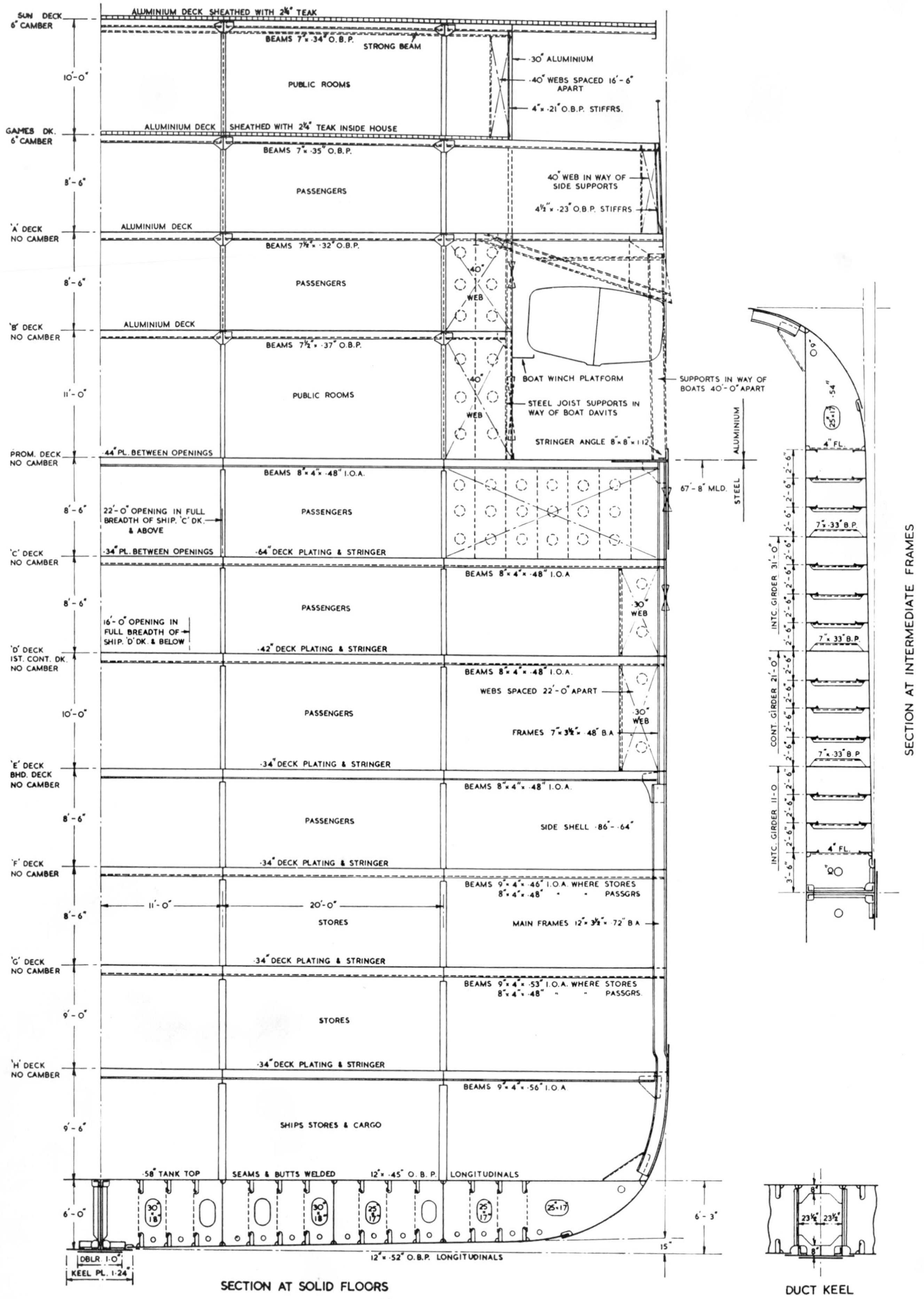

Fig. 9.—Midship Section.

ss *Canberra*

Turbo-electric passenger liner

Statistics and Technical Data

Completed 1961 by Harland & Wolff Ltd., Belfast.

Yard no. 1621.

Gross tonnage	49,073 tons
Net tonnage	25,190 tons
Length overall	249.5 metres (819 feet)
Breadth	31.3 metres (103 feet)
Draught (full)	10 metres (33 feet)
Service speed	23.5 knots (maximum designed speed 27.5 knots)
Engines	2 x British Thomson Houston
Propellers	2
Stabilisers	2 x Denny Brown Fin
Bow thrusters	1
Rudders	1
Crew	805
Passengers	1,750 maximum passenger capacity
	1,665 regular passenger capacity
Passenger space ratio	27 tons
Passenger decks	10
Passenger cabins	787: 285 outside
	4 suites
	320 inside
	178 court

Maiden voyage commenced 2nd June 1961 – Southampton – Sydney, Auckland.

Last voyage – 10th - 30th September 1997 – Southampton – Mediterranean cruise.

(Photograph by FotoFlite, Ashford, Kent TN23 1ES, England.)

Published by Ships Monthly Ltd., 222 Branston Road, Burton-on-Trent, Staffordshire DE14 3BT and presented with the September 1997 issue of 'Ships Monthly'.

plant in conjunction with a condensate cooled distiller. All make-up feed is passed through an Ionostat.

The auxiliary machinery is electrically-driven with the exception of the air ejectors, the main turbo-feed pumps, one harbour feed pump, the large boiler forced-draught fans and the air-conditioning compressors, which are all steam turbine driven.

STRUCTURAL ARRANGEMENT

From the midship section drawing (Fig. 9) it will be observed that a large amount of welding has been worked into the hull structure. The shell plating is generally flush but outside strakes have been used for the sheerstrake, bilge strake and flat-plate keel. With a scantling of 1·25in. the keel plate is fitted with a 1-in. doubler in way of the centre girder. Ordinary bulb plate longitudinals, 12in. by 0·52in., are fitted on the bottom shell and these extend for 0·4 L amidships. The main frames, which consist of 12-in. by 3½-in. by 0·72-in. bulb angles, are joggled in way of the bilge strake and are bracketted to the tank top and to the beams supporting E deck. Above E deck the side frames are of 7-in. by 3½-in by 0·48-in. bulb angles and 0·30in. plate webs are spaced 22ft. apart.

In way of the aluminium superstructure, supports are spaced 40ft. apart in way of the boats. At a higher level, *i.e.* between A deck and the Games deck 0·40in. plate webs are arranged in line with the lower supports, and the side frames consist of 4½-in. by 0·23-in. ordinary bulb plate stiffeners.

All decks beneath the Games deck are worked without camber while both the Games deck and Sun deck have 6in. of camber.

The double bottom is 6ft. 0in. deep at the centreline, rising to 6ft. 3in. in the half breadth and there is a 15in. rise of floor.

The decks are of all-welded construction and are flush-plated. The tank top also has welded butts and seams and the flush-plating, 0·58in. thick, is supported by 12-in. by 0·45-in. ordinary bulb plate longitudinals, and these extend for 0·4 L amidships.

All decks below D deck are of 0·34-in. plating while the plating for D deck is 0·42in. thick and that for C deck 0·64in. thick, but a scantling of 0·34in. has been used between openings. The plating for the Promenade deck, the uppermost steel deck, is 0·44in. thick. H deck is supported on 9-in. by 4-in. by 0·56-in. inverted ordinary angle beams while on all other decks the beams consist of inverted ordinary angles but the scantlings generally are 8in. by 4in. by 0·48in. However, in way of stores spaces, the scantlings are increased to 9in. by 4in. by 0·46in. at F deck, 9in. by 4in. by 0·53in. at G deck and 9in. by 4in. by 0·56in. at H deck.

The frame spacing generally is 33in. but is reduced to 27in. in way of the panting area and 24in. at the ends.

Curves of floodable length are shown in Fig. 10.

Special anti-corrosion paints, supplied by Hangers Paints, Ltd., are based on the Shell Chemical Company's Epikote epoxy resins. The hull coating is an Epikote/polyamide paint and was specially developed for marine use by Hangers Paints, Ltd. The Toxion anti-fouling system has been provided by Messrs. F. A. Hughes & Co., Ltd., for the protection of the underwater portion of the hull. Internal installation work was carried out at Belfast, and the external pipework was fitted in dry-dock prior to the vessel's maiden voyage. No anti-fouling paint was applied to the hull and the Toxion system will be operated whenever the vessel is at anchor or in port.

The underwater hull is cathodically protected against corrosion by a system in which a direct low voltage electric current is made to flow through the sea on to the hull to suppress the electro-chemical corrosion that would normally occur. This system has been developed by Messrs. E. Reader and Sons, Ltd.

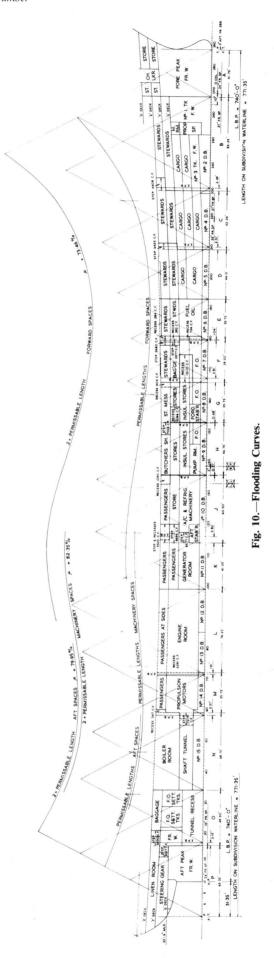

Fig. 10.—Flooding Curves.

LAUNCH OF "CANBERRA"

A Day to Remember at Belfast

THE 16th March, 1960, was indeed a memorable day for Northern Ireland for, in addition to constituting an outstanding event in the lives of many people resident in the immediate vicinity of the Musgrave Yard, the launch of the *Canberra* created immense interest throughout the United Kingdom and other countries. The fact that the *Canberra* is the largest merchant vessel to be built in a United Kingdom shipyard for over 20 years no doubt helped to increase the interest aroused.

The launching ceremony was very gracefully performed by Dame Pattie Menzies, G.B.E., wife of the Prime Minister of Australia, in the presence of a great and enthusiastic assembly of people. A novel touch was introduced by Dame Pattie Menzies when she pinned a sprig of white heather, which she had carried 6,000 miles, to the ribbons attached to the bottle of Australian wine with which she performed the launching ceremony. The heather had been sent to her in Australia by Sir William C. Currie, G.B.E., who, at the time of the launch, was chairman of the P. & O. Company.

Photographs of this momentous occasion are reproduced in Figs. 11, 12 and 13, while Figs. 14 and 15 show the make-up arrangement in the way of the forward and after poppets.

Among the guests were the Governor of Northern Ireland, Lord Wakehurst, the Prime Minister, Viscount Brookeborough, the Lord Mayor of Belfast and members of the Northern Ireland Government. Sir Frederick E. Rebbeck, K.B.E., D.Sc., D.L., J.P., presided at the luncheon after the launch. The Prime Minister proposed the toast of the Peninsular & Oriental Steam Navigation Company, and stated that he felt that the *Canberra* had not been built by Messrs. Harland & Wolff alone but by all the people of Northern Ireland.

Sir William Currie replied and he recalled that at the

Fig. 13.—"Canberra" Entering the Water—Note the Impressive Poppet Arrangement.

launch of the *Arcadia* seven years ago he had said that it was not without very careful consideration that his company had decided to build, in conjunction with the Orient Line, a fleet of large, fast passenger vessels, but much reduced in numbers compared with pre-war.

Since they took that decision the inflationary spiral had caused each successive ship to cost more than her predecessor, but they felt that there could be no going back. It was a question of carrying on or getting out and the answer was certainly not the latter.

He said that both inside and out, the *Canberra* would be different in plan and detail from any other ship the company had, but she would not be different for the sake of being different. "She will only be different when we judge that we have found some new and better solution to the old problems or where the advance of techniques and the standard of comfort we can offer has enabled us to add to the pleasure which we hope she will give her passengers.

When I say "we," I mean all those many people whose child she is, our own advisers, the top ranks at Harland and Wolff, Sir Hugh Casson and Mr. McBride, with Mr. Wright and Mr. Rendle, Miss Oakley and a list which might be much further extended if we had the time, and all the drive and vision of Sir Donald F. Anderson.

Sir Frederick Rebbeck replying said that the launch of the *Canberra* had been one of the very greatest in their history. Every time he had driven to the works he had instructed his driver to pass the *Canberra*, and he had watched her rising in the stocks to the huge magnificent vessel she was now.

The *Canberra* was one of the heaviest ships they had launched, as they had been able to put in her a lot of machinery which would normally go in later. They were proud to build such an outstanding vessel and he hoped that the skill and experience of the two great companies would produce a ship, when complete, of which they had every reason to be proud, and that the long association between them would continue.

Fig. 12.—Dame Pattie Menzies Performing the Launching Ceremony.

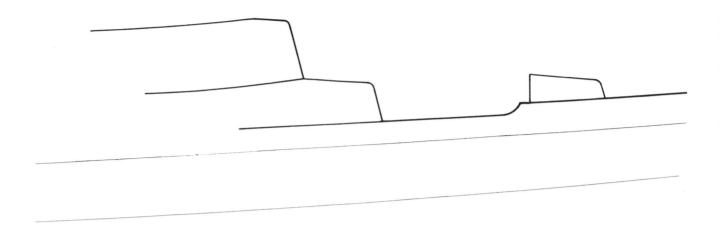

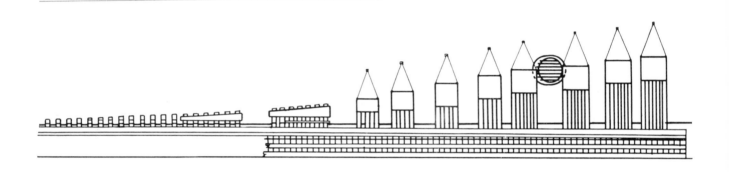

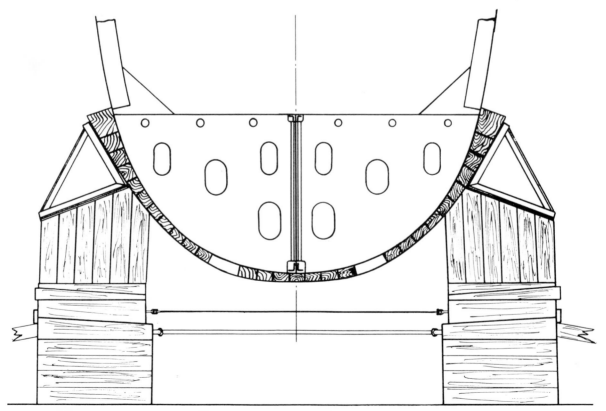

Fig. 14.—Make-up in Way of Forward Poppet.

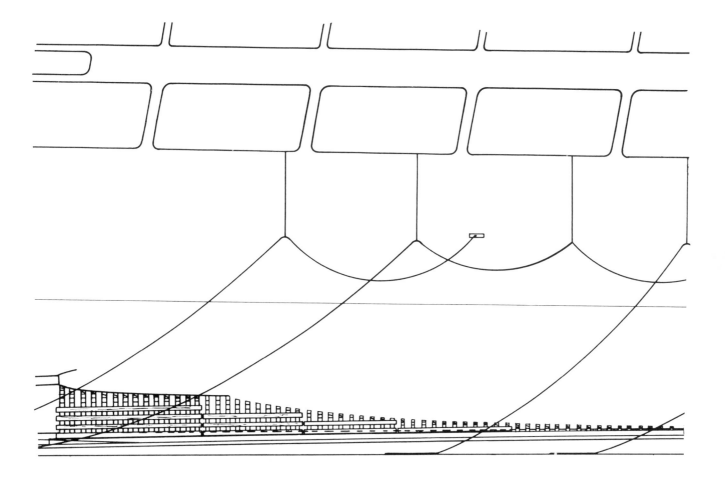

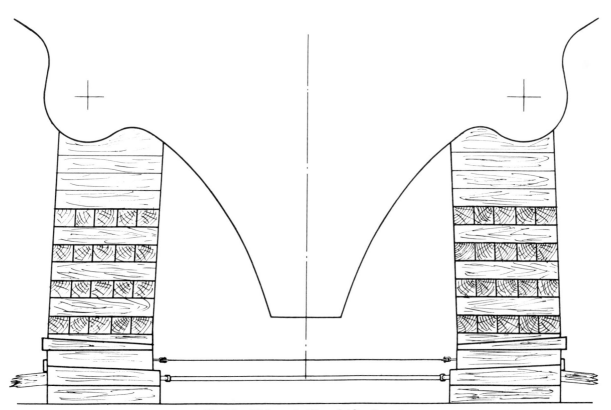

Fig. 15.—Make-up in Way of After Poppet.

SPECIAL FEATURES

ALUMINIUM SUPERSTRUCTURE

ONE of the outstanding features of the *Canberra* is the extent to which aluminium has been used in the superstructure. The use of this metal—totalling about 1,000 tons—has enabled a saving in structural weight of about 1,500 tons, and this has enabled arrangements to be made for the accommodation of more than 200 additional passengers.

There are four tiers of passenger accommodation in the superstructure, above which there are another four tiers of bridge decks. The twin funnels and the mast are also made of aluminium.

Of the total quantity of aluminium employed in the upper works of the *Canberra*, more than 800 tons of plates and extruded sections, all in B.A.28 alloy, have been provided by the British Aluminium Co., Ltd., while 140 tons of plate and sections in the alloys Noral B54S and Noral A56S, including all the material for the Games deck and the houses on that deck, have been supplied by Alcan Industries, Ltd.

Welding has been adopted exclusively in the construction of the superstructure. Panels of deck plating and deckhouse sides have been prefabricated in the welding shops by the inert-gas metal-arc process, using both automatic gantry and manually-operated machines. Deck panels up to 30ft. square were supplied complete with deck beams ready for erection on board, where they were welded to neighbouring panels.

The deep deck girders have also been prefabricated from plate webs and heavy bottom flanges, cut from plate or extruded sections. This method of manufacture has given the designer an unlimited choice of strength properties for each length of girder, which could only be matched in extruded sections by making a large number of costly dies. The extent

Fig. 15.—Aluminium Superstructure under Construction.

to which welding has been employed is, of course, one of the outstanding features of the aluminium superstructure. The British Aluminium Co., Ltd., have always played a leading part in the development of aluminium for shipbuilding, and of welding techniques. In 1954, the 72ft. welded aluminium yacht *Morag Mhor* was built for the company to demonstrate the application of the inert-gas metal-arc welding process to ship construction, and following the success of this venture the company co-operated with Clan Line Steamers, Ltd., London, and the Grangemouth Dockyard Co., Ltd., Grangemouth, in the construction of the first all-welded wheelhouse on an ocean-going merchant ship—the *Clan Robertson*.

Before aluminium shipbuilding sections were standardised by the British Standards Institution, the British Aluminium Co., Ltd., designed and manufactured two ranges of sections, one of which, specially for welded construction, was used on the *Clan Robertson*. In the *Canberra*, another new range of sections has been used, triangular bulb-plates, again first introduced by British Aluminium as an improvement on the square-bulb British Standard sections, to facilitate fillet welding on the periphery of the section.

Prior to building *Canberra*'s superstructure, Messrs. Harland & Wolff, Ltd., invited the co-operation of the British Aluminium Company in the design and construction, at Belfast, of a representative portion of a ship's superstructure. This provided practical experience of making many of the welded joints likely to be employed on the ship and confirmed that the shipbuilder's design proposals were well suited to the material.

Some of the plates used in the *Canberra* have been welded at the British Aluminium Company's rolling mills at Falkirk, where plates up to 14ft. wide may be made by automatically welding together two 7ft. components. Although 7ft. is the maximum width of plate which can be hot rolled, greater widths are often preferred by shipbuilders since 'tween deck heights are seldom less than 7ft. 6in. The welded plate manufactured at Falkirk has the welding bead removed and is virtually indistinguishable from unwelded plate.

Welding of the aluminium posed many problems and close collaboration between Quasi-Arc, Ltd., and Messrs. Harland & Wolff, Ltd., at an early stage in the planning, led to the design of two new automatic-welding gantries for work on the superstructure. These machines have spans of 35ft. and 54ft., and have been used very successfully for the high-speed welding of the large bulkhead and super-structure sections.

The gantries are each equipped with two welding heads, and can be employed either for the butt welding of aluminium plates or for the simultaneous production of two fillet welds between stiffeners and bulkhead panels. Welding is carried out at high speeds using the argon-shielded bare-wire (Sigma) process, and the machines are designed to operate at high duty cycles.

Among additional equipment supplied for work on the aluminium superstructure was a total of 40 semi-automatic Lynx machines which were used in the prefabrication shops and also on board the ship.

Much of the steel structure on the *Canberra* was welded with the prototype portal-frame gantry, developed in collaboration with Messrs. Harland & Wolff, Ltd., some years ago. This machine is equipped with two Unionmelt submerged-arc welding heads for simultaneous fillet welding on both sides of stiffeners, on bulkhead and deck panels.

TRANSPORTERS AND CONVEYORS

CARRON TRANSPORTERS

VARIOUS items of cargo, including passengers' baggage and motor cars will, of course, be carried in the *Canberra*, and if conventional cargo-handling equipment had been employed it would have imposed limitations on the design of the superstructure. Hatches would have had to be trunked up through a considerable number of decks, or the superstructure would have had to be cut away to provide deck space for the hatchways and handling equipment. As either method would have involved a considerable loss of valuable passenger accommodation it was decided to install Carron transporters which operate through the ship's side and leave the superstructure unaffected.

Two transporters are installed and they are identical units, very simple to use and requiring only one operator. Each consists of a steel boom, carried on rollers within the ship, and arranged to be power driven to project through doors in the ship's side, to suit docking arrangements. When not in use the boom is housed centrally within the ship.

In the operating position the boom extends some 30ft. from the side of the ship, and it is fitted with a travelling carriage from which is suspended a hoist with a cargo platform (see Fig. 16). Traversing, hoisting and lowering of the cargo platform is controlled by an operator who is accommodated in a cab on the carriage. The photographs reproduced in Figs. 17, 18 and 19 show details of the working mechanism.

To commence loading or unloading operations the ship's doors are opened and the boom is traversed outwards to the limit of its travel. Control is from a push-button panel inside the ship, power being provided by an electric motor and winch hauling on wire cables. To prevent the boom from moving if the ship's doors are closed there is an electrical interlock, which also stops the boom when it reaches the limit of its travel. It takes less than 1½ minutes to extend the boom, and when it reaches its working position the power supply is connected to the carriage.

Overhead conductors carry the power for the carriage, and these are mounted on the underside of the boom, but they are not energised until a power cable is plugged in manually. Two plug points are provided, one for port operation and the other for starboard operation, and they are so positioned that the power supply can only be connected when the boom is out.

A winch mechanism, from which hang four wire lifting ropes, is mounted on the travelling carriage. The wire ropes are led over pulleys on the car platform and returned to a fixed point on the carriage to give a double purchase, which gives a lifting capacity of three tons. Two crane-type controllers enable the operator to traverse the cab in either direction and to hoist or lower the platform as required.

To load a car, the carriage is traversed to the end of the

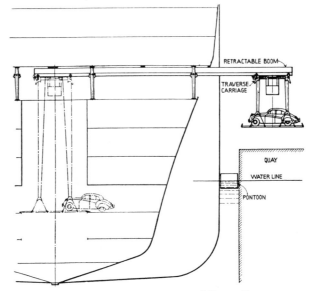

Fig. 16.—Diagrammatic Arrangement of Carron Transporters.

boom, the platform is lowered to the quay and the car is driven on. The platform is then raised, at a speed of 60ft. per min., until it is just under the carriage where it is automatically locked in position. The carriage is then traversed along the boom into the ship at a speed of 125ft. per min. At the inner limit of its travel the carriage is above a hatch trunk which leads to the lower decks where stowing arrangements are made.

It is necessary for the platform to be guided in the trunking, as it has a possible vertical travel of 45ft. and is only supported by the wire ropes. For this purpose four rigid guides are fixed to the sides of the trunking and there are slippers on the platform which engage with them. These slippers are bell-mouthed to ensure initial engagement as the platform is lowered.

The operator has full control over the motion through braking gear which is operated by the crane-type controllers in the cab.

Three decks are used for storage and on the lowest of these the platform rests on the deck, but for the intermediate levels easily removable stops are fitted to the guides to hold the platform while the car is removed. Warning lights are fitted to notify the operator when the platform is approaching the stops.

The transporter can also be used for handling cargo but a different platform is used and is connected directly to the ropes with a single purchase to give a lifting capacity of 1½ tons. Change-over from one platform to another can be carried out in a few minutes, as quick-change shackles and

Fig. 17.—The Carriage is Traversed by means of Endless Cables Wound Round Winding Spools Electrically Driven Through Reduction Gearing.

Fig. 18.—Boom Winding Winch with Endless Cables Arranged to Provide Port or Starboard Movement.

Fig. 19.—Electrical Collector Heads Pick up Current from the Overhead Conductors to Supply Power to the Hoist and Traverse Motors.

pins with safety locks are used to connect the hoisting ropes to the two platforms.

P.C.P. fully guarded overhead current collection equipment for the transporters has been provided by British Insulated Callender's Cables, Ltd. This fully guarded equipment ensures that all current-carrying parts of the conductor system are adequately insulated at all times and that the bare conductors are completely enclosed. This is attained by the use of an extruded rubber compound (P.C.P.) protective guard over conductors, and insulated shrouds over exposed metal fittings which support contact wires. An additional advantage is provided in situations where corrosive dust is present, since by the use of the protective guard the dust is prevented from settling on the conductors.

BAGGAGE CONVEYORS

Another impressive feature of the *Canberra* is the integrally-fitted automatic baggage conveyors which have been constructed by Messrs. J. Collis & Sons, Ltd. These conveyors will considerably reduce the periods lost in turn-round and minimise passengers' waiting time. With a full complement, approximately 5,000 separate pieces of baggage will have to be handled and the importance of an efficient loading system is underlined by the fact that one second lost per piece will increase the loading time by 75 minutes.

From the outset the owners have expressed a desire to maintain the clean lines of the vessel and to have a conveyor system which operates as a built-in portion of the ship's equipment.

It was necessary for the equipment to be able to load into and out of the baggage room on *F* deck and also from five cabin decks, as well as to be able to accommodate wide variations in berthing facilities. Variations in the vessel's displacement had also to be accounted for and up to 16ft. difference in tide levels.

These various requirements were met by designing a dual system, one part to carry baggage not wanted on voyage, direct into the baggage room, and the other taking wanted baggage for transfer to a Vertiveyor elevator which carries it to the required deck.

The deck conveyor installation consists of a horizontal section of Collis Statveyor with a ship-to-shore section at each end. This is supported by a gantry which can be moved either to the port or starboard side. From either side delivery is made to a point at which the baggage is sorted manually for the various upper decks and fed into the Vertiveyor.

Each of the five cabin decks served has a loading and discharging station, with a loading table. To enter the Ventiveyor the load has to pass through pneumatically-operated shutters, which are smoke and fire-proof, and which are automatically locked or opened in accordance with a press-button deck-selection mechanism. The transfer of baggage into or out of the Vertiveyor trays is operated pneumatically.

The baggage room conveyors comprise a fixed double installation, one on each side of the ship, running from shell

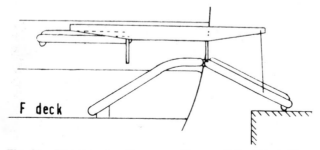

Fig. 20.—Baggage-room Conveyor with one of the Ship-to-Shore
Sections Lowered to the Quay.

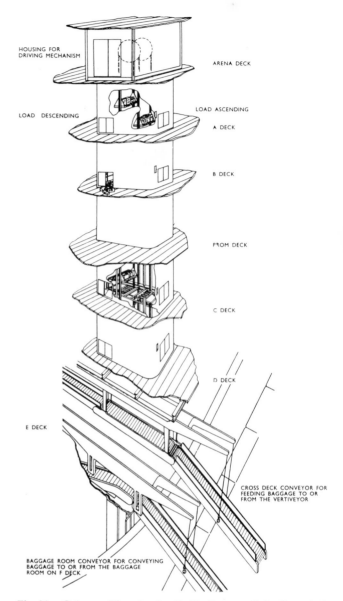

Fig. 21.—Cut-away View showing the Vertiveyor and the Cross-deck
and Baggage-room Conveyors.

doors on *E* deck, through the decking and down into the baggage room on *F* deck. These are swan-necked slat conveyors which can be connected with the quays by means of straight sections of conveyor carried by a travelling overhead gantry located on *E* deck. When the conveyor is to be connected to the quay the gantry is extended through the ship's side to the appropriate position and the conveyor is then lowered to ground.

The baggage room conveyors can be operated in either direction and can be remotely controlled from the baggage room or from either end. The installation has been designed for a unit load capacity of 50 ℔ per running ft. at 60ft. per min.

The original plans provided for four stores conveyors which are also installed on *E* deck and three of these units are attached to retractable gantries which lower them from the ship to the quay and raise them off the deck when not in use. They discharge on the deck for manual stowage of stores. The fourth stores conveyor is portable and is not provided with a supporting gantry. As already mentioned, the original plans were to have four stores conveyors, but as a result of development since the work started an additional conveyor has been provided. Diagrammatic drawings of the Vertiveyor and the cross-deck and baggage room conveyor are reproduced in Figs. 20 and 21.

To drive the *Canberra's* conveyor system there are 23 Crompton Parkinson motors fitted with magnetic brakes, including 18 geared units. They range from 5 H.P. to 1 H.P., and are all suitable for operation from the ship's 440-volt three-phase supply.

Each conveyor is separately driven and the magnetic brakes are so connected that they apply a positive arresting of the load in the event of a power supply failure.

HYDRAULIC SYSTEMS

HYDRAULIC systems which operate removable partitions on the passenger decks of the *Canberra* have been supplied by Messrs. Short Brothers & Harland, Ltd.

The *Canberra's* large ballroom partition is arranged to be raised vertically through a slot in the deck, the operation being carried out by a single hydraulic jack and associated linkage. Two auxiliary jacks ensure a smooth start and also bring the partition to rest without shock when it is lowered to the stowed position. A hydraulic lock positively fastens the partition in the raised or stowed position. Control is by electro-hydraulic methods from two push buttons positioned near the partition. An emergency button is provided to stop the partition at any time during the raising or lowering operation.

The Games deck screens are hinged at their upper edges and are swung upwards by hydraulic jacks through an arc of 90 deg. These jacks are also designed so that they bring the screens slowly to rest without shock. Although the jacks are capable of holding the screens in the raised position by hydraulic lock, positive mechanical catches are provided for each screen. These catches automatically engage or disengage when the appropriate force is applied by the jacks; their design is based on a well-proven type of aircraft under-carriage lock.

The port and starboard groups of screens are independently operated by an electro-hydraulic push-button control system similar to that of the ballroom partition. An emergency stop button is provided for each group to arrest the movement of the screens and to hold them in any position by hydraulic lock.

A manual hydraulic control system for the partition and screens is provided for use in the unlikely event of the failure of either the electrical supply or electro-hydraulic selectors.

STABILISERS

THE stabilising equipment in the *Canberra* is of the well-known Denny-Brown activated-fin type, which is in world-wide use in some 250 vessels. Ships fitted with this equipment range from small cross-channel vessels to the very largest, including the *Queen Mary* and *Queen Elizabeth*. In the *Canberra*, as in the two *Queens* and a number of other large ships, two pairs of fins are fitted, to form, in effect, two separate stabilisers which can be operated synchronously or independently.

The active part of the installation is the fins, which can be housed within the hull when not required. These fins are of aerofoil shape with a flap at the after end, and each is carried on a shaft which can oscillate the fin through a maximum angle of 20 deg. above or below the mid position to give the required angle of attack of the fin on the water. The photo-

Fig. 22.—Work in Progress on Forward Port Stabiliser.

graph reproduced in Fig. 22 shows work in progress on the forward port stabiliser, while the recess for the forward starboard stabiliser is shown in Fig. 23.

Each of the fins in *Canberra* has an area of 90 sq. ft. and, when in use extends horizontally 12ft. 6in. from the ship's side at a point about 22ft. below the surface of the water. When it is desired to stabilise the ship the fins are extended and then oscillated synchronously and in opposite senses so that the pressure on the angled fins, due to the ship's forward motion through the water, gives a righting moment which opposes the roll.

It is essential that the reversal of the angle of the fin be effected rapidly (in the *Canberra* the time required is about 2·9 seconds) and this is effected by means of a V.S.G. variable-delivery, servo-controlled pump driven by a 35-H.P. electric

Fig. 23.—Recess for Forward Starboard Stabiliser.

motor, which provides the pressure fluid for operating the rams which oscillate the fin. This same motor also drives a small auto-controlled V.S.G. pump which provides servo pressure for the main pump control and also for extending or retracting the fin. One power unit is provided for each fin and flywheels are fitted to the motor to absorb the peak horse-power demand.

Solenoid-operated valves, controlled either from the bridge or stabiliser compartment provide control over fin extension and retraction. The output from the variable-delivery pumps is controlled by special equipment designed and manufactured for this purpose by Messrs. Muirhead & Co., Ltd. This apparatus is of the latest compensated-control type and is entirely automatic in action. It consists of two gyroscopes which, in conjunction with a mechanical differentiator and fin angle transmitter, produce five control functions—roll angle, roll velocity, roll acceleration, fin feedback and natural list—which are combined automatically in the required proportions to give the best results obtainable from the fins in any sea conditions.

The natural list feature causes the gear to stabilise about the mean rolling position thus saving ship's propulsive power in that the stabiliser fins do not attempt to compensate for an out-of-trim or listed condition. If required, the natural list can be switched off for stabilisation to the true vertical. The resultant output signal from the gyroscope unit controls a small hydraulic servo, the output of which is hydraulically amplified in a second stage to control the main V.S.G. pumps.

Control panels located in the bridge and in the stabiliser compartment contain indicator lamps and signalling switches, etc., and a control switch on the bridge starts and stops the fin oscillation.

BOW PROPELLERS

TO assist in docking and manoeuvring a Pilgrim lateral-thrust unit has been supplied by Messrs. Brown Brothers and Co., Ltd., who have worked in conjunction with the Manganese Bronze & Brass Co., Ltd., to designs evolved by the P. & O. Research and Development Company.

The unit is fitted with a two-blade propeller mounted in an athwartships tunnel, 6ft. 7in. diameter which is located about 70ft. from the bow. By turning the propeller in one direction or another a jet of water is formed, and the resultant force applied to the vessel is of considerable assistance when manoeuvring alongside docks and in similar situations.

Power is provided by a Harland & Wolff horizontal, variable-speed, uni-directional, synchronous electric motor (60 cycle, three-phase) capable of developing 800 H.P. at a maximum speed of 1,200 r.p.m. This prime mover is mounted on the deck over the bow thrust unit compartment and the drive is transmitted by means of Crofts flexible couplings to a Hindmarch/MWD oil-operated reversing gear, type MW-special, designed and manufactured by Modern Wheel Drive, Ltd.

The reverse gear is arranged with a right-angle drive and the output shaft is vertically below the gearbox seating. This drive then goes down to the propeller which has another right-angle drive in its supporting hub, and the reduction gearing in the thrust unit itself results in a maximum propeller speed of approximately 300 r.p.m. The drawing reproduced in Fig. 24 gives the layout of the bow propeller and also shows the arrangement of the driving motor and the Hindmarch/MWD oil-operated reverse-reduction gearing.

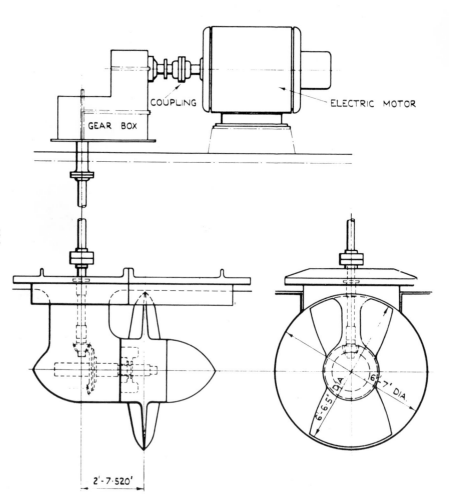

Fig. 24.—Layout of Bow Propeller showing Arrangement of Driving Motor and Reverse-reduction Gearing.

Fig. 25.—Bow Propeller Fitted in the Athwartships Tunnel at the Forward End of the Ship.

A mechanically-driven lubricating oil pump is incorporated in the Hindmarch/MWD gearbox, which also has an additional pump for circulating oil round the propeller gearbox.

Start, stop, speed variation and direction of thrust are all effected electrically by means of a control stand mounted on the bridge.

An interesting feature of the installation is that the thrust-unit compartment forms a watertight cofferdam space which can be pressurised, and into which the complete unit can be withdrawn for overhaul while the vessel is still afloat. The photograph reproduced in Fig. 25 shows the bow propeller and also the aperture through which it can be raised. Every precaution has been taken, however, to prevent damage to the propeller blades, and louvre-like slats are fitted across both the port and starboard apertures to prevent fouling by flotsam and cables, etc.

As the prime mover has a synchronous speed of 1,200 r.p.m. and a full load speed of 1,183 r.p.m. giving a slip of 17 r.p.m., the Allen West starting equipment is designed to operate the motor at a first speed of 800 r.p.m. (247 H.P.), a second speed of 935 r.p.m. (395 H.P.), a third speed of 1,105 r.p.m. (650 H.P.) and a fourth speed of 1,183 r.p.m. (800 H.P.).

Hand-operated turning gear is fitted to the gearbox and the propeller pod has an input shaft speed of 1,200 r.p.m. (1,183 r.p.m. under load), but the bevel gear ratio of 51 : 13 gives an output shaft speed of 301·5 r.p.m. under load.

The blades and cone of the propeller are constructed of Nikalium having an electro potential of 0·22 volts. The diameter of the blades over the tips is 6ft. 6½in. and the pitch, which is non-uniform, has a mean value of 5ft. 9in. A thrust of 8·5 tons is available with the propeller operating at the fourth speed of 300 r.p.m. This reduces to 6·7 tons at the third speed of 266 r.p.m., 5·1 tons at the second speed of 233 r.p.m. and 3·8 tons at the first speed of 200 r.p.m.

STEELPLATE TOUGHENED GLASS

Considerable use has been made throughout the passenger decks of steelplate toughened glass, manufactured by Steele's (Contractors), Ltd. Steelplate is toughened polished plate glass manufactured in thicknesses of $\frac{3}{16}$ in. and upwards. The main difference between ordinary and annealed glasses and toughened glass, is that the former has strain removed from it by annealing and the latter has stable balance stresses deliberately introduced by heat treatment. The high compressions in the surface zones are balanced equally by high tension in the centre. Toughened glass is no more resistant to scratching or abrasion than annealed glass.

When glass is passed through the toughening process, the result is to produce a stronger finished product which is more resistant than ordinary annealed glass, to impact, pressure or wave shock. The degree of strength varies, of course, with the thickness and composition, but Steele's toughened glass produces far greater strength—at least four times stronger than annealed glass.

The remarkable increased resistance to sudden temperature changes found in all toughened glass is because the inherent properties are not greatly altered by the ambient temperature within the range 90 deg. F. to 563 deg. F. A window of Steele's toughened glass can be exposed to a radiant furnace heat to the extent that the surface of the glass attains a temperature of 482 deg. F. while the reverse surface is exposed to ambient air temperature. Steelplate—and other products of Steele's (Contractors), Ltd.—Steelcast and Steeltuff—will also withstand the test rigours of molten metal and hot scale splashing.

Providing the exposure is not prolonged, or too frequent, toughened glass remains stable up to 563 deg. F. and can be used at temperatures a little in excess of this figure.

Steelplate, Steelcast and Steeltuff provide considerably greater flexibility than annealed glass of the same thickness, due to the high compression stress in the surface.

When broken, Steelplate and other toughened glass disintegrates into small segments which prevent serious injury—a most important feature when installed in crowded areas.

In the *Canberra* there are 38 Steelplate toughened glass doors and assemblies in the first-class spaces, and the average sizes are 84in. by 36in. These doors have a top and bottom rail with a side stile on the inner edge. One face of the stile stands proud of the glass by 1in. and this serves as a handle. Aluminium has been used for the rails and stiles. The doors are pivoted on double and single-action floor springs with a top pivot concealed in the timber transome bar.

In the tourist-class spaces there are 31 Steelplate toughened glass doors and assemblies, the average sizes again being 84in. by 36in. Delta metal No. 2 has been used for the 3¼in. top rail, L-shaped bottom rail and side stile. Screwed to the top of the L-shape is a specially designed silver-bronze handle. Here, again, the doors are pivoted on double and single-action floor springs with a top pivot concealed in the timber transome bar.

Steelplate toughened glass has also been used for seven showcase doors in the first-glass shop area (sizes 76in. by 32in.) and for the transomes (30in. by 32in.). The whole assembly has a metal channel down both long edges and incorporated in one side of the door are two hinges on which the door swings. On the other side of the door, welded to the channel, is a 6-in. by 1-in. handle.

A total of 12 Steelplate toughened glass weatherproof doors, with dimensions of 73in. by 36in., situated in external parts of the ship, have also been provided. Around the door is a top and bottom rail with a side stile, and on the fixed edge are special hinges on which the door swings—these hinges serve to thoroughly weatherproof the doors. On the other edge of the door is a channel which stands proud of the glass on each side and serves as a handle. Aluminium finished metal has been used for the door fittings, and an additional feature of the doors is a plate which has been welded to one channel on the inner edge, in such a way that it overlaps the channel on the other door making the gap between the doors waterproof.

Fig. 26.—First-class Observation Lounge on Games Deck.

IN the *Canberra*, an attempt has been made to produce a layout which meets the needs of every occasion and yet remains new and exciting, and the public rooms, therefore, differ considerably from normally accepted practice, as also do many of the staterooms.

New materials have been used to a large extent, and very special care has been given to the lighting effects. Each public room in the *Canberra* has been treated individually and each has its own special appeal. Photographs of the accommodation are reproduced in Figs. 26 to 60.

ACCOMMODATION

Fig. 27.—Enclosed Area on Promenade Deck.

The task of decorating and furnishing the interior of the vessel has been shared between a number of designers. Heading this group, under Mr. John West, who has been responsible for the design of the *Canberra*, are Sir Hugh Casson, Neville Conder & Partners, whose work, together with that of his assistants, led by Mr. Timothy Rendle, is seen in the first-class spaces; Mr. John Wright, who, with his assistant Mr. Frederick Hickman, has been largely responsible for the tourist-class spaces; and Miss Barbara Oakley, who has designed and decorated all classes of passenger accommodation, alleyways, all officers' quarters and crew mess rooms. Heal's Contracts, Ltd., have carried out the work in the first-class observation lounge (Crow's Nest), in association with Mr. John Wright, and the eight *de-luxe* suites on C deck, in association with Miss Barbara Oakley. Other firms have, of course, worked in close association with the designers.

The first-class public rooms include a lounge (Meridian Room), writing room and library (Menzies Room), Century Bar, a private room for dining or entertaining (Crystal Room), and observation lounge (Crow's Nest), a ballroom (Bonito Club), children's playroom and playground, ladies' and gentlemen's hairdressing salons (the ladies' salon includes a beauty parlour under the supervision of a trained beautician), shops, etc., and a restaurant.

The tourist-class public rooms include a lounge (William Fawcett Room), reading rooms and library, the Cricketers' Tavern, smoking room and card rooms (Peacock Room), a pool café (Alice Springs), a ballroom (Island Room), a teenagers' room (Pop Inn), children's playroom and playground, ladies' and gentlemen's hairdressing salons, a shop, and a restaurant.

A large cinema, capable of accommodating 332 people, is situated centrally on A deck for the use of either first-class or tourist-class passengers. The cinema is equipped to show CinemaScope as well as standard screen films, and Stereophonic sound equipment is installed. The ceiling has been designed as a suspended acoustic shell stopping short of the walls and, within the space, continuous lighting is concealed round the perimeter of the room to throw up in relief the textured wall treatment. The shell ceiling, which has a sculptural form, is illuminated indirectly for stage productions, and for this purpose footlights and spotlights are provided.

There are separate ladies' and gentlemen's hairdressing salons in both classes. The first-class ladies' salon has special backwash chairs designed by Kenneth Gibson, A.R.I.B.A., for Richard Henry, Ltd.—the first time that Richard Henry's exclusive chair has been fitted in a liner.

FIRST-CLASS PUBLIC ROOMS

Restaurant—

The chief aims in designing the restaurant were to counteract the effect of the very large area of the room (extending the full 100ft. width of the ship), together with the rather low ceiling height, and also to design an artificial lighting scheme which would be bright and cheerful and would counteract any feeling of oppression that the lack of side windows might give, the room being too low down in the ship to allow natural lighting to be used. To solve the first problem the room has been broken up visually by means of raising a portion of the ceiling; by designing a sunken area to the centre of the floor, to which access is gained by steps; and by using pillar-casings to form screen walls which prevent the whole of the room being visible from any one point. Further visual dividers are designed in the form of high-backed banquette seating in bays on each side of the ship, each bay seating 12 and forming, as it were, small rooms on their own. It was considered essential that the bright, cheerful lighting required for breakfast and lunch should be subdued and varied in form for dinner. During the day there will be bright ceiling lights, formed by clusters of glowing cylinders specially woven from glass reinforced plastic, and continuously along each side of the ship there will be the effect of strong sunlight filtering through woven straw screens. For evening this lighting is replaced by glowing lanterns placed in the centre of each table. Finishing materials for the room are mainly natural wood and leather and the floor is carpeted. A type of inlay is worked as a frieze into the wooden balustrade around the centre lower section of the floor and an inlaid relief forms the main feature on the wall behind the captain's table.

Meridian Room—

In planning the lounge area, several smaller and related spaces were also required; a sit-up bar, writing rooms, library, magazine room, service rooms, and a space for a staircase which rises up to the observation lounge (Crow's Nest). The chief feature of the design is the use of a type of open-planning, the area being designed virtually as one room and, by means of a series of curving walls, rooms have been formed within the "folds." Within one dark panelled fold the staircase rises up as a brightly-lighted white spiral. In another part of the room the curving walls enclose the sit-up bar, the counter for which has been designed as a sculptural shape formed by laminations of very darkly coloured hardwood. Acting as a foil to the curving screen walls, the main central seating area of the lounge is illuminated by a spiky and angular ceiling light fitting 30ft. long and formed of glittering metal facets. Decorative effect in the lounge is obtained chiefly from the lounge chairs which have been specially designed of glass reinforced plastic. Brightly coloured removable covers fit over the foam plastic upholstered plastic shells, which give a light and shiplike character

J

for the furniture; this is a departure from the tradition of "club" armchairs in ships.

Bonito Club and Pool Area—

The swimming pool, with its terracing, and the adjacent pool café, have been designed, so far as possible, as one space. The teak boarding of the pool terrace continues into the centre of the pool café to form the dance floor, and the whole of the glass wall, which is the only division between the terracing and the café, has been designed to slide vertically into the floor to form one continuous deck surface so that dancing can continue out on to the terrace. In the pool café, as in the first-class restaurant, a special form of artificial lighting has been designed for the evenings. Over the whole of the dance floor area a cellular glass reinforced plastic ceiling gives a soft, golden diffused, light through honeycomb-shaped cells. The café tables at each side of the room are illuminated internally, giving a soft glow through their decorative top surfaces, and the orchestra is spot-lighted against a dark richly-coloured mural decoration. The swimming pool, which is of white mosaic, is set within the enclosing tiers of sunbathing terraces, forming an arena which gives ample protection from the wind.

Fig. 28.—First-class Pool and Bonito Club.

Fig. 29.—First-class Two plus One Court Cabin.

Fig. 30.—First-class Court Alleyway.

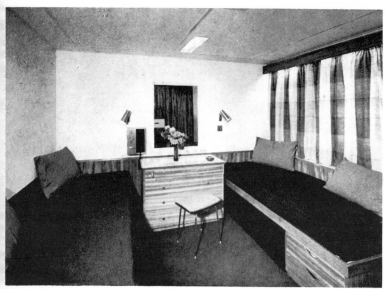

Fig. 31.—First-class Two-berth Cabin.

Bureau Area—

The first-class shop, designed as a group of brightly lit floor-to-ceiling showcases, is the focal point of the bureau concourse. Leading off this area are the ladies' and gentlemen's hairdressing salons (which have luminous ceilings to give an ideal form of lighting) and a card room which is also designed to be used for private parties and dinners. One wall of this room is treated with mosaic formed by large fragments of coloured glass faced with a transparent film of clear resin.

Crystal Room—

To be used for parties and cards, the Crystal Room has a carpet of dark mottled leaf green and black with the surrounding edging of white terrazzo. The walls are light grey wood veneer in parquet strips, while the whole of the ceiling is covered with a white plastic louvred grid, illuminated to give an overall diffused lighting effect which can be adjusted by means of a dimmer. The tables are in satin chrome and have reversible tops—baize one side and black leather the other, and the glass-reinforced plastic chairs, with satin chrome legs, have bright orange covers. The focal point of interest is a decorative panel in resin and glass fragments—employing a technique, on a very large scale, that is used for setting small botanical specimens into clear resin blocks.

Crow's Nest—

Designed for recreational purposes, on traditional ship lines, the Crow's Nest emphasises the sweeping curves and radiused structure. The forward bulkhead has 41 full-height windows which give a magnificent frontal view, with similar windows aft looking out onto the enclosed Games deck. The entrances are placed to port and starboard from the Games deck, and the spiral staircase from the first-class lounge terminates in the centre of this room. All wall surfaces are flush and painted eggshell white. Ceilings are close-boarded in yacht fashion, also painted white, with concealed cold-cathode lighting to the periphery. Main lighting is from clusters of small spotlights inset flush to the ceiling boards, and concealed fluorescent tubes running fore and aft. A conical perspex light fitting is placed centrally over the spiral staircase. The main floor area is covered in teak boarding and the forward seating area is close covered in carpet which has a black ground with white, lemon, gold and brown motifs. Roller blinds are fitted to all windows for screening purposes at night and these are made in thin wood slats woven into a coloured cotton backing. Two large rectangular screens conceal the bar and pantry service areas and contain illuminated feature maps in relief of Southampton Water and Sydney Harbour. These maps have small illuminated flashing marker buoys which indicate pictorially the channels of both ports. Other interesting features of the room are the scale model navigation buoys, to correct detail, of the type seen in the approaches to the ports of call. A magnetic repeater compass forward of the staircase balustrade is linked to the main ship's compass and gives an accurate recording of the ship's course. Chairs are from the famous Bertoia designs in chrome-plated wire basket construction, upholstered in yellow and white tweeds, with small stools to match and occasional tables with white plastic tops and satin chrome underframes. Special 24-in. television receiver sets are installed and the room is fully air-conditioned.

Playroom—

This room is mainly pale blue in colour with a blue rubber floor, and on the walls is a plasticised mural of children at play and famous characters from children's books, all in the soft drawing and colours of Edward Ardizzone. One half of the room can be opened up, when the weather is good, to give access to an outside deck space. There is a miniature cabin, mainly for small girls, and, for the boys, a rocket into which they can climb and view the deck above through a periscope; these and other special toys, such as the climbing boxes, small house and mobile crocodile in the tourist-class playroom, were designed by Margaret Redfern. There is a water tank for sailing boats and, as in the other nursery, a rocking-horse, doll's pram and chairs and tables, etc.

TOURIST-CLASS PUBLIC ROOMS

Restaurant—

It is understood that this is the largest restaurant afloat and has seating accommodation for some 704 people at one sitting. Outboard, the seating each side is divided by free-shaped fins covered in white Everflex. The bays thus formed prevent the possibility of a canteen atmosphere but, as each fin is cut away in the centre, the vista across this vast room is not spoiled. The shape of the room is dramatised at night by the white ceiling which describes a parabolic curve almost to the outer edges, where there is a margin of darkness. The centre ceiling is of brightly lit white glass fibre. There is a two-way control on the lighting so that it is possible to make it softer for dining at night. The walls are of irridescent greeny-gold glass fibre, that changes tone with position; the floor is dark blue and the leather upholstered plywood furniture is in dark blue and khaki-green. At the main entrance and in each bay there are screen sculptures in metal by Geoffrey Clarke.

William Fawcett Room—

This is the main tourist-class lounge, and as such is the central meeting point. The room is very large, and is flanked on each side at one end by writing rooms and a library. It is designed on the lines of the "palm-court," with fountains and a considerable amount of mirror glass. The outer walls are of translucent silver-white glass fibre, and cutting in at right angles are screens with tinted mirror-glass murals, designed by Professor Robert Goodden, two more of which (much larger and set in black bean wood) face each other in the centre of the room fore and aft. Also placed centrally are two fountains, and the bubbling fluorescent water surges in a glass tank and spirals upwards through pipes. Balls are arranged to be captured by the water and the effect is to provide a scene of continually dancing balls. Bent plywood, veneered in black bean, has again been chosen for the furniture, which is covered in bronzed green leather and also pure silk tweed in a pattern of purples, from Bianchini Ferier. The curtains are in alternate blocks of greyish mauve and pink, and the carpet is dull gold.

Peacock Room—

Designed specially to provide a quiet atmosphere for smoking and reading, the Peacock Room has two adjoining rooms where passengers can enjoy a quiet game of cards. There is a waiter service bar, and a small floor which can be cleared in the evenings for dancing. The walls are curved and are covered in a dyed blue wood veneer, and the same theme has been used for the ceiling. When drawn, the curtains are continuous around the sides, and are of matching blue stripes, with orange and gold. The furniture is all made in bent pine plywood and is covered in leather, and some of the large "club" easy chairs are joined together to make a serpentine sofa. The floor is white, the dance floor being marked with diagonal black stripes, and there is carpeting in the card-rooms. Over the centre part of the Peacock Room hangs a canopy, designed by Robert Adams, who also designed the "bas-relief" mural opposite the bar opening.

Island Room—

It is intended to use this space for dances, concerts and also as a games deck, while during some part of the day a portion

Fig. 32.—First-class Outboard Two-berth Cabin.

Fig. 33.—First-class Nursery Cabin.

Fig. 34.—First-class Two-berth Outboard Cabin with Bath.

Fig. 35.—De-luxe Cabin Arranged as a Bedroom.

will become a playground for children. Both sides open up in hot weather to give access to the deck. All round the inner walls is a vast immensely colourful mural of Ceylon and the Pacific Islands by Robert Buhler, R.A., which is laminated into the wall panels so as to be indestructible. Down each side of the room are hinged seat screens which swing round so as to divide the space up athwartships when needed. The furniture, which is laid out in islands on white Indian rugs, is a design evolved for the *Canberra* and is used throughout the tourist class. It is made from a simple drum of laminated plywood, from which four different chair designs, as well as

Fig. 36.—Corner of De-luxe Cabin.

a table, have been cut. The idea gave a cheap and clean design of furniture that can easily be re-polished or re-upholstered during the lifetime of the ship.

Cricketers' Tavern—

This is the main bar in the tourist-class, incorporating the all-important atmosphere of a "pub" with cricket as its theme, and it is fitting that Colin Cowdrey, the famous England cricketer, was called in as consultant and as a specialist. The long, narrow room is divided down its length into groups by individual tables with semi-circular seating. Behind this on the inboard wall (all the walls are made of willow wood strips) is a montage of bats, balls, caps, pads, gloves and stumps, designed by Margaret Redfern. Cutting at right angles into the outboard wall are screens on which are painted life-sized portraits by Ruskin Spear, R.A., of W. G. Grace, Sir Donald Bradman, Learie N. Constantine and K. S. Ranjitsinhji. The bar, which is of willow and white marble, is backed with a row of nearly 200 ties representing famous clubs. A wooden hand hold at the front of the bar is wound round with black twine in the manner of a bat handle.

Alice Springs and Lido—

There are two swimming pools in the tourist-class, one of which, called Alice Springs, includes an undercover bar-café, and the other—the Lido—combines with a paddling pool for children. Alice Springs is distinguished by an overall use of glass mosaics, which form a multicoloured feather-like design, by Arnold Machin, R.A., round the pool and the walls of the café. Elsewhere the mosaics are white. Canework seating has been chosen for this room, and the bar front is also of cane. Flooring is in white vinyl. The Lido is on an upper deck and is a rather larger pool. It is intended that the adjoining paddling pool will be supervised by "nannies." The whole area is decorated in coloured mosaics in abstract

Fig. 37.—De-luxe Cabin Arranged as a Sitting Room.

designs and in the paddling pool, as an imaginary garden, by
Edward Bawden.

Playroom—

This room is large and light with a colour scheme basically
white and yellow. Laminated into the white plastic walls is a
mural of imaginary birds and animals by Mary Feddon, and
this mural runs along each end of the room and in a semi-
circle behind the carousel. Both in this room and the first-class
playroom the carousels are worked by every other child
riding a small bicycle, with round dished baskets for the
smaller children set in between. Also for the smaller children
there is a play house and climbing boxes. A magnetic wall
with letters and numbers, is provided for the older children,
who also have a wheelhouse and a chute, together with the
traditional rocking-horse and doll's-pram. For quieter play,
or in rough weather, all the children in both playrooms can
be seated at chairs and tables. For organised games tourist-
class children have the use of a section of the Island Room as
a playground at certain times of the day.

Pop Inn—

This is designed for the teenager and younger passenger. It
is rather on the lines of a coffee bar, with drink-dispensing
machines and a juke box, only larger to allow for dancing and
table tennis, etc. The walls are of ordinary deal into which
free poker-work designs have been burnt. There are also
paintings by Royal College of Art students. The bar tops are
made up of hundreds of strips of coloured perspex placed
against each other and, at intervals, a fluorescent strip is
inserted. The upholstery is of nylon fur and the room is lit
from a continuous multicoloured strip in the shape of a
scribble on the ceiling. In the small sitting-out room
at one end there are lighting panels made in the same
way as the bar tops and they are suffused with light from
behind.

Entrances—

The walls of the tourist-class entrances are lined with
removable panels of white leather cloth so that there will
be as much light as possible. Each bank of entrances is
distinguished by a different colour slip behind the deep
rosewood handrail. On the walls of the principal entrances are
moving waterscapes, which have been designed by Mr. John
Wright, in conjunction with Comyn Ching & Co. (London),
Ltd. The movement is provided by continuous jets of water,
and the effect is most pleasing, giving added charm to these
spaces.

Fig. 38.—De-luxe Cabin Bathroom.

Fig. 39.—First-class Restaurant.

HOSPITALS

The *Canberra* has a main air-conditioned hospital for passengers, together with an isolation hospital and crew hospital. There is an operating theatre, dispensary, consulting rooms, and a dark room for developing X-rays. The staff includes two surgeons, three nursing sisters, one dispenser, one hospital attendant and stewards.

Situated on *D* deck, the main hospital is particularly spacious. It consists of six wards and has a total of 16 beds. Four of the wards have three beds in each and the other two have two beds in each.

The isolation hospital and the crew hospital are located on *C* deck aft. The three isolation wards contain nine beds in all, and adjoining are two verandas. There are two crew wards, one having three beds and the other four.

STATEROOMS

All tourist and some grades of first-class cabins have upper berths which fold away against a matching bulkhead, leaving the maximum of clear space available in the daytime. Heaton Tabb & Co., Ltd., did much experimental work on this arrangement before it could be made to work smoothly in all circumstances. This firm also made the pre-fabricated glass fibre shower and w.c. units and wash basin recesses. The showers, with cylindrical perspex screens, were designed by Mr. John West, and it is largely due to their compact shape and lightness that it is possible to provide showers in so many tourist cabins. Naturally, there are bathrooms or showers adjoining all the first-class staterooms.

There are blocks of tourist cabins which can be used as four-berth rooms, but as two-berth cabins they are complete with shower and w.c. Both these convertible cabins and the standard tourist-class cabins have plastic bulkheads in pale colours, with simple beach furniture. Some of these cabins have soft grey bulkheads and bedspreads and curtains printed in a bright pink and tangerine design. Others have pale blue bulkheads with white, sky blue and lettuce green bedspreads. Both schemes have large squares of Templetex—a curly pile carpet, backed with P.V.C., in aubergine, and these squares virtually cover the entire cabin floor. Deep aubergine is also the colour of the specially-designed rubber flooring in the alleyways. This forms a link and gives continuity to all the tourist alleyways which have bulkheads in varying shades of pale grey and focal points of coral.

In the first-class, the passageway bulkheads are white, broken up with blacks and periwinkle blue, egg shell blue and straw yellow. All through these decks the flooring is deep Mediterranean blue and black rubber, providing continuity without monotony. The bulkheads of the first-class cabins are covered with Vynide, a soft plastic, with a texture something like linen, but the surface is dirt and moisture resistant. A large amount of white has been used with dark close-fitted charcoal carpets. Simple grained woods of deep colours with occasional bright highlights have been planned to provide the passengers with an atmosphere that is restful without being dull.

The largest proportion of first-class accommodation is arranged in groups looking on to courts which have three large windows on the ship's side. Each room has a control panel for radio, temperature variations, two-way light switches, and service telephone. Deckheads are flush with lights recessed above.

In the first-class shower cabins the dressing table, writing table and small nest of drawers can be fitted into a minimum space or spread out, with a continuous top linking them all together and still giving them a tailor-made appearance. In order to avoid a working top impression the hard plastic used for some of these has an exclusive pen and ink design by

Fig. 40.—Side Section of the First-class Restaurant.

Joan Hope on a white background, and in some others a dark blue and green cotton by Jacqmar has been laminated in Perstorp plastic by Skanska Attikfabriken A/B.

An unusual feature in the tourist-class cabins is that the single chairs and the dressing stools (for the four-berth cabins only) have been specially designed by Wood Brothers (Furniture), Ltd., in glass fibre.

For those who want more space and luxury, there are four veranda suites and eight *de-luxe* cabins. Two of the suites and four of the *de-luxe* cabins have communicating doors. Each cabin has its dayroom, convertible to a bedroom by use of folding beds and settees, with entrance lobby, bathroom, toilet and luggage space. All ceilings to the cabin areas are of white painted strip-boarding, with white plastic sheet and P.V.C. cloth to bathroom, toilet and entrance lobbies. Lighting is from concealed and suspended fluorescent fittings with table lamps to the cabin area and flush recessed tungsten fittings to toilets and lobbies.

Fig. 41.—Part of the First-class Observation Lounge.

Fig. 42.—First-class Swimming Pool.

Walls are covered in grass cloth, wheat cloth and wall paper to cabin areas, with plastic and P.V.C. fabric to entrances. The bathrooms and toilets are lined out in specially designed ceramic tiles and glass mosaics. Specially woven mottled carpets are fitted to cabins and entrance lobbies, elsewhere linoleum and translucent white vinyl tiles are used.

There are four colour schemes for the eight cabins, and the furniture is in teak, Swedish pine, elm and Rhodesian rosewood. Each cabin has a folding bed, bed-settee, writing table, double wardrobe, dressing table and a bedside table which houses all lighting, air-conditioning and ventilation controls, telephones and radio. The main item of furniture is a unit which houses a refrigerator, clock, radio, 17in. television set, and storage for glasses. Upholstery consists of a settee, two easy chairs, writing chair and dressing stool, covered in linens and woven fabrics from the latest ranges of several manufacturers. Curtains are in matching or contrasting Thai silks with white Venetian blinds to the window areas. Each suite occupies approximately 400 sq. ft. of floor area with four large windows to each cabin, and all are completely soundproofed.

CREW ACCOMMODATION.

Senior officers, who have considerable entertaining to do, have individual schemes, and their furniture is designed to give as light an effect as possible. Refrigerators and television sets are incorporated in a general scheme of bookshelves, cupboards and drawers. Danish woollen fabrics are used on upholstered chairs so that a masculine tailored effect has been achieved, and deep coloured close-fitted carpets make the rooms really comfortable for men who have so much responsibility and are away from home for long periods.

Furniture for junior officers has been designed on the same principles as for passengers and is very simple but provides good storage space. The bulkheads are covered with white Vynide and on the lavender-grey linoleum deck there are large charcoal coloured carpets. The beds and easy chairs are covered in a very heavy closely woven cotton in pink, scarlet and plum coloured stripes, which was specially developed by Donald Brothers, Ltd. For the curtains over the washbasins and the covers on the glass-fibre writing chairs, a plain coloured cotton and rayon weave has been used.

The officers' smoking room is panelled in larch and the room is equipped with television. Full length midnight-blue and navy-blue check curtains run across one side of the room and the chairs are of midnight-blue and emerald green wool.

Leading hands and the crew have recreation rooms with the same facilities, and cool-coloured plastic bulkheads make a less sophisticated background for strong coloured chairs and tables.

Dining arrangements for the European stewards take the form of a mess room which is decorated in pale grey, black and red. Boxes of green plants are arranged to break the square lines of tables and chairs, and transparent glass-fibre screens with abstract designs by Allan Day run along the whole of one side.

Goanese stewards have a large room for mess and recreational purposes. The background colour for plastic bulkheads is grey but in the mess room side there are two large panels of a gay orange spring laminated in plastic, and on the recreation side the same print is used for curtains. Bookcases, writing tables and an altar are all veneered in straight grained elm and the screens across the sidelights are a translucent blue glass fibre.

Fig. 43.—Cinema.

WALL COVERINGS, FURNISHINGS AND DECK COVERINGS

Fitted throughout the *Canberra* are 1,250,000 sq. ft. of Swedish Perstorp plastic laminate. This is believed to be the largest single order ever placed for plastic laminate to be used in a ship.

Swedish Perstorp has been used on every kind of surface in cabins and alleyways, bathrooms, toilets, nurseries, galleys as well as on doors.

All bonding of Perstorp to plywood cores was carried out by Heaton Tabb & Co., Ltd., at their London and Belfast works.

Postforming grade Perstorp has been used extensively for corners where it has been applied to both plywood and Marinite cores, to ¾ in. external radius, the height of the corners being 8 to 9ft. Skirtings have also been provided for use in conjunction with these corners, formed to a similar radius. Approximately 1,000 corners and 1,000 skirtings have been supplied, roughly 750 with plywood cores and 250 with Marinite.

In addition to the bulkheading material, Heaton Tabb have supplied 1,900 cabin doors, most of them faced with Swedish Perstorp in various colours. Heaton Tabb have bonded more than 22,000 panels, some faced on one side and others on two sides.

In the tourist-class cabins, 142 convertible units were specially designed by Heaton Tabb in conjunction with the owners, each unit giving a choice of either two additional berths or separate shower and w.c. The internal bulkheads of these units are all faced in a light blue mottled Perstorp specially produced for the *Canberra* by the manufacturers of Perstorp—Skanska Attikfabriken—who have been making plastic laminates for more than 35 years.

For the tourist-class dance space, one of the largest plasticised murals ever fitted on board ship contains approximately 90 full-sized mural panels. The artist was Robert Buhler, working for John Wright. The panels were painted on impregnated paper provided by Perstorp and the paper was then returned to Sweden for processing into finished Perstorp panels.

The artist for the first-class nursery mural was Edward Ardizzone, and the mural provided here is in three sections, one showing children playing, bathing, boating, fishing and swimming with a wooded island background, another depicting nursery rhyme characters and the third with a Treasure Island theme.

In the tourist-class nursery the artist was Miss Mary Feddon, whose mural covers three walls, her theme being birds, flowers and plants, and animals.

Other uses of Swedish Perstorp in the *Canberra* include pale green Perstorp (PP307) for surfacing dumb waiters in the tourist-class restaurant, white Perstorp (PP30) for surfacing the outboard deckhead and window linings of the first-class lido café. Black Perstorp (PP15) has been used for the back panels of the artists' decorative plaques on both port and starboard sidescreens in the tourist restaurant, and this material has also been used for the revolving doors in the first-class restaurant, while for the tourist-class restaurant, pale green Perstorp (PP307) has been chosen.

In the tourist dance space the free standing and swivelling divisional screens are faced in white Perstorp (PP30).

With the exception of the mural area, the tourist-class nursery is also panelled in white Perstorp (PP30), while in the first-class nursery, pale blue Perstorp (PP304) has been used.

Fig. 44.—Longitudinal View of the Tourist-class Restaurant.

Fig. 45.—Section of the Tourist-class Restaurant.

Fig. 46.—Athwartships View of the Tourist-class Restaurant.

White Perstorp has been used for the bar fitments, in the tourist-class smoking-room bar.

A process for incorporating fabrics into plastic panels has been used for surfacing dressing table tops in some of the first-class cabins.

Miss Barbara Oakley, who is responsible for the décor and furnishing of the first-class cabins, has used a Jacqmar printed cotton which has been laminated into Perstorp panels. The design is dark blue with turquoise daisy heads. Another design, incorporating black and white grasses and insects was designed by Joan Hope. A special photogravure roller was produced by Perstorp to carry out the printing of this design.

The use of Perstorp in the *Canberra* will undoubtedly reduce maintenance considerably. Repainting in alleyways and in other areas where there is frequent traffic is often necessary every two years. With Perstorp there will be little or no maintenance required during the lifetime of the ship.

Nearly 200 clocks, of the electric-impulse type, with their attendant master control panel and two navigating chronometers, all manufactured by Thomas Mercer, Ltd., have been fitted throughout the *Canberra*.

Just over half of the clocks in the ship have been designed by the staff at Thomas Mercer, Ltd., and these are installed in officers' and crew's quarters and in all crew spaces. The remainder of the clocks—those fitted in public rooms, *de-luxe* suites and special cabins, etc.—have been designed by some of the country's leading industrial designers, including Sir Hugh Casson, Neville Conder & Partners, to match the décor of the areas of which the clocks are part.

All clocks are controlled by Mercer navigation chronometers, of the type which has been made in St. Albans for over 100 years, the first of which was made by the present chairman's father. These chronometers are accurate to as little as half-a-second per day, and are equipped with electric contacts which, through the master control panel, give an electric impulse to the whole of the clock system every half-minute. By this method, extremely accurate time-keeping is available for navigating, and for passengers and crew.

The control panel is equipped with a means of advancing or retarding, by a pre-determined amount, all the clocks on the ship, a facility which is used nearly every night when the ship is travelling in an easterly or westerly direction.

The 200 clocks are wired in groups of ten, so that, if one of the clocks sustains accidental damage, only the clocks in that particular circuit are affected, and the remainder of the clocks are not stopped.

In all, some 17,586 sq. yds. of Semtex deck coverings have been applied in the *Canberra*. The largest proportion of the work is in the first-class accommodation where 10,000 sq. yds. of Semtex SX.559B underlay has been used. Some 3,200 sq. yds. of Supreme extra with Elasdec topping has been laid on the promenade deck and various smaller weather deck areas.

Underlays in bathrooms, toilets and showers, have accounted for 1,328 sq. yds. and a similar area of Semflex has been laid in the same spaces.

Above the promenade deck level, 650 sq. yds. of Vinylex on SX.547B underlay has been provided for pantries and bars. Some 260 sq. yds. of underlay and the same area of rubber has been supplied for the wheelhouse and chartroom and the entrance to these spaces, while 560 sq. yds. of Gripdec has been applied to the fan rooms and ventilation spaces.

Bonding positively to the clean sub-deck, the various Semtex underlays provide an anti-corrosive, resilient and tough surface for taking decorative and weatherdeck top finishes.

Leyland rubber floors are fitted in the tourist-class dining saloon, tourist-class smoking room, tourist-class ballroom and in the first and tourist-class nurseries and playground.

Leyland rubber floors are not restricted to tile size and as there is a range of 130 colours available there is no difficulty in meeting the requirements of decorative architects to match any decorative scheme.

The carpet selected for the cinema has been manufactured by Messrs. S. J. Stockwell & Co. (Carpets), Ltd., and supplied through Heaton Tabb & Co., Ltd. The carpet is of Curlax, plain wilton, dyed to a special shade of green. The quantities supplied were 185 yds. of 36in. width and 255 yds. of 27in. width to match. Curlax is the original crush-resisting plain carpet and it is claimed to be the first British carpet to be sold with an unconditional free-replacement guarantee against attack by moth grubs (1937). It is now produced in eleven grades, to satisfy various degrees of potential wear and six of these grades are made in any width from 2ft. 3in. to 33ft. 0in. seamless.

The carpets in the tourist-class ballroom are handmade plain white Indian carpets woven in Mirzapur in the very heavy, deep pile, tough Everest quality made by O.C.M. (London), Ltd.—the Oriental carpet manufacturers, and supplied through Heaton Tabb & Co., Ltd.

A large quantity of the linoleum supplied for the *Canberra* is of Stains Colourama sheet marble in heavy gauge, made by the Linoleum Manufacturing Co., Ltd. The wide colour range from which the selection was made has been designed by an International colour scientist so that it is specifically correct for floor coverings in respect of light reflectivity, strength of hue and distance from basic colour.

Other linoleum has been supplied by Barry, Ostlere and Shepherd, Ltd., and the contract fulfilled by this firm covered 9,000 sq. yds.

A rather unusual type of fitting has been used for the curtain rails throughout the *Canberra*. These are known as Silent Gliss, and they are manufactured by Silent Gliss, Ltd. In the *Canberra*, some 4,000ft. of rail of this type has been used. It is much more streamlined than the average type of curtain rail, and it is very light, being made of anodised aluminium. Silent Gliss is extremely silent in operation, as virtually indestructible white nylon gliders slide noiselessly in the anodised aluminium rails, which are siloconised to give permanent lubrication.

For the wall coverings in the senior officers' cabins and also in the first-class private bathrooms, Mural Texturide, manufactured by Arlington Plastics Development, Ltd., has been used. Mural Texturide has been used for marine purposes for many famous vessels including the *Queen Mary*. This wall covering is resistant to stains, burns, scuffing, ozone and sea water, and as it is completely washable, stands up to years of wear, thus reducing the need for frequent redecoration. There is a wide range of colours and design to choose from, and these can be arranged to blend or contrast with any decoration scheme.

Fine decorative woods have been chosen for the first-class and tourist-class accommodation. They were selected and specified by Miss Barbara G. Oakley and supplied by Messrs. William Mallinson & Sons, Ltd. Some 155,000 sq. ft. of different decorative veneers were provided including white beech, fruit cherry, European elm, African elm, muninga, Australian blackbean, Australian walnut, Canalletta, Indian laurel, Bombay rosewood, figured teak and French walnut.

Hardwoods in various sizes and thicknesses both in square edge wood and cut through logs were supplied in muninga, Australian blackbean, Australian walnut, Fresh walnut, Indian laurel and English fruit cherry.

For the Peacock Room, Messrs. W. I. Brine & Sons, Ltd., have provided blue bird's eye maple and pine veneer and the same firm have supplied blackbean for the William Fawcett Room, willow for the Cricketers' Tavern, Dorenz teak for the

Fig. 47.—A Wing of the Tourist-class Restaurant.

Fig. 48.—Starboard Side of the Tourist Ballroom.

Fig. 49.—Alice Springs.

Fig. 50.—Cricketers' Tavern.

first-class Bureau area, first-class shop and cinema foyers and Rio rosewood for special handrails and tourist-class entrances.

Mallite plastic faced panels have been used for the deck-heads in the accommodation. This factory-made panel incorporates a semi-rigid plastic bonded to Lydney W.B.P. plywood, and when necessary it can be wiped clean with a mild detergent. Some 74,000 sq. ft. of Mallite panel have been supplied for the cabin accommodation in the *Canberra*.

Prominent among the furniture on board the *Canberra*, are the Tripos chairs and footstools. The Tripos design was evolved by Ernest Race, R.D.I., PP.SIA, and the manufacturing work has been carried out by Ernest Race, Ltd. In all, some 60 chairs and footstools, together with 120 additional

Fig. 51.—Detail of Wall Decoration in the Cricketers' Tavern.

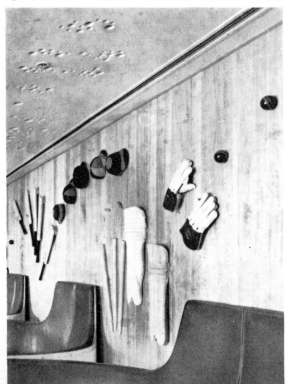

sets of loose covers, have been provided. The chairs are located in the first-class enclosed decks.

A detailed programme of research into materials able to withstand prolonged exposure to sea air, spray and severe climatic changes experienced in round-the-world voyages, was behind the development of the Tripos. The main frames are of square section steel tubing finished with an entirely new fused nylon process. Seats, backframes and arms are in Afromosia treated with a modern resin finish and the upholstery filler is Aeropreen flame-retardent polyether foam. This material not only reduces the risk of fire spreading, but is unaffected by extremes of heat and cold and humid climatic conditions.

A new type of action allows the chair to be simply adjusted to upright or reclining positions, and the loose cushions are effectively secured by dowel rods slotted in the fabric and clipped to the underside of the frame. This device prevents the cushions from slipping in use, yet allows them to be rapidly removed when the zipped cover needs changing. Suspension of cushions in both chair and footstool is by means of resilient rubberwebbing.

Tubular armchairs and easy chairs for the crew have been provided by the British Tubular Manufacturing Co., Ltd. These chairs are made of Brytalloy tube with a black Anosil finish. One of the most serious disadvantages with tubular furniture, when it was first introduced, was that the finish—whether chromium plating or enamel—wore off and the tube became rusty making the furniture shabby. This corrosion has, of course, been most active on ships and in humid climates where, however well the outside of the tube is protected, the corrosion eats through from the inside, penetrating the steel wall and destroying the tube.

To overcome this destructive rust, a new tube—Brytalloy—was produced several years ago, and extensive tests were made at sea under very severe conditions and the tube was not affected and stood up to all that was required of it. As a result of these successful tests, Brytalloy tubular furniture has been installed on hundreds of ships.

Fig. 52.—Part of the Peacock Room.

Accordo Blinds' units are installed throughout the first-class passengers' and officers' accommodation. Two types of blind unit have been employed—the Accordo combined blind and window unit and the Accordo outboard blind unit. Accordo blinds, which are completely housed within their own anodised aluminium window frames, comprise pleated P.V.C. coated fire-proofed nylon cloth and are finished in a variety of colours.

Lurashell settees and chairs have been provided for the first-class lounge and Lurashell pedestal chairs and terrazzo tables are fitted in the first-class dining room.

Other items from the Lurashell range have been used in the tourist-class accommodation, junior officers' quarters and ladies' hairdressing salon.

An important item in the *Canberra's* outfit, and one which is of prime importance to the comfort of the passengers, is the quality of the pillows. This important contract was entrusted to the Puritan Feather Co., Ltd., who have supplied no less than 6,388 pillows for the *de-luxe* cabins, first-class rooms, tourist-class rooms, hospital, officers' accommodation, and also for the European and Goanese crew. The qualities range from a good class half down to a soft poultry feather, all of which conform to B.S.I. specification both so far as the cover is concerned and the contents.

The pillows are covered in different coloured materials according to the class for which they are intended, in order that they may easily be distinguished, and all are marked with the Insignia of the company.

A further important item with the beds are the mattresses, and these have been supplied throughout the ship by the Dunlop Rubber Co., Ltd.

Some 32,000 sq. ft. of Connolly Vaumol brand upholstery leather, in nine different shades, have been supplied to the various furnishing contractors. The colours are black, copper, brown, Guardsman red, indigo blue, Khaki green, light beech brown, mink brown, orange and turbid green.

Over two miles of Susan Williams-Ellis's textile design Ravenna have been used in the *Canberra*. Ravenna is one of Hull Traders' range of printed fabrics, and about 4,000 yds.,

in black on a deep crimson ground, have been printed on deep textured cotton for the vessel.

It is used in the first-class cabins for bedspreads, curtains for wash-basin recesses, squabs for glass-fibre chairs and covers for convertible bed-settees. The bold design and rich colour of this fabric, which is based on the Ravenna mosaics shows to great advantage against the charcoal coloured carpets and white walls with areas of soft peacock blue, in which the cabins are decorated.

Throughout the *Canberra* a very great variety of materials have been used, and although these materials such as plastic, glass-fibre, etc., are ideal for the purpose for which they have been designed, their application has presented several problems.

Fig. 53.—Centre of the Peacock Room.

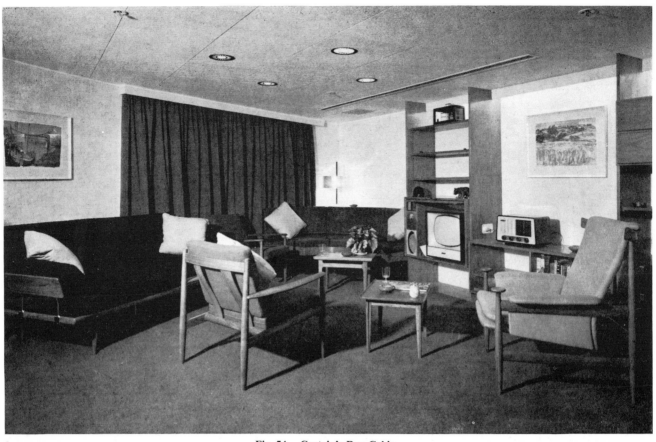

Fig. 54.—Captain's Day Cabin.

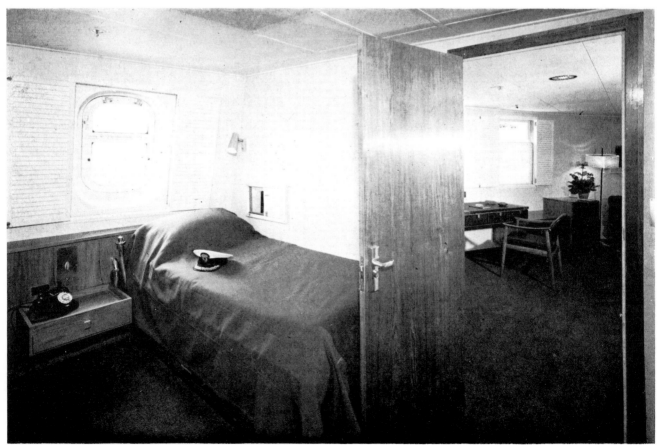

Fig. 55.—Captain's Night Cabin.

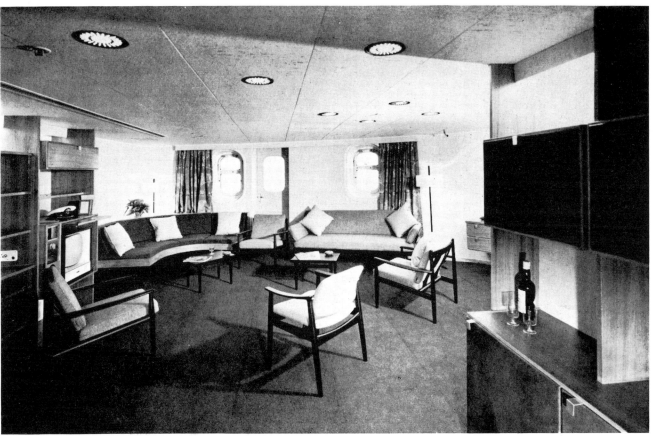

Fig. 56.—Staff Captain's Day Cabin.

Fig. 57.—Purser's Cabin.

Fig. 58.—Tourist-class Two plus Two Cabin with Shower.

Fig. 60.—European Crew Mess.

One of the most difficult to solve was how to bond together wood, aluminium foil and a plastic material to produce the gold and silver panels which decorate the tourist-class restaurant and lounge. The normal bonding method is by high-pressure hydraulic press, but, under heat, wood shrinks, metal expands and plastic to some degree remains stable. Experts from Heaton Tabb & Co., Ltd., tackled this baffling problem with a series of experiments. Fifty-three prototype panels had to be produced before a solution was found. The secret is the length of time the panels remain in the giant presses at just the correct temperature and pressure.

Employing this process more than 1,000,000 sq. ft. of plastic materials have been bonded to wood for the *Canberra*.

Windows and Hardware—

The complete installation of windows has been supplied by Bull's Metal & Marine, Ltd., a member of the Stone-Platt group, and comprises some 1,200 individual items ranging from horizontal sliding windows on the navigating bridge to specially designed types on *C* and *D* decks. The extensive air-conditioning of the ship has allowed the use of many fixed windows which, to suit the requirements of the architects responsible for decoration, were made as large as possible without impairing the structural strength of the ship.

All windows have been supplied with frames of aluminium alloy, and where they have been fitted into steel plating in

Fig. 59.—Tourist-class Two-berth Cabin Converted for Daytime Use.

the lower decks suitable insulation is provided to prevent the two metals coming in contact and producing electrolytic action. Toughened glass of varying thicknesses has been incorporated in the complete outfit.

A special feature of the *Canberra* has been the creation of large recreation spaces, many of them enclosed by fixed and power-operated screens, which have also been designed and manufactured by Bull's, in close co-operation with the owners and builders. In all, approximately quarter of a mile of partitioning of this type has been used, involving a total glass area of 5,000 sq. ft. On the extensive Games deck, side screens have been erected to provide protection from the wind for passengers taking part in deck games or bathing in the adjacent swimming pool. To prevent down draught, other screens run athwartships at intervals, and one is designed to slide into the engine casing when the full games area is required. Between the dance area and first-class swimming pool, a screen 30ft. long is powered hydraulically to slide vertically to form a division between the two areas or disappear 'tween decks, as required. The children's playground is enclosed by upward-hinging screens in sets of five and these are also operated by hydraulic power.

Various other screens of sliding, folding and fixed design are located in other parts of the vessel, providing a measure of flexibility in the use of space never before attained on a passenger vessel. All screens are constructed from light alloy extrusion and sheet and are fitted with toughened glass.

The entire master key system of control locks throughout the ship, together with the associated Marinalium alloy hardware fitments in way of the cabin accommodation, bathroom accommodation, crew accommodation and also all the Marinalium alloy hardware required in the public rooms has been provided by N. F. Ramsay & Co., Ltd. Marinalium alloy is a magnesium aluminium alloy and has been specially designed for marine use.

Frameless mirrors have been provided by T. & W. Ide, Ltd. The glass is British polished plate glass manufactured by Pilkington Brothers, Ltd. Great attention has been given to the protection of the silver to withstand the rapid changes in the atmospheric conditions encountered at sea. The film of silver is about 50 per cent. thicker than would normally be applied, and to this a film of copper plating has been deposited as an initial protection. This has then been backed with a specially resistant paint and finally lead foil has been applied using a neutral varnish as adhesive.

Perspex baths, manufactured by Thermo Plastics, Ltd., are installed. These baths are made from Acrylic material and are available in white and various British standard colours.

AIR-CONDITIONING, VENTILATION, INSULATION AND REFRIGERATION

PASSENGERS in both classes will enjoy the luxury of comfortable temperatures no matter what variations there are in the climatic conditions. To ensure that all spaces are served, the *Canberra* is fitted with one of the largest marine air-conditioning installations ever designed. The total length of the air ducts is $17\frac{1}{4}$ miles and the fans move the equivalent of 50 tons of air per day. As a further step towards passenger comfort, specially-designed sound-resistant cabin bulkheads have been erected throughout the passenger spaces.

Air-conditioning and Ventilation—

The air-conditioning system, which was designed, manufactured and installed by Thermotank, Ltd., is served by 70 central air-conditioning units in which the air is filtered, heated or cooled according to atmospheric conditions, and its humidity adjusted to a comfortable level before being distributed to cabins, public rooms and other accommodation throughout the ship. To cater for maximum cooling requirements, 4,400 gallons of chilled brine are circulated per minute to the finned-tube heat exchangers in the air-conditioning units.

With a total capacity of 22,000,000 B.Th.U. per hour, the central refrigerating plant, which supplies the cooling medium, has been manufactured by Messrs. J. & E. Hall, Ltd.

Individual control of the conditioned air is provided by means of re-heaters. In the first-class accommodation, as well as the officers' and engineers' cabins, these re-heaters are in the branch ducts serving the accommodation. A bulkhead indicator in the various cabins governs the operation of a thermostat which, in turn, actuates a valve controlling the supply of warm air to the re-heater. If the occupant of the cabin sets the indicator to maximum cooling, the valve shuts off the supply of warm water and the conditioned air enters the cabin at the lowest temperature available from the system. Any subsequent change in the setting of the cabin indicator brings the thermostat into operation and this allows the valve to supply warm water to the re-heater, consequently raising the temperature of the air to the required level.

The air-conditioning units serving the tourist-class accommodation and the crew's spaces are fitted with re-heaters which operate, for the groups of accommodation they serve, in the same way as the individual cabin re-heaters with the exception that the zone thermostats function automatically as a group control. The quantity of air entering the accommodation, which is covered by this section of the system, can be controlled to suit individual requirements, and automatic pressure controllers ensure that the pressure in the system is maintained at the correct level, irrespective of the fluctuating demands created by passengers operating their individual volume controls.

There are separate automatic temperature controls in all the public spaces available to passengers and for two of these rooms, the Bonito Club and Island Room, there are additional fresh-air units which come into operation automatically when the number of passengers accommodated rises above normal.

When heating is required, a calorifier, which is fitted in association with the refrigerating machinery, supplies warm brine to the air-conditioning units, which then function as pre-heaters. The final temperature of the conditioned air delivered to the accommodation is again governed by the operation of the re-heaters.

Control of the warm water supply to these re-heaters is arranged in accordance with outside conditions. As an example, the water temperature in tropical climates will be at a moderate level and, although high enough to provide for individual variations, it would not create any possibility of overheating. In winter conditions the temperature of the

Fig. 61.—Underdeck Pipe Arrangement.

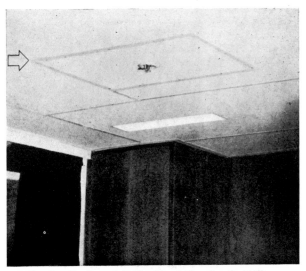

Fig. 62.—Perforated Ceiling Panel Covering the Diffusers.

water is greatly raised to enable interior temperatures of 70 deg. F. to be maintained when the outside atmospheric temperature is 20 deg. F.

Automatic humidifier valves come into operation at each air-conditioning unit when heating is required.

One of the features of the system is an entirely new type of air terminal developed by Thermotank, Ltd., specially for the *Canberra*. Known as the Sofflo distributor, it is a very compact and unobstrusive fitting which diffuses the conditioned air into the accommodation through a perforated fascia. The distributor fits flush with the ceiling and not only houses the equipment for introducing the conditioned air in a draughtless, diffused pattern but also accommodates, where necessary, the automatic sprinkler and the Tannoy-system loudspeaker. To suit the varying requirements of the accommodation served, the Sofflo distributors have been designed in a range of sizes. It was necessary to accommodate these distributors in very shallow ceiling voids and this posed many problems in achieving efficient diffusion of the conditioned air at the unusually low noise level specified. The photograph reproduced in Fig. 61 shows how the installation is arranged under deck, while Fig. 62 shows all that is visible to the passenger.

Over 14,000ft. of Flexflyte ducting has been used in the installation of the Sofflo distributors, and the flexibility of this type of duct has greatly relieved the innumerable problems encountered in the very restricted spaces available.

In the public rooms the conditioned air is introduced through Stripline grilles. These continuous strip diffusers fit flush to the bulkhead and function by continually projecting a thin blanket of air over the room through a series of elongated slots.

Spot coolers are fitted in the laundry, printers' shop and electricians' and engineers' workshops, as well as in the dairy, bakery, larder, pantries and various food preparation rooms.

For serving the galleys and their various dependencies, refrigerating machinery compartments, pump room, stabiliser compartments, laundry, duct keel and lift shafts there is a comprehensive system of mechanical supply and exhaust ventilation. Mechanical supply ventilation is also arranged for the Stadium, steering-gear compartment, baggage rooms and bow-propeller space, while a mechanical exhaust system serves the passengers' public rooms, pantries, bars, laundrettes, cofferdams, cargo holds and various other service and machinery spaces.

A Thermotank de-humidifying system is installed for the bulk store and flour store.

In all, the fans serving the complete Thermotank installation, including torpedo exhaust fans for the cargo spaces, together produce a total of 717 B.H.P.

To ensure full efficiency of the Thermotank air-conditioning installation at all times, the owners have selected Aqua-Clear for the prevention of corrosion and scale deposits in the system. Aqua-Clear, supplied by Messrs. Kinnis & Brown, Ltd., is ideally suitable because of the harmless and non-toxic qualities of the chemical.

A unique feature of all the lavatories for both the passengers and crew is that they are all fitted with the new Silavent system, which provides individual ventilation of each lavatory bowl. This is the first major order for Silavent, which is marketed by Morphy-Richards (Installations), Ltd., and it is, in fact, the first order for marine use.

Polluted air and the bacterial aerosol, caused during flushing of the w.c. are withdrawn from the bowl through a chromium-plated collector fitted at the hinge of the Silavent seat, *via* Polyorc BH high-impact rigid P.V.C. tubing and cemented fittings, manufactured by Yorkshire Imperial Metals, Ltd.

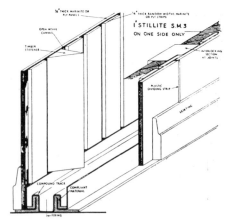

Fig. 63.—Arrangement of Panels for Special Cabin Bulkheads.

Connections are then taken to the ship's exhaust ventilation trunking.

Sound-resistant Cabin Bulkheads—

Usually, in large passenger ships, the best accommodation is located as far as possible from the engine-room in order to minimise cabin noise. Although this arrangement provides the best living conditions, it also raises problems, because if the ventilation system is quiet, or turned off, the cabin bulkheads, which often consist of one skin of 1-in. thick plywood, are generally found to be inadequate as sound barriers. Thus, in the accommodation, conversation in adjacent cabins often is clearly audible.

For the *Canberra* the problem of cabin noise was very carefully considered at the design stage and several innovations have been adopted to ensure maximum passenger comfort.

The engine-room is situated as far aft as possible in order to minimise cabin noise, and special arrangements have been made to reduce noise in the high-velocity ventilation system. Special cabin bulkheads have also been developed to provide conversational privacy with little increase in weight over the conventional 1-in. plywood. The bulkheads consist of two specially treated skins of $\frac{1}{2}$-in. plywood, mounted on a metal track designed to structurally isolate the skins from the structure and from each other. The drawing reproduced in Fig. 63 shows the arrangement of the plywood panels. To prevent amplification of sound in the air sandwich the cavity formed by the two plywood panels is lined with Stillite mineral wool mat, type S.M.3. The bulkheads are 3in. thick and have been designed by A.I.R.O. (Acoustical Investigation and Research Organisation, Ltd.) to provide high sound insulation throughout the speech frequency range. These special resistant bulkheads have been constructed by Sound Control, Ltd.

The design of the public rooms was also the subject of an investigation carried out by A.I.R.O., who considered the acoustic treatment in the form of sound absorptive finishes necessary to provide satisfactory conditions. The problems associated with the cinema were of particular interest as an initial reverberation analysis showed that when two-thirds full the reverberation time would be considerably shorter than the optimum value of 0·9 seconds required at the reference frequency of 512 cycles per second. This effect arose from the large amount of absorption afforded by the plywood panelling, fixed drapes and carpeting which had been proposed. In order to avoid the excessively "dead" effect that would have resulted, recommendations included the substitution of wood-strip panelling for the fixed drapes. Further modifications included the replacement of heavy carpeting with a thinner type with a suitable impervious underlay to maintain the impact insulation.

Insulation of Brine Mains—

Extending to many thousands of feet in total length, the brine mains form the cooling system of the *Canberra's* air-conditioning installation. Emerging from the central plant in the machinery space adjoining the ship's engine-room as pipes of relatively large bore, the mains branch off into separate circuits to serve the air-conditioning unit rooms in various parts of the ship, and the run is in smaller bore piping to serve the various spaces.

For the insulation of these complex circuits of brine mains, with their numerous bends and branches, flanges and control valves, the Anchor Insulating Co., Ltd., have used a relatively new material—Polyurethane rigid foam—first developed by the Imperial Chemical Industries, Ltd., some three years ago. Much work has been done on the application techniques of this remarkable material since it was first produced, and it is now claimed that Polyurethane has some outstanding advantages over conventional insulating media.

For the brine mains on the *Canberra* a timber framework of rectangular section was constructed in suitable stages along the full extent of the mains to provide grounds for encasing. Linings of $\frac{3}{8}$-in. resin-bonded plywood were attached to this framework, with the effect that each run of mains pipework was enclosed in square or rectangular tube—square for single runs of pipe and rectangular where multiple pipes were running together. The cavity so formed round the mains served to contain the Polyurethane rigid foam later to be injected. The last operation was performed by a skilled operator after suitable holes had been drilled at intervals in the casing to admit the special dispensing gun—part of the portable apparatus used in this technique of insulation.

Polyurethane rigid foam is currently being applied for insulation purposes informulated from a mixture of two liquids, both supplied by Imperial Chemical Industries, Ltd. These are Daltolac 41 and Suprasec D/Arcton 11. In the foaming apparatus the two liquids are contained in separate tanks, from where they are fed to an air-driven motor unit. This unit drives two pumps, each of which is calibrated to dispense exactly the quantity of liquid required. The liquids pass through hoses to the dispensing gun where they mix together and are at once injected into the receiving cavity. It is inside the cavity that chemical interaction begins, some 15 to 20 seconds after injection. This produces a foam which rapidly expands to a volume many times than that of the original mixture, and soon becomes quite rigid, adhering by virtue of its own properties to the metal walls of the pipework and the interior of the plywood linings.

The services for which Polyurethane rigid foam is suitable are many and varied. For example, the material has been used by the Anchor Insulating Co., Ltd., in the *Canberra* for water-proofing and forming supports beneath the baths and shower trays throughout the ship. In this particular instance, its anti-corrosive qualities are of paramount importance.

A considerable amount of insulation work was also undertaken by Messrs. Andersons Insulation Co., Ltd., who were responsible for the insulation of the class "A" fire-resisting divisions, the engine-room and boiler-room casings, domestic steam and exhaust pipes, turbines and pipe systems throughout the engine-room and boiler-room, and the boiler uptakes and main funnels. This company also undertook the deckhead insulation in the generator room and fireproof insulation below the boiler flat.

Cold Storage—

In many parts of the ship—galleys, pantries, restaurants, saloons and bars—cold storage cabinets and lockers of various designs and capacities have been provided for the safe accommodation of foodstuffs, liquor and mineral waters.

The Anchor Insulating Co., Ltd., were called upon to construct these cabinets to the specifications of Messrs. J. & E. Hall, Ltd., and to install them on board.

In most cases the method used to construct these cabinets was to erect a timber framework which was then lined with slab cork insulation. Outer casings and linings were then applied in various specified materials, the cabinets for the galleys being finished in highly polished anti-corrosive sheet metal, and those for the saloons in polished timber or plastic panelling to harmonise with the general décor of the ship.

Refrigerating Machinery—

To satisfy the demands of the air-conditioning plant and also to serve the various insulated storerooms, there is a most extensive installation of refrigerating machinery.

The plant comprises four two-stage centrifugal compressors and four eight-cylinder veebloc compressors, together with various Hallmark units.

Operating on Refrigerant 11, and each coupled to a 547-B.H.P., single-stage, steam turbine, the centrifugal compressors deal with the requirements of the air-conditioning plant and each set is capable of abstracting 5,500,000 B.Th.U. per hour. Speed regulation enables the output to be controlled to give a smaller duty when the vessel is in temperate waters, and below this duty the air-conditioning demand will, in general, be handled by the standby compressor which forms part of the provision chamber machinery. The three remaining eight-cylinder compressors are each directly coupled to 100-B.H.P. electric motors and operate on Refrigerant 12. Their capacity is quite sufficient to deal with the demands of 19 independently-cooled provision chambers which have a total insulated capacity of 88,000 cu. ft.

Cooling in all the provision chambers is effected by means of plain pipe air-cooling batteries with air-circulating fans, air coolers being arranged for brine circulation.

In addition to these duties, the plant provides cold brine for about 40 cold cupboards in way of galleys, saloons and pantries. Seven drinking-water coolers, of capacities ranging from 100 to 300 gallons, are fitted on various decks and these are also cooled by brine from the main plant.

Three special brine-cooled cabinets have been fitted in service counters in the confectioners' shop, tourist cold pantry and fruit and salad rooms. These spaces are all situated on *E* deck.

Seventeen automatic cocktail ice-makers are fitted in, or adjacent to, various bars and pantries, and these units are capable of producing about 95,000 ice cubes (3,715 ℔) per 24 hours. For working in conjunction with beer and mineral lockers and draught beer cabinets, there are ten independent Hallmark units.

Also installed are four water-coolers of 30 to 200 gallons capacity, which are fitted with independent Hallmark water-cooled condensing units. In the dairy there is a 6-H.P. water-cooled unit to maintain the required temperature in the ice-cream hardening room, which has a capacity of about 4-cu. ft. Hallmark units also work in conjunction with two 5½-gallon Giustic ice-cream freezers.

In the locker adjoining the fish-preparing room there is a Hallmark flake ice-making machine, and in the café pantry on the Games deck a 17-cu. ft. domestic refrigerator is fitted, while 27 Electrolux refrigeration cabinets of various sizes are sited throughout the ship.

The insulated, refrigerated provision rooms are situated in two 'tween decks and comprise 19 separate compartments with temperatures ranging from –5 deg. F. to 50 deg. F. These compartments are insulated with Fibreglass and cork slabs, lined with aluminium or galganised-steel sheets which have been erected by Messrs. McEwan Insulators, Ltd., on the Gregson Patent Insurail system.

Fig. 64.—View of the Main First-class Galley.

HOTEL SERVICES

TO cater for the needs of a maximum of some 3,200 persons, the main galley in the *Canberra* extends the full width of the ship on the same deck as the restaurants, with the first-class dining room immediately forward and the tourist-class dining room immediately aft. In fact, the whole of the midship section on *E* deck is set aside for this 150-ft. long space. A photograph of the first-class galley is reproduced in Fig. 64.

Situated on the deck below, the fish-preparing room, bakery and butchers' shop are connected to the main galley by lifts. The confectionery shop, still room and cold pantries are all within the main kitchen area. The galley, main pantries and service pantries are equipped with the latest designs of electrically-heated and steam-heated stainless-steel cooking apparatus. This includes ovens, grills, fryers, bakers' ovens, hotpresses, salamanders, hotplates and toasters, in addition to ice-making machines, potato peelers, doughmixers and dishwashing machines.

Service pantries (Fig. 65) are arranged on all decks for serving morning tea and light snacks and a buffet service is provided for the open decks.

Perhaps the most striking innovation in the bakery is the adoption of electrically-fired reel-type ovens, which have been supplied by Messrs. G. & R. Gilbert, Ltd. This type of oven affords great advantages over the conventional chamber-type in low fuel consumption and space saving. The two Pedigree ovens are each fitted with eight carriers having dimensions of 20½in. by 5ft. 8in., to give them a nominal holding capacity of 16 baking sheets, which represents 192 2-lb loaves. Messrs. Gilbert have also supplied a dough-dividing machine, for scaling-off bulk dough into pieces of requisite size, a flow conveyor for taking the dough pieces to a moulding machine which shapes the dough into final form for baking. They have also provided a machine for dividing and moulding rolls or buns, and a multi-bladed machine for slicing the baked loaves.

To provide, instantly, cups of tea or coffee with the minimum attention, Messrs. W. M. Still & Sons, Ltd., have supplied seven sets of their tea-brewing machines and three sets of coffee-making equipment, which are installed in various parts of the ship. The insulated boiler cabinets have been specially designed for the *Canberra* and have the particular advantage of reducing heat radiation to a minimum. At the back of the insulated cabinets are situated heat extraction ducts through which the heat rises to a suspended hood, where it is dissipated to the ship's ventilating system. In the coffee-making machines, the coffee is infused under pressure in a sealed vessel and is automatically transferred to Pyrex-lined storage containers. The tea-brewing units employ a similar system to ensure that as one container is being used, the other is being re-charged.

Fig. 65.—*A* Deck Pantry.

After every meal that is served in the *Canberra* there will, as may be imagined, an immense amount of washing up to be done. To provide an easy means of effecting this mammoth task, the Hobart Manufacturing Co., Ltd., have supplied four of their model XXM-4 fully-automatic dishwashers. These units have a dual-drive arrangement which provides for the automatic dwell of each dish-filled rack in the wash and rinse compartments, in which they are moved back and forth. Subsequently, the racks are once more rinsed before leaving the machine. The Hobart company have also supplied—in addition to various items of food-preparing machinery— two fully-automatic model XM-3E, three semi-automatic model LE-3C and fifteen semi-automatic model SM-6E dishwashers, together with seventeen Sani-quik glass washers, which employ cold water into which a sanitiser detergent is automatically charged to wash each glass individually.

In a large ship, the problem of serving hot meals to those who cannot attend the normal dining spaces is most important, and to solve this Messrs. C. H. Blackburn & Co., Ltd., have provided five electrically-heated food conveyors. Two of these serve the passengers' sick bay and three are for various sections of the crew. Those for the crew's dining room were specially designed to suit the dimensions of passage ways, etc., and to carry standard P. & O. containers and trays, both in the hot cupboard and on a baine-marie type hob. All the conveyors are constructed on a strong steel framework, upon which double aluminium panelling serves as a cavity to house the insulation.

Table Settings—

An entirely new range of patterns has been designed for the crockery used in the *Canberra*, which was manufactured by Messrs. Geo. L. Ashworth & Brothers, Ltd. In designing the various items, Lady Casson has achieved high aesthetic qualities in addition to providing a form and strength most adequate to arduous shipboard use. All of well-proportioned but functional form, the pieces (Fig. 66) employ as a motif, an endless and intricate maze of gun-metal grey which contrasts with an attractive creamy-white body glaze. The motif has been used as a wide and uniform border on such pieces as the dinner plates, as a centre medallion on circular dishes and as a wide band on such straight-sided items as teapots.

In collaboration with Sir Hugh and Lady Casson, Mr. E. C. Clements has designed spoons, forks, cutlery and hollow-ware in Mappin Plate specially for the *Canberra*. The flatware is of an exceptionally simple pattern, completely undecorated and relying for effect on its classic lines. Spoons and forks have long handles, with the slightly rounded-off ends turned up— a form which has been found most comfortable in use. An innovation—and a concession to the international character of

the passengers—is the inclusion of an oyster fork and cheese scoop *en suite*. A complete setting comprises soup ladle, sauce ladle, table knife and fork, fish fork, dessert fork and oval-bowled spoon, table spoon, round-bowled soup spoon, cheese scoop, preserve spoon, oyster fork, leaf-bladed butter knife, leaf-bladed fish knife, tea and coffee spoons, and fruit eaters. The hollow ware continues the same pattern of classical simplicity.

A wine service (Fig. 67) has been specially designed for the *Canberra* by M. R. Stennett-Wilson, M.S.I.A. on behalf of Messrs. T. Wuidart & Co., Ltd.

Laundry—

To obviate the necessity of carrying large stocks of linen, the vessel is equipped with a full size laundry (Fig. 68) for which the machinery has been supplied by Messrs. Isaac Braithwaite & Son, Ltd. The work which accrues from the needs of more than 3,000 passengers and crew, including personal garments, is handled in half-day lots. The work is fed into a classifier—divided into a number of containers for the various items—the feed side of which is a sorting room and the discharge side the wash house.

Passengers' personal garments are classified and taken to a section of the washouse specially equipped for this purpose. The machinery has been designed especially for the various phases through which the work passes and includes washing machines, hydro extractors, a flatwork ironer, drying tumblers, shirt presses, garment presses, collar-finishing plant, and ironing and finishing equipment.

Additional to the main laundry in the *Canberra*, are small self-service launderettes, available on almost every deck in both first and tourist-classes for those passengers who prefer to launder their own personal garments. These launderettes are equipped with suitable domestic-type washing and spin-drying machines, and there are airing and ironing facilities. In addition, every first-class cabin contains facilities for passengers to use the electric irons and ironing boards which are available.

Television—

A completely co-ordinated closed-circuit and off-air Marconi television service is installed in the *Canberra*. This employs some 50 Ekco receivers which provide for the reception of broadcasts employing the 405-line (50 frames) system used in the United Kingdom, the 625-line (50 frames) used in Australia, and the greater part of Europe, or the 525-line (60 frames) system used in the United States of America, Canada and Japan. The receivers are located in the veranda and *de-luxe* suites, in most public rooms, in children's rooms and in certain crew spaces. Incoming broadcast programmes

Fig. 66.—Crockery Patterns.

Fig. 67.—Wine Service.

Fig. 68.—Laundry.

are processed as appropriate in a central control room before distribution to the individual receivers.

A small public room has been wired for use as a television studio, and here a camera can be added to the circuit for plays, interviews and amateur shows presented on board. An interesting feature is that outside shots, particularly from the bridge, which is close to the control room, will give passengers a picture of what is going on on deck and on the navigating bridge. There are two cinema projectors for closed-circuit television programmes while the ship is at sea and out of the range of broadcasting stations.

Material for programmes used in the closed-circuit system while at sea is provided by Programme Exchange, Ltd. A similar system to this was installed in the *Oriana* and was found to be so successful that it was decided to include commercial advertising in the programmes presented in the *Canberra*. This provides for eight minutes of commercial time in each day.

Fig. 69.—Broadcast Master Control Station.

Broadcasting System—

More than 1,000 cabins accommodating first and tourist-class passengers, officers and crew are served by a broadcasting system provided by Tannoy Marine, Ltd. This gives a choice of two programmes, emanating either from radio services or from live programmes from public rooms. If they so wish, passengers can have continuous music in their cabins while the ship is at sea, the music being fed into the broadcasting system from tapes specially pre-recorded by Reditune, Ltd.

An outstanding feature of the communications system is the means providing priority for messages emanating from any of seven master microphones. From the associated master controls (Fig. 69) it is possible to select, individually or collectively, first- or tourist-class public rooms or cabins, circulating areas and crew messes or cabins. With this system, priority announcements can be broadcast from all loud-speakers or from selected circuits, automatically cancelling any other programme or over-riding volume controls which have been turned to the "off" position. The original programmes are restored automatically when the priority announcement is concluded.

Another innovation is the boat-order system, featuring "call-back" facilities which enable officers on the bridge to speak to each lifeboat station, and *vice-versa*. This is effected through transistorised amplifiers and a special control panel, which have also been designed by Tannoy, Ltd. The system enables the officer in charge of each boat station to communicate with the centre of operations during an emergency.

Telephones—

Two special radio-telephone terminals in the *Canberra* enable passengers to make calls from all first-class cabins and from the ship's two telephone kiosks, and privacy of radio-telephone converstaions is ensured by the provision of speech inverters. Two Redifon V.H.F. radio-telephone sets link the bridge with the telephone kiosks and the whole telephone system. A unique feature, developed by Mr. P. A. Bendelow, of the owners' Electronics Department, so that all this equipment can be used as a unit, is that all inputs and outputs go through a special switch unit designed and made by the owners.

To ensure that both passengers and officers of the watch can send and receive radio messages without delay, a Lamson tube system has been installed to connect the radio office with both the purser's bureau and the chart room. This system is operated by vacuum and the messages travel at some 30ft. per second through either incoming or outgoing 2¼in. internal-diameter brass tubing. This material has been employed to obviate corrosion trouble, and as the ships' superstructure is of aluminium, a plastic insulation has been incorporated where the tube passes through the plating to prevent galvanic action.

Lifts—

The lifts on board the *Canberra*, which have been manufactured and installed by Messrs. J. & E. Hall, Ltd., include two first-class passenger lifts; one serving G deck to the Captain's Bridge and the other from E deck to the Sun deck. There are also two passenger lifts for tourists serving from F deck to the Games deck.

The engineers' and crew's lift serves from the tank top to the Navigating Bridge. There are three lifts for passengers' baggage, two for goods only, serving from G to A deck and the other which can also be used for passengers, serving from F to A deck.

Six goods lifts deal with stores, two from the tank top to E deck, two from H to E deck and two from G to the Games deck. For pantry service two lifts have been installed, one from E to A deck and the other serving H to E deck. The other lift, making up the total installation, is for laundry and serves from F to E deck.

Fig. 70.—Wheelhouse.

EQUIPMENT

WITH a vessel built to such a high specification as the *Canberra*, it is not surprising to find that the equipment throughout has been constructed to a very high standard. All the requirements of Lloyd's Register of Shipping have been adhered to and the latest recommendations of the Ministry of Transport have been fully implemented.

Navigating—

The navigating departments in the *Canberra* are, of course, equipped with the most up-to-date instruments to assist the deck officers in their arduous duties. A photograph of the wheelhouse is reproduced in Fig. 70.

A comprehensive range of Marconi Marine communications equipment includes a single-sideband installation for long-range high-frequency radiotelephony. In addition to the world-wide communication facilities provided, the *Canberra* is equipped with a completely co-ordinated internal and off-air television service, permitting standard television broadcast receivers to be used for the reception of local television transmissions in any port along the liner's route.

The growing use of radiotelephony in the marine intermediate and high-frequency bands has led to the development by Marconi Marine of single-sideband communication equipment for marine applications. Single-sideband equipment has many advantages when compared with double-sideband equipment, the most important being a reduction in the transmitter power necessary for effective communication and improved intelligibility and speech quality due to a reduction in selective fading distortion.

As already mentioned, the *Canberra* has a single-sideband transmitter and there are two Atalanta receivers which will deal with normal radiotelegraph and radiotelephone traffic in the medium, intermediate and high-frequency bands. Special radiotelephone terminal equipment enables passengers to make calls from first-class cabins and from telephone kiosks, and privacy of radiotelephone conversations is ensured by the provision of speech inverters.

Emergency equipment consists of a Reliance medium-frequency transmitter, an Alert guard receiver and an Autokey automatic keying device. In addition, two of the vessel's class "A" motor lifeboats are fitted with permanent Salvare combined transmitters and receiving installations.

Located on the wheelhouse bulkhead is a console—constructed by Messrs. Clifford & Snell, Ltd.—which comprises, perhaps, the most comprehensive centralisation of control, communication and indicating equipment ever to be installed in a ship. The section on which all the instruments are mounted faces forward, and viewed from port to starboard, the equipment on the sloping front contains the loudaphone loudspeaking and transistorised telephones for direct communication with the engine-room, forecastle, mooring spaces and all other control stations of the ship. The three panels on the starboard side carry the Tannoy sound broadcast and boat-station control assemblies, together with the Kidde fire detector panel.

On the vertical section, the top panel accommodates the switches for controlling the ventilation fans and, mounted on a ship's outline plate, is a group of nine indicators connected to the Grinnell sprinkler alarm indicator panel in the centre, and this device enables the officer on watch to observe a fire immediately and to switch off the fans in the appropriate sections. Below this panel is a seven-way lights indicator, including two anchor lights, and the control switches for the navigation lanterns. Next follows the indicator for showing

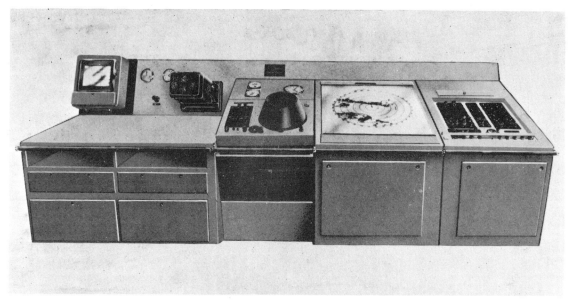

Fig. 71.—Navigation Console Housing the 16-in. Master Radar Display and the 24-in. Projected Display.

that a lifebuoy has been released and a push switch for launching liferafts. Below the coloured block plan associated with the sprinkler alarm panel is a specially designed control panel for operating the two sets of stabiliser fins.

The next panel accommodates the G.E.C. fire alarm indicator and telephone, while the two panels alongside house three de-gaussing indicators and three rotary switches for crew, engine-room and general emergency alarms. The Stone watertight-door indicator and controller panels feature the latest design in this equipment and like the stabiliser control

Fig. 72.—Assembly of Twin, 10-ft. Slotted Waveguide Radar Scanners on the Foremast.

forms a clear compact assembly. Two small panels at the starboard side of the console are for indicating faults on the gyro compass, steering motors and telegraphs.

All the panels conform to a definite pattern and finish to meet the requirements of the owners' naval architect, and they are constructed in such a way that immediate access can be gained by the use of rapid release devices, so that the panels, which are hinged at the base, can be opened outwards for inspection and servicing if necessary.

The after section of the console is constructed in a similar way to the panel arrangement on the forward side and all equipment can be inspected from the rear as well as through large access doors. On the sloping section are all the lighting switches for the bridge, wheelhouse, chart room and the bridge deck area, the labels for which are illuminated through a dimming control. A similar dimming control is provided for complete internal illumination of the console.

All the ship's cables are brought up to sections of appropriately engraved and protected terminals so that each cable can be immediately identified as required. In the construction, use has been made of Perstorp, mounted on robust hardwood framework, the effect being to provide an exact matching of the pleasing and workmanlike décor of the wheelhouse.

Built into a console, constructed by Messrs. Kelvin and Hughes, Ltd., are the 16-in. and 24-in. master displays for two separate radar systems. This radar equipment embodies a number of features which are unique in marine radar practice, and there is little doubt that the Canberra has the most comprehensive and versatile radar system ever to be fitted in a merchant vessel.

Essentially, the installation consists of two true motion radar systems, each complete with its own basic units and controls. There are two scanners, two transmitters, two display units, two motor-alternator assemblies, and an additional slave display is provided to work remotely off either of the master displays. The two radar systems are arranged so that they can be operated separately or simultaneously, and changeover switches enable any unit of either system to be used with units of the other system if required. This arrangement not only achieves valuable operational flexibility, but allows routine maintenance service to be effected without interrupting the availability of normal radar information.

Located in the wheelhouse, the console (Fig. 71) is an integrated combination of tactical chart table, radar display systems, echo sounder, Decca Navigator, clocks, logs, etc. It

Fig. 73.—The Complete Auto-electric Steering Control Equipment under Test. View Shows Main Wheelhouse Steering Control Unit, Secondary Steering Control Unit for Steering Gear Compartment, Steering Control Position, Change-over Switch, Two After Power Units and Selector Switch, Three Bearing Repeaters, Steering Repeater for After Steering Control Position, Two Heading Indicators, Rudder-angle Indicator and Miniature Indicator.

also serves as a housing for units concerned with the S. G. Brown autohelm, Kelvin & Hughes transmitting magnetic compass, bridge wiring to the telegraph communication system and wheelhouse lighting control.

Of the two master radar displays, one is an adaptation of the well-established Kelvin & Hughes equipment designated type 14/16P. This provides relative motion or true motion presentation on a 16-in. P.P.I. display with built-in reflection plotter. The other master display is a 24-in. diameter "Bright Display" of radar information in either relative motion or true motion presentation. This large screen bright display is produced by use of the photographic rapid processing technique, pioneered by Messrs. Kelvin & Hughes, Ltd., for defence purposes, which has now been developed for marine

radar application and is ship-borne for the first time in the *Canberra.*

This equipment presents P.P.I. information by projecting on to a 24-in. display surface a sequence of rapidly processed photographs of a special cathode ray tube. The time cycle between successively projected pictures can be varied between $3\frac{1}{2}$ seconds and 60 seconds. This means that in a time cycle of $3\frac{1}{2}$ seconds the information on the cathode ray tube is photographed, processed and projected to the plotting screen. By comparison, a conventional radar display, using an aerial rotation of 20 r.p.m. renews the radar data once every three seconds. Black on white, or white on black, are available for the projected image for daylight viewing. For use at night there is a choice of coloured shades. Apart from the obvious

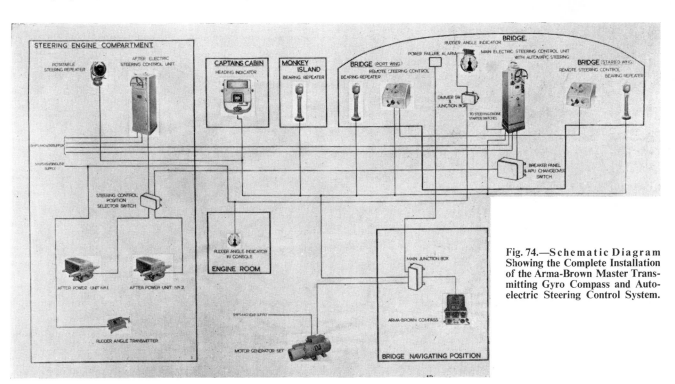

Fig. 74.—Schematic Diagram Showing the Complete Installation of the Arma-Brown Master Transmitting Gyro Compass and Auto-electric Steering Control System.

Fig. 75.—Arma-Brown Master Transmitting Compass.

advantages of the large-screen bright display achieved by this method of presentation, the photographic projector provides the most up-to-date radar plotting facilities, since the P.P.I. image is projected on to a paper surface and direct plotting is possible.

The slave display is situated at the forward end of the wheelhouse and can be a slave to either of the two master displays. It presents a relative motion P.P.I. display and has a reflection plotter. Although designated slave, this unit is, in fact, virtually independent in operation of the master. Range of view, gain, and ranging by means of calibration rings or range marker, can be carried out quite independently, and, so far as the navigator is concerned, the slave can be regarded as another radar installation.

To make up the aerial system there are two 10-ft. slotted wave-guide scanners installed adjacent to each other on the main mast above the crow's nest (see Fig. 72). Despite the close proximity of the two scanners, both radar equipments can be operated simultaneously without the appearance of mutual interference. This unique feature represents a further substantial advance in marine radar progress and has been made possible by a specially synchronised power-supply system which, in itself, is duplicated to allow for continuity of operation during servicing periods.

An inter-system switching arrangement enables each scanner to operate with either transmitter which, in turn, can operate with either master display unit. Alternatively, all three display units can be operated from one transmitter and one scanner. Located in the navigational console is an indicator panel, which shows at a glance, by means of coloured lights, which particular units of the system are in operation at any time.

Included among the other navigational equipment is a Kelvin & Hughes transmitting magnetic compass, which is a standard unit of conventional design installed on the roof of the wheelhouse. It feeds information to a specially designed repeater at the steering position which reproduces a 30 deg. sector of the compass card as well as a defined image on an

8-in. wide screen, and this is presented to the steersman in the vertical plane. The binnacle incorporates a direct wheelhouse reflector unit for standby purposes.

An entirely automatic pressure-operated Sal log provides speed indications on a scale graduated from 0 to 30 knots. The pressure-receiving unit takes the form of a pitôt tube which is installed in the bottom of the ship, and which can be retracted and locked in position when not in use. A repeater is fitted in the navigation console and remote control facilities are provided on the bridge for raising or lowering the tube.

The Decca Navigator is one of the Mark V, nine-chain receivers mainly for use in North-West Europe, but it is significant that the Australian Government are now holding evaluation trials with a chain in the Sydney area for both marine and aerial navigational purposes.

The *Canberra* is equipped with the S. G. Brown auto-electric steering control system. This has been designed to provide three methods of steering control from one small wheelhouse unit for ships fitted with electro-hydraulic or steam-operated steering gear. Rudder application is brought about through two S. G. Brown after power units which are directly coupled to the control valve of the steering gear, and primarily controlled from the wheelhouse unit. This system provides electro-mechanical, as well as completely automatic, steering control, using the Arma-Brown gyro as datum, and has the further advantage that only one after power unit is used at one time, the other being in the standby condition ready for instant use when required. It is not necessary to have hydraulic piping from the steering engine, the wheel-house transmitter or the large wheel.

The main hand-electric control is by means of a handwheel, the movement of which operates port or starboard switches and these, in turn, operate breaker switches. Situated in the wheelhouse unit, these breaker switches govern the operating field circuit in whichever after power unit is selected.

Auto-control is by means of a "brains" unit, which is situated in the wheelhouse unit and is operated from a datum provided by the Arma-Brown gyro compass. The "brains" unit provides an impulse to operate the breaker switches in the control unit to govern the operating field circuit in the after power unit selected for main control.

Secondary hand-electric control is by means of a lever located on the front of the unit. When the lever is moved to port or starboard, switches are made which, in turn, operate a second system of breaker switches. These breaker switches govern the operating field circuit in the after power unit not employed for main or auto control.

From the foregoing, it will be apparent that there are two completely separate operating circuits, one of which can be used for main and auto control and the other for secondary. In addition, there are two separate input supplies from the ship's mains. To provide protection in the event of a mains power failure on one line, the two ship's main inputs are connected to a four-pole two-way switch situated in the bridge unit. This provides change-over switching between either supply, while a power failure alarm unit gives an audible and visual indication of any major power failure from the output side of the motor generator.

The main bridge unit also incorporates an indicator showing the rudder movement transmitted to the steering engine, a course trimmer to enable small alterations of course to be made while main control is in automatic steering, a rudder and weather control and a rotatable steering repeater.

To provide a complete secondary steering-control position within the complete system, a second control unit is incorporated, and this unit is located in the steering gear compartment. It provides two separate methods of hand-electric steering control similar in every respect to those provided at the primary control position, but using entirely separate breaker switches to govern the operating field circuit in either of the two after power units. As with the primary control, power supply inputs are duplicated and a rudder movement indicator is incorporated.

The two steering positions operate entirely independently of one another within the complete system, selection of the control position being made by a special change-over switch. Safe operation of the system is assured by the inclusion of an S. G. Brown clear-view, rudder-angle indicator, positioned in the wheelhouse and actuated by a rudder-angle transmitter connected to the rudder stock. A second rudder-angle indicator is included in the main engine-room control console.

Mechanical and electrical interlocks are incorporated to ensure that the auto-electric steering control system will not operate until the power supply switch to the steering engine has been made. Three bearing repeaters are fed from the Arma-Brown gyro and a special silent-running, clear-view repeater is installed in the captain's cabin on a table mounting. A wide-angle viewing heading indicator, including a manually-operated "course to be steered" indicator is included in an instrument panel at the forward end of the wheelhouse. The photograph reproduced in Fig. 73 shows the complete equipment under test, while a schematic diagram of the installation is shown in Fig. 74.

The unique characteristics of the Arma-Brown gyro compass (Fig. 75) that make it impervious to vibrations and ship movement, make it unnecessary to provide a special gyro compartment. The compass is, in fact, installed in the chart table at the after end of the wheelhouse, and this arrangement enables the navigating officer to take advantage of the heading indicator built into the top of the compass.

Emergency—

Believed to be the largest single contract ever to be placed for equipment of this type, the construction of the *Canberra's* lifeboats was entrusted to the Viking Marine Co., Ltd., who have extensive experience in the building of reinforced plastic craft. Their lifeboats and rescue boats are well known to most shipping companies and have proved to be sturdy and reliable during many years of service in all parts of the world. The installation on the *Canberra* comprises 24 boats providing accommodation for 3,362 persons.

Six of the craft are class "B" motor lifeboats, 36ft. 0in. by 12ft. 0in. by 5ft. 0½in., each with seating capacity for 144 persons and powered by a Parsons-Peregrine air-cooled Diesel engine. Viking hand-propelling gear is installed in 16 of the lifeboats, each of which has dimensions of 36ft. 0in. by 12ft. 0in. by 5ft. 0½in. and a seating capacity for 153 persons. The remaining two craft are class "A" combined rescue/accident motor lifeboats with dimensions of 26ft. 0in. by 8ft. 10in. by 3ft. 7in. Each has a seating capacity for 25 persons and is propelled by a Petter air-cooled Diesel engine. As part of their equipment, each of these boats is fitted with a fully-equipped wireless cabin. It is intended that the six class "B" motor lifeboats will be used for ship-to-shore service. A photograph of the boats is reproduced in Fig. 76.

The boats have all been constructed from reinforced plastics, the polyester resin employed being Crystic 189, made and supplied by Scott Bader & Co., Ltd. Crystic 189 was introduced by Scott Bader in 1954 and it was the first British polyester resin specifically developed for the contact moulding of large boat hulls. This polyester resin is specifically designed for all contact and low-pressure moulding applications where outstanding water and chemical resistance are called for, particularly in boat hulls and chemical plant. It is made to match the latest types of glass mat and so produces mouldings of a quality not possible with earlier resins. Since the correct viscosity of the resin is a major factor in the production of high quality reinforced plastics laminates and mouldings,

Fig. 76.—Interior of Lifeboat, Showing Hand-propelling Gear.

Crystic 189 can be supplied in three different viscosities, and the fabricator can blend these when necessary to obtain any particular viscosity. In this way the physical characteristics of Crystic 189 can be used to full advantage. Samples of Crystic 189 glass-mat laminates have been subjected to five years continuous immersion in sea water without any signs of deterioration. Samples have also been immersed for six months off the west coast of Africa, at Aden and in Lake Maracaibo, Venezuela, without any adverse effect. Some thousands of boat hulls of all types have now been made with Crystic 189, ranging from dinghies and rowing eights to lifeboats and 60-ft. Diesel cruisers, illustrating the great confidence placed in this resin by the shipbuilding industry.

The boats are carried in Welin-Maclachlan underdeck davits which have been specially designed to suit the structure of the vessel. In order to take advantage of all the available space, the trackways have been built neatly into the cabin space. The fact that this arrangement has not interfered in any way with the layout and size of the cabins proves the close liaison between the owners, shipbuilders and davit company during the initial design period.

This underdeck davit has a straight trackway and in view of the restricted space available between the two decks, the trackways are angled at 18 deg. to the horizontal and to give the outboard turning moment at 25-deg. list, balance weights are fitted. In this trackway there runs a special davit cradle or carriage which carries the boat from the stowed position to the outboard position. The cradle has steadying arms to hold the boat rigid athwartships and fore and aft during the turning out action.

In view of the fact that it has been necessary to fit balance weights with the 18 deg. trackways, the cradle had to be as light as possible and, for this reason, aluminium-bronze has been employed in the manufacture. At the same time problems of stability were raised due to the cradle running in a

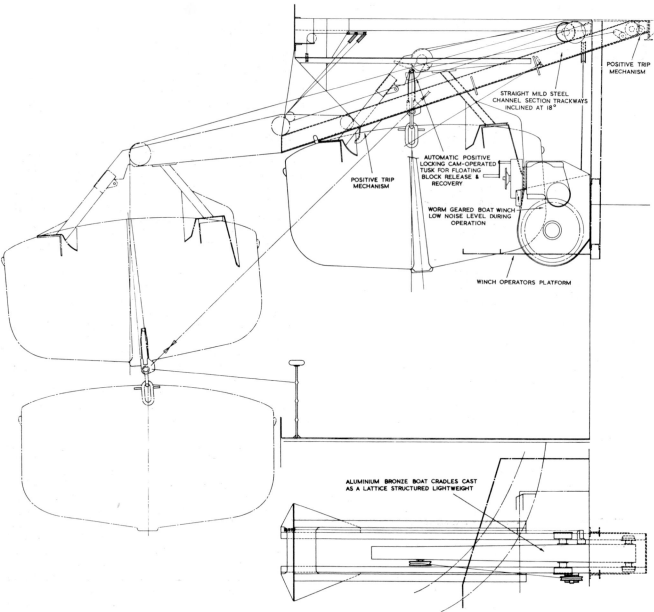

POSITIVE TRIP
MECHANISM

STRAIGHT MILD STEEL
CHANNEL SECTION TRACKWAYS
INCLINED AT 18°

AUTOMATIC POSITIVE
LOCKING CAM-OPERATED
TUSK FOR FLOATING
BLOCK RELEASE &
RECOVERY

POSITIVE TRIP
MECHANISM

WORM GEARED BOAT WINCH
LOW NOISE LEVEL DURING
OPERATION

WINCH OPERATORS PLATFORM

ALUMINIUM BRONZE BOAT CRADLES CAST
AS A LATTICE STRUCTURED LIGHTWEIGHT

Fig. 77.—Arrangement of Lifeboat Davits.

straight trackway, and these could only be overcome by fitting an automatic moving tusk. This moving tusk, which is operated by a cam running on the davit trackway, ensures that the boat is only released when the davit is fully outboard, and when this releasing action takes place the cradle itself is automatically locked to the trackway. By using an automatic tusk arrangement it is possible to launch a lifeboat at any adverse list condition either by gravity or some other external force. It also ensures that under all conditions of list, whether adverse or favourable, the davit is stable. A drawing of the davit is reproduced in Fig. 77.

The boat davit winches, which have been specially designed to mount on the side of the ship's casing between the two deck levels, have been streamlined to blend with the surrounding ship's structure and to give clear decks underneath the boat and davit. The winch design is also new, as instead of the conventional spur gearing, a silent worm gearbox has been incorporated to reduce noise to a minimum when in operation. This is a very important feature as the winches are situated in close proximity to the cabins.

An Elliot four-man Seiner inflatable liferaft has been supplied for use in "man overboard" emergencies. The liferaft is housed in a glass-fibre container, which is fitted at the stern of the vessel and held in place by a lashing incorporating a Schermuly quick-release link.

The installation in the *Canberra* is the first in a British ship incorporating the quick-release link manufactured by the Schermuly Pistol Rocket Apparatus Ltd.

Within a matter of about 30 seconds of the alarm being given and the release switch operated, an inflated liferaft is floating on the water in the wake of the ship for rescue purposes.

Sound signalling is by means of a Tyfon, type T575 DVEL, steam whistle, complete with push-button and full automatic control, manufactured by Kockums Mekaniska Verkstad A/B., and supplied through their United Kingdom representatives, the Industrial & Mining Supplies Co., Ltd.

Also fitted is a Secomak double G whistle which comprises two separate type G, Mark IV., whistles, each of 6 H.P. mounted one on each side of the platform on the mast. These whistles will be operated simultaneously by one set of control gear and since each is of a different tone the result is a two-tone

Fig. 78.—Fitting Rocksil Mattress to Aluminium.

Fig. 79.—Rocksil Wired Mattress Being Fitted to Bulkhead.

whistle. Fully automatic fog signalling is incorporated. Since it is independent of steam or compressed air the Seco-mak electric whistle is always ready for instant use at sea or in harbour so long as electric power is available.

As is to be expected in a vessel of this class, extensive precautions have been taken to guard against the possible outbreak and spread of fire. There is a complete Grinnell automatic sprinkler and fire alarm system which incorporates an additional automatic-starting Diesel engine-driven pump.

For protection against the spread of flame and smoke through necessary openings in all the class A.60 bulkheads, fire-resisting doors have been fitted in accordance with the recommendations of the International Convention for the Safety of Life at Sea (1948). Doors manufactured by Caston Barber, Ltd., were selected.

For the smaller openings in gangways, galley, air-conditioning into rooms, etc., the hinged-type fire door, known by the registered name Barbador, has been used. Of this type alone, there are more than 240 doors throughout the ship. Each door is constructed from steel sheet and asbestos, and is as fire-resistant as the A.60 bulkhead in which it is fitted. They are all designed to be self-closing and to latch automatically, and have stainless-steel "flush with deck" threshold plates and flush-type handles on the gangway side. Any variation in deck level is overcome by the use of rising butt hinges which lift the door panel on opening by ½in. in 90 deg. and 1in. in 180 deg.

A new approach in the installation and decorative treatment has been made with the fire doors, to blend them with the surrounding décor. To this end a special grade of flame-proof laminate sheet matching the surrounding panels on gangway linings, etc., has been applied to the surfaces of the steel doors. These doors, after having been faced with plastic sheet, were let in flush with the gangway lining, to form part of the ship's decoration. All door handles and fittings are of flush design and their colour and finish match adjacent metal furniture on cabin door handles, storm rails, etc.

For the larger openings in main class A.60 bulkheads, sliding telescopic Castodors have been selected to give clear openings 5ft. 0in. wide by 7ft. 4in. high. When open, these doors slide and telescope into recesses at the side of the opening. Due to the multi-leaf construction, storage space taken is only approximately 18in. by 8in.

Throughout the vessel there are 40 Haskins Firola fire-resisting steel shutters. The Firola shutters have been designed to conform to the exacting specifications and requirements of such authorities as the London County Council, London Fire Brigade, Fire Offices Committee and the Ministry of Transport to provide an efficient method of preventing the spread of fire in buildings and ships, particularly passenger ships. For many years, the Firola shutter has been used extensively for such applications as openings in party walls, lifts, staircases, corridors and escalators, as well as for petrol pump enclosures, abutting well holes, ledger recesses, safes, etc. Following exhaustive tests carried out by the Ministry of Transport, it was realised that the Firola shutter would meet an urgent need for the prevention of the spread of fire on board ships under the International Convention for the Safety of Life at Sea, class "A" risk. Apart from its efficiency as a means of preventing the spread of fire, the appearance of the Firola shutter and the method used for its installation enable any decorative treatment to be maintained. The shutters are fitted singly or in double sets, one on each side of an opening, to give a minimum fire-resistance grading of two hours and four hours respectively.

In the *Canberra*, the shutters are of push-up operation and are equipped with automatic fusible-link release apparatus. Also installed in the *Canberra* are two Haskins Rolador shutters, each measuring 29ft. by 31ft. and constructed of 14-gauge aluminium. They are mounted horizontally to provide a covered section on the open Games deck. The shutters, each of which weighs 2,000 lb, are electrically operated and, by means of a continuous chain drive, can be extended or retracted onto spring-loaded coils in a housing at a speed of 28½ft. per min. The shutters are mounted on a slope to follow the deck camber and this slope in turn facilitates the shedding of rain water from the shutters.

An extremely large contract for thermal insulation has been carried out by Andersons Insulation Co., Ltd., mostly in Caposite amosite asbestos and Rocksil rock wool. Caposite amosite asbestos blocks, manufactured by Cape Insulation and Asbestos Products, Ltd., a subsidiary of the Cape Asbestos Co., Ltd., have been used for the linings of insulated

Fig. 80.—Marinite Partitions with Caposite Fire-resisting Insulation on Deckhead. Grounds for Suspended Ceiling are in Position.

class "A" fire-resisting divisions. The $1\frac{1}{2}$in. thick Caposite blocks are covered with hard-setting cement keyed to wire netting. All insulation on fire divisions has had to be carried 15in. along the abutting structure—the deckhead ribbon—and for the most part this has been carried out in Caposite. Where the deckhead is of aluminium, Rocksil rock wool has been used.

At every entrance, where lift shafts, ventilation shafts and stair wells are potential flame and smoke funnels, the area has been made into a completely incombustible compartment by lining walls, ceiling and floor with fire-resisting and non-combustible materials. Two-inch thick Caposite blocks line the walls and also the undersides of the floor in most of these entrance areas.

The insides of all cable ducts entering a fire area through class "A" bulkheads have been packed with Caposite and the outside protected with the same material. Control valves in the ventilation ducting have been similarly protected, as have the fire-resisting shutters.

Other potential fire hazards on the ship have been treated in similar fashion. For example, the ceiling beneath the ventilation unit room is protected with $2\frac{1}{4}$-in. Rocksil, while the deckhead over the entire area of the galleys—some 20,000 sq. ft.—is protected with Caposite blocks and similar treatment has been afforded to the deckhead of the baggage room. The fore and aft inside walls of the boiler room have been insulated with $1\frac{1}{2}$-in. Rocksil extra-light density slab on top of $2\frac{1}{2}$in. thick Rocksil mattress.

Insulation of the boiler panels was carried out by Messrs. Harland & Wolff, Ltd., in their boiler shop, and again Caposite has been used for this work, as well as for the boiler drums and funnel uptakes.

In way of the forced-draught fans the deckhead is covered with Rocksil wired mattresses, $2\frac{1}{2}$in. thick and the false steel ceiling with $2\frac{1}{2}$in. thick Rocksil extra-light density slabs, serving both fire and acoustic purposes.

Inside the engine-room and other machinery spaces, the principal auxiliaries, in addition to the high-pressure and low-pressure turbine cylinders, have been lagged with Caposite. Ventilation trunking, both in the engine-room and boiler room, has been insulated with $1\frac{1}{2}$in. and 2in. Caposite blocks.

In various parts of the ship the shell has been insulated with Rocksil type "A" mattress and this material also lines the deckhead of the captain's bridge and cinema.

Fire-protection for the aluminium bulkheads of the tourist-class lounge is by means of Rocksil, while for the Lido and first-class ballroom, Caposite gives "A" class protection

Fig. 81.—Cutting Marinite Before Erection for Fire-protective Lining in Crew's Stores Space.

behind the band platform and Rocksil protects the ceiling, where the whiteness of the rock wool effectively reflects the electric light through the translucent suspended ceiling. In the aluminium structure, where the aluminium plating joins the steelwork, a protection ribbon of Rocksil wired mattresses has been fitted to comply with the requirements of the Ministry of Transport. In all, the Andersons Insulation Company have fitted more than 500,000 sq. ft. of Caposite and Rocksil. Photographs of Rocksil being applied are reproduced in Figs. 78 and 79.

An extensive amount of Marinite incombustible material has been used as the final facing for many of the fire-resistant bulkheads. In all, about 200,000 sq. ft. of the material in $\frac{1}{2}$in., $\frac{3}{4}$in., $\frac{7}{8}$in., 1in. and $1\frac{3}{16}$in. thicknesses have been used. Finishes are paint, natural wood veneers, laminate plastic and soft plastic veneers. The uses of the Marinite are many and varied. For example for the fire protection of class A.60 divisions in steel and aluminium, including engine-room casings, hatch trunking and stairwells. All the public room subcontractors concerned in a space bounded by one or more class A.60 divisions, used Marinite as a decoratively finished lining insulation. Lightweight Marinite has been used for the fire protection of class A.60 aluminium superstructure.

Cabins and doors adjacent to main entrances have been built up of Marinite bulkheading to form fire stops and Marinite has also been used for the underside of the shipside lifeboat embarkation stations, insulating ventilation trunking passing through passenger accommodation and galley ceilings. The ease with which Marinite can be worked is clearly illustrated in Figs. 80 and 81.

For the protection of 16 cargo and baggage spaces, the Walter Kidde Co., Ltd., have supplied and installed a smoke-detecting and CO_2 fire-extinguishing system. Samples of air in the spaces are continually taken through piping to a smoke-detecting cabinet situated on *E* deck. From this cabinet air samples are drawn through a single pipe to a single-line cabinet installed in the wheelhouse. Should smoke be present in any of the air samples, it causes an audible alarm to be sounded from the wheelhouse cabinet. Further investigation is carried out in a cabinet on *E* deck where the actual space affected is determined. By opening the appropriate valve the sampling of air from the space is arrested and CO_2 can be injected through the same piping to extinguish the fire. A total of sixty-three 80-℔ capacity, CO_2 cylinders are provided for this installation, and connections are also available for the protection of the boiler room.

Where the subdivision bulkheads are penetrated for reasons of access the openings are fitted with watertight doors. For this purpose, Messrs. J. Stone & Co. (Propellers), Ltd., a member of the Stone-Platt Group, have supplied 21 power-operated watertight doors, and these units are fitted in the engine-room and on *G* and *H* decks.

Power is obtained from a central hydro-pneumatic pumping plant, which is fully automatic and complies with the latest Ministry of Transport regulations. The doors can be operated from either side of the bulkhead or collectively by a controller on the bridge. This controller incorporates a warning device which gives an audible warning at the doors before and during closing. Located adjacent to the controller is an indicator panel with illuminated discs for each door to show their open and closed positions. In the event of an emergency, the doors can be closed by hand pumps situated at each door and at positions above the bulkhead deck.

A further 17 hand-operated doors are installed on *F* deck, in addition to the power system. Operation is by the Hanston system, in which each door is opened or closed individually, locally and at remote positions on the bulkhead deck, by hand pumps.

Deck—

As already mentioned, the *Canberra* has been built in accordance with the requirements of Lloyd's Register of Shipping for their highest classification and the outfit and equipment also fulfil, in every respect, the latest recommendations of the Ministry of Transport.

To satisfy the extremely high specification, deck equipment of the most modern type has been provided, and included are anchors supplied by Messrs. Samuel Taylor & Sons (Brierley Hill), Ltd. Three Dreadnought bower anchors, each weighing 201 cwt., are installed, together with one Dreadnought stern anchor weighing $69\frac{1}{2}$ cwt. The same firm have also provided 330 fathoms of $3\frac{9}{16}$-in. Tayco chain cable with integral studs, shackled in 15 fathom lengths with Kenter shackles. Two of the lengths are divided at $3\frac{1}{2}$ and $11\frac{1}{2}$ fathoms. Also provided are 150 fathoms of $2\frac{1}{16}$ in. Tayco chain cable with integral studs for use as stern chain. This ground tackle is the largest outfit that Messrs. Samuel Taylor and Sons have supplied since they provided the anchor gear for the *Queen Elizabeth*.

Included in the mooring arrangements are Taylor, Pallister Dunstos warping guides, and the same firm have supplied the outfit of steel blocks and shackles together with MCI blocks.

Two Pitt-Scott (Johnson-type) mooring winches are fitted. These winches are capable of maintaining constant tension at any desired value within the designed range. This is from 2,500 ℔ to 15,000 ℔ with automatic control, with an increase to 20,000 ℔ in manual control. The line speed, with a pull of 15,000 ℔, is 80ft. per min., while the units have a free line speed of 400ft. per min. Operation is from Ward-Leonard motor generator sets.

Even though much of the *Canberra's* cargo will be handled by transporters, arrangements have been made for a limited amount of gear of more orthodox type. This takes the form

Fig. 82.—Forward Deck Gear.

of two derricks, one of 10 tons and the other of 3 tons safe working load. These derricks have been supplied by Stewarts and Lloyds, Ltd., and are each 57ft. long and supported on two streamlined derrick posts at the forward end of the ship (see Fig. 82).

Welded aluminium hatch boards for Nos. 2 and 3 hatchways on each of *D*, *H* and *J* decks have been provided by Saro (Anglesey), Ltd.

Steering is effected by means of an electro-hydraulic steering gear manufactured by Messrs. Brown Brothers & Co., Ltd. Of the four-cylinder Rapson-slide type, the gear has two power units each consisting of a 275 B.H.P. electric motor driving a size 50, mark III. V.S.G. variable-delivery pump. Each power unit is capable of full duty, the other being a standby but it can be brought into operation immediately for use in entering or leaving harbour or for operation in confined waters.

The steering gear is arranged so that five combinations of hydraulic cylinders can be used—all four, two port, two starboard, two forward or two aft, the necessary change-over valves, which are all housed in one chest, being arranged for this purpose. Control is by the S. G. Brown automatic helmsman, already referred to, from the navigating position, but mechanical control is provided from a handwheel fitted in the steering gear compartment.

With all four hydraulic cylinders and one power unit in operation, the steering gear is capable of exerting a maximum working torque of 2,050 tons ft. and of moving the rudder from 35 deg. port to 35 deg. starboard and *vice versa*, in a period not exceeding 30 seconds when the vessel is proceeding at full ahead speed. With two power units in operation the time from hardover to hardover is about 18 seconds.

A substantial rudderhead bearing and carrier have also been supplied by Messrs. Brown Brothers, and this bearing takes the full weight of the rudder, etc., as well as the radial loads imposed by the sea on the rudder. Special lubrication is provided to ensure that lubrication of this important item is available even when at a rudder angle of about $4\frac{1}{2}$ deg.

James Gordon Valves, Ltd., a member of the Elliott-Automation Group, have supplied special valves for fuelling and ballasting the *Canberra*. In all, 64 of these special Pilgrim valves are installed. Pilgrim valves are designed for remote operation from a control console, with provision for rapid and fool-proof operation during the quick turn-round in a fuelling port which is imperative with a fast liner.

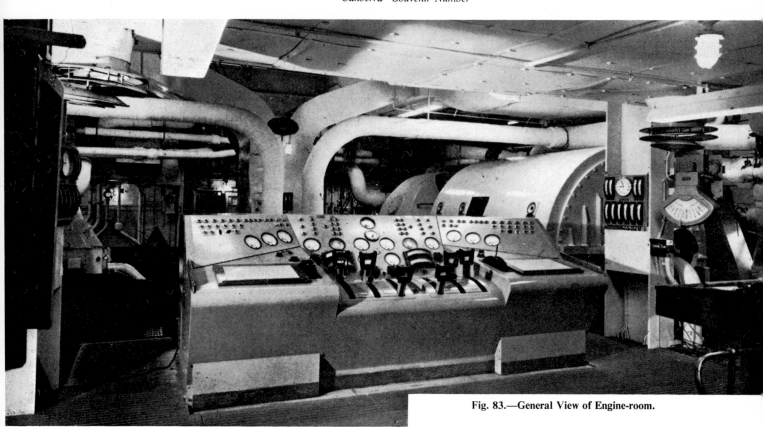

Fig. 83.—General View of Engine-room.

PROPELLING MACHINERY

BEFORE deciding on the type of machinery most suitable for a ship such as the *Canberra*, extensive design studies were undertaken, on behalf of the owners, by the Yarrow-Admiralty Research Department. It was finally decided to adopt a turbo-electric system capable of developing 85,000 S.H.P., driving twin propellers, which gives the *Canberra* the most powerful British-built turbo-electric propulsion installation to date. Her power per shaft—42,500 S.H.P.—also slightly exceeds that of the French pre-war liner *Normandie*, whose turbo-electric machinery was rated at 160,000 S.H.P. on four screws. There have, however, been more powerful ship-borne turbo-electric installations, such as those in the American aircraft-carriers *Lexington* and *Saratoga*, completed in 1920. In each of these vessels the power developed was 180,000 S.H.P. on four screws and the machinery comprised turbo-alternator sets supplying induction motors which drove the propellers.

Soon after these vessels were built, induction motors were superseded by synchronous propeller motors, and this type of motor, fitted with a squirrel-cage winding for starting and reversing, is still used to-day. It is lighter, smaller, more efficient and has a larger air gap than an equivalent induction motor.

The synchronous propeller motors installed on the *Canberra* have a gap between the rotor poles and the stator cone increasing from a minimum of 0·43in. at the centre of the pole face to 0·645in. at the pole tips. An equivalent induction motor, from an electrical design viewpoint would, ideally, have an air gap of 0·05in., which is not acceptable mechanically, and would probably be 0·15in. as a result of mechanical considerations causing the power factor to drop to less than 0·1.

The equivalent induction motor has an air gap of about ⅛in. and operates at a poor power factor, while the lighter, smaller and more efficient synchronous motor installed in the *Canberra* has a minimum air gap of nearly ½in. and operates at unity power factor.

In the *Canberra*, the engines have been placed aft, to allow improved accommodation for passengers and to obtain unimpeded public rooms. A photograph of the engine-room is reproduced in Fig. 83.

A feature of electric transmission is the flexibility possible in the arrangement of propulsion machinery, arising from the mechanical independence of propeller motors and propulsion alternators. The drawing reproduced in Fig. 84 shows the engine-room arrangement, while sections through the engine-room are shown in Fig. 85. Above and aft of the propeller motors are the boilers, allowing short runs of steam piping to the propulsion turbines, located aft of the alternators.

In the simplest turbo-electric system, a propulsion turbo-alternator powers a synchronous propeller motor direct-coupled to the propeller shafting. The ratio of the number of poles chosen for the alterator, usually two, and the number chosen for the propeller motor determine the speed reduction between turbine and propeller. This reduction permits optimum speeds both at the turbine and the propeller.

With the turbine running light, at 25 per cent. full speed, the propeller motor stator is connected by contactors, for ahead or astern rotation, to the alternator stator. The alternator is then excited, usually with a boost value of excitation, and the motor is started as an induction motor, a squirrel-cage winding being embedded in the rotor pole faces.

When the motor is approaching synchronous speed, *i.e.* 25 per cent. of full speed, its field is excited to bring the

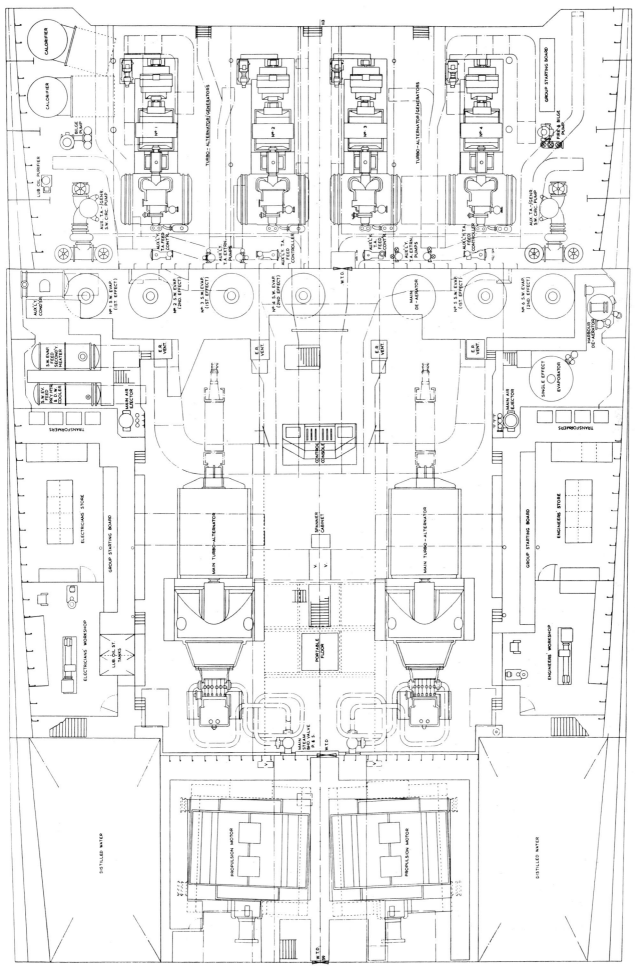

Fig. 84.—Layout of Engine-room and Generator Room.

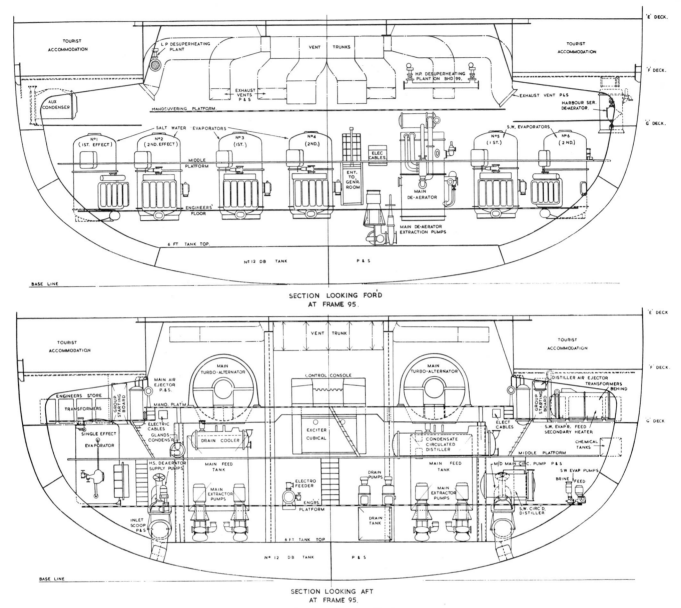

Fig. 85.—Sections Through Engine-room.

motor into step. Both the alternator and the propeller motor excitations are reduced to the normal operating values, and any propeller speed between dead slow and full speed is obtained by controlling the turbine speed.

The drawing reproduced in Fig. 86 shows the circuits available for supplying the two propeller motors from one or both of the two propulsion turbo-alternator sets.

Each motor is of double-unit construction, *i.e.*, there are two separate motors within a common frame and on a common shaft.

The switchgear allows any one or more half-motors to be connected to either of the turbo-alternators, *i.e.*, the two alternators cannot be paralleled.

The usual combinations available are port turbo-alternator supplying the two port motor units and, independently, the starboard turbo-alternator supplying the two starboard motor units, up to 85,000 S.H.P.; one turbo-alternator set completely shut down, and the other set supplying both propeller motors at powers of up to 40,000 S.H.P. (this arrangement allows economical running at reduced powers should the *Canberra* be required for cruising); port and starboard propellers synchronized, and this is attained by the port alternator

providing power for the forward port and starboard propeller motor units, with the starboard alternator powering the aft propeller motor units. These combinations are, of course, separate from the emergency running arrangements.

Fig. 86 also shows the method of reversing the direction of rotation of a propeller motor by interchanging phases A and C. The reversing contactors are operated with the propulsion circuit "dead" and are, in effect, set-up switches.

The arrangement of the propulsion control gear, set up in the factory for test purposes, is shown in Fig. 87. In the ship, the outboard cubicles are dropped below the turbine platform level on which only the console and lever gear are accommodated. In the centre is the console and below it the excitation cubicle. Outboard are pairs of cubicles containing all the H.T. equipment. In each pair, one being associated with each drive, the upper cubicle contains the propulsion set-up switches, and the lower cubicle the reversing contactors. This propulsion control gear is placed forward of the propulsion turbo-alternator sets and the operator at the lever gear, Fig. 88, faces aft.

On the console behind the propulsion levers are horizontal edgewise tachometers in pairs to indicate the associated turbo-alternator and propeller motor speeds. Circscale instruments give propulsion A.C. voltages and currents, S.H.P., exciter D.C. voltages and currents, the actual movement of each propeller and a count of its revolutions using Selsyn drives, the relative movement of the two propellers using a differential Selsyn, and rudder angle. Lamps indicate the switching of propulsion and excitation circuits, faults, excessive machine temperatures, essential auxiliaries operating, and if propeller turning gear is engaged.

At each end of the console is a "short-circuit" relay which trips the excitation in the event of a heavy overcurrent in the propulsion circuit, a temperature indicator connected to thermocouples in the alternator and propeller motor stators and ventilating systems, and an alternator output kWh. meter.

There are two sets of three propulsion levers, one set for each drive. From outboard to inboard, each set comprises a direction lever, a speed lever, and a starting lever. The direction lever is mechanically coupled to the reversing contactors, and closes these for ahead or astern operation. The starting lever is concerned only with applying alternator and propeller motor excitations. At its first position, boost excitation is applied to the alternator only which, during

starting, is driven by the turbine at a governed quarter full speed, and the motor runs up almost to its synchronous speed as an induction motor. At the second position, reduced boost excitation is applied to the motor as well as to the alternator, and the motor is synchronized. The final position of the lever reduces alternator and motor excitations to the normal values for continuous running.

Mechanically coupled to the associated turbine governor control system, the speed lever has a worm, for fine adjustment, which engages with a rack. Above the quarter speed position of the lever, increasing steam flow can be obtained only by adjusting this worm, but the worm can be disengaged for reducing the steam flow. To guard against faulty operation, lever interlocking is provided, and further interlocking ensures that the propulsion and excitation circuit set-up switches cannot be re-set, or access gained to the H.T. or excitation cubicles, unless the direction and starting levers are in their "off" positions.

Outboard of the direction levers are the telegraph reply actuators, and outboard of each of these is a desk giving access to a sub-standard kW. meter, which provides accurately the alternator power output for trials purposes.

Each H.T. set-up switch cubicle, contains two groups of

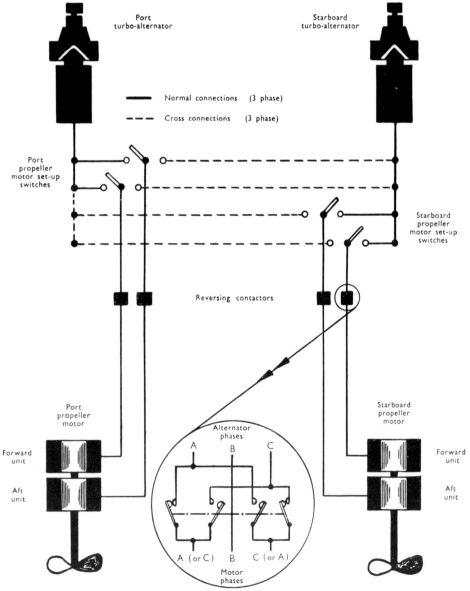

Fig. 86.—Simple Key Diagram of Propulsion Circuits, Showing Switching Arrangements.

Fig. 87.—Propulsion Control Gear as Assembled in the Factory.

three switches, one group for each half of the associated propeller motor. These switches have three positions—starboard alternator, "off," and port alternator. They are operated manually, the operating arms carrying the mechanical interlocking which ensures that they can only be re-switched when the direction and starting levers are "off," and that these levers can only be moved from "off," when the switches are positively in one of their three positions.

Below each set-up switch cubicle is the associated H.T. reversing contactor cubicle. This contains two groups of four contactors, which determine the direction of rotation of the associated propeller motor, and are mechanically closed in pairs, for ahead or astern, by the direction lever.

Full power conditions carried by each contactor, are 6,000 volts, 1,550 amps. but interlocking of the lever gear ensures that no contactor can be opened unless excitation has already been removed from the alternator and propeller motor. To obtain a rapid decrease in excitation, the automatic control units incorporate a voltage suppression circuit which operates when the starting lever is brought to the "off" position. The reversing contactors will, therefore, not be

called upon to open on load. This voltage suppression circuit is also initiated by the "short-circuit" relay which trips excitation in the event of a heavy overcurrent due to a fault in the propulsion A.C. system.

Below the control console is located the excitation cubicle, which contains the relatively low-voltage control gear including excitation switchgear and contactors. Propulsion exciters are driven in tandem with the auxiliary turbo-alternators. Each of the four auxiliary turbo-alternator/propulsion exciter sets comprises a pass-out turbine with combined condenser; a 6,000/1,200-r.p.m. reduction gearbox; a 1,500-kW., normal rated, 0·8-p.f., 440-volt, 3-phase, 60-cycles alternator; the tandem driven 300-kW., 300-volt, 1,000-amp. D.C. continuously rated, 1,200-r.p.m. propulsion main exciter; and a Vee-belt driven 1,800-r.p.m. exciter set, including the pilot exciter for the propulsion main exciter and also the main exciter and small permanent magnet alternator for the auxiliary 1,500-kW. alternator.

The commutators of the propulsion main exciters are of Pollock construction, and anchor the copper segments over practically their whole length and are excluded from the closed-air circuit.

Set-up switches in the excitation cubicle, enable one propulsion main exciter to be connected to the port excitation busbars and another to the starboard busbars. Two exciters are standby. Built into the excitation cubicle are four Magnestat excitation control units, two associated with each drive. Of the two, one is normally working, but automatic changeover is provided to transfer control to the second regulator in the event of failure of the first. If the second regulator fails, control is transferred automatically to "hand." In the event of such a transfer to "hand," maximum excitation is applied but this can be reduced by the operator to the value appropriate to the power.

The regulators control excitation on a volts-per-cycle basis when the propeller motors have been synchronized, but give fixed values of boost excitation during the starting sequence. Each regulator comprises a voltage sensitive circuit and a two-stage magnetic amplifier. It excites the pilot exciter that serves the main exciter which, in turn, serves the alternator and propeller motor. The resulting combination of time constants necessitates the voltage suppression circuit.

With the switchgear in the excitation cubicle, each half

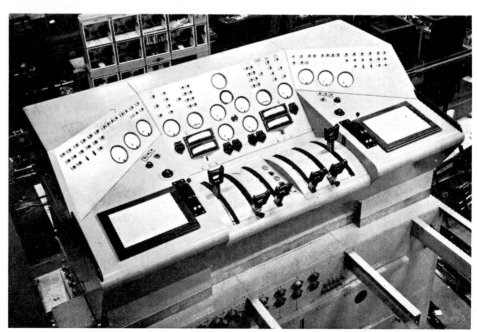

Fig. 88.—Propulsion Console, Showing the Twin-screw Lever Gear and Instrumentation.

propeller motor field can be connected either to port or starboard excitation busbars. Alternator fields can be switched to their associated busbars only.

When setting-up for any running condition involving two alternators, the pattern of connecting alternator and motor stators is repeated when connecting their fields to the propulsion exciters, so that there are, at all times, two completely independent electrical systems. Consequently, if a fault was to develop in one system, it could not affect the other.

If the port alternator is supplying both port propeller motor halves, the three fields are connected to the port excitation busbars and are, therefore, excited by the same machine. The starboard alternator and propeller motor fields are connected to the starboard excitation busbars, and supplied by a second exciter. Similarly, when the propellers are synchronized, the port alternator and the two forward propeller motor fields are connected to the port excitation busbars, and the starboard alternator and the two aft propeller motor fields to the starboard excitation busbars. However, under the cruising condition of one alternator powering both propeller motors, the alternator field is supplied by one exciter and the four motor fields by a second exciter.

Each propulsion turbo-alternator set is rated 32,200 kVA, 1·0 p.f., 6,000 volts, 3-phase, 51·5 cycles, 3,100 amps., 3,087 r.p.m., equivalent to 85,000 S.H.P. on two sets; and 30,700 kVA., 1·0 p.f., 4,670 volts, 3-phase, 40 cycles, 3,800 amps, 2,400 r.p.m., when powering both propeller motors, at 40,000 S.H.P. The alternator size, therefore, was determined by the cruising power.

Turbines—

Developed from a land machine, supplied for power stations where fuel economy and reliability are of the greatest importance, each single-cylinder turbine has seventeen stages and cam-operated multi-valve control. Steam conditions are 700 ℔ per sq. in. gauge, 950 deg. F., the vacuum corresponding to the service power being 28½in. Hg. A fundamental change from the land design lies in suiting the machine to variable-speed operation, particularly in terms of blade vibration.

Vibration characteristics of individual blades were calculated in the design stage and checked, initially by single blade tests, where necessary with bladed segments, and finally in the completed rotor. The axial blade clearances, diaphragm to banding, of the early stages, are 0·08in. increasing to 0·272in. at the last stage. A fixed thrust is combined with the governor end bearing.

Another departure is the provision of twin governors. One controls the turbine speed at 25 per cent. full speed during manoeuvring, when the propeller motor is brought up to this speed during starting. The other is adjustable between about 85 per cent. full speed and above the running speed when it is available as a pre-emergency governor to catch the set before it trips out on overspeed.

In common with large land turbines, supervisory gear is provided. The need for this equipment is particularly important during the starting-up and shutting-down periods, when thermal differences in the machines are liable to give rise to a variety of difficulties. For example, on starting up the turbine, the sudden entry of hot steam causes the machine to expand and as the rotor is entirely surrounded by steam it expands more rapidly than the more massive stator. In a typical marine turbine, the axial clearances between the side of the h.-p. blades and the outer casings are only about 0·1in. Since the machine may expand axially by up to 0·75in. it is obvious that a control of both rotor and stator expansion must be maintained. The electro-magnetic sensing heads developed for turbine supervisory equipment are capable of measuring differential expansions as small as 0·005in. Again, a small amount of eccentricity of the rotor may easily result in

Fig. 89.—Rotor Being Entered into Stator.

serious damage if the rotor is allowed to run up to speed. Eccentricity may be produced either by thermal stresses (a temperature gradient of 1 deg. to 2 deg. C. across the rotor may easily produce distortions sufficient to damage the machine), or by standing idle. A.E.I. turbine supervisory equipment can detect an eccentricity of 1–2 thousandths of an inch before any dangerous speed is reached.

Another important indication of a turbine's running condition is the amount of vibration, since any defect in rotor balance, alignment or bearing condition is quickly reflected by the vibration level. The equipment, therefore, measures vibration levels at a number of points on the turbine. An important feature of this equipment is the very small size of the electro-magnetic sensing heads used for these measurements. The overall dimensions of the differential expansion and eccentricity sensing heads are 2¾in. diameter by 1¼in. wide, enabling the head to be placed at the most strategic point, *i.e.*, under the existing bearing pedestal caps. The vibration sensing heads have dimensions of 2in. diameter by 6in. long, and are mounted externally.

Two standard ranges of A.E.I. turbine supervisory equipment, are available and have been developed and manufactured by the Electronic Apparatus Division of Associated Electrical Industries, Ltd.

On two-cylinder machines the differential expansion between the h.-p. rotor and stator, vertical and horizontal h.-p. shaft eccentricity, rotor speed, and governor and pedestal movement are measured. On three-cylinder machines an extra differential expansion and an extra eccentricity measuring circuit are added for the i.-p. cylinder, and vibration is measured on the bearings. Equipment for single-cylinder turbines is most valuable, as in the case of the *Canberra*, where measurements of eccentricity, differential expansion and vibration are taken for each turbine.

All circuits of the equipment are transistor-operated to give increased life. Each individual transistor and circuit is built as a plug-in sub-assembly which can be replaced with a spare if a fault develops. All control circuits are mounted in a single 16in. deep tray, 19in. square.

The differential expansion of the rotor and stator is found by determining the clearance between a fixed sensing head on the stator, placed facing a suitable smooth radial surface (such as a coupling or disc), on the rotor. The sensing head contains an iron-cored coil, the inductance of which is the inverse function of the gap length, and the value of this

Fig. 90.—22,250-H.P. Propulsion Motor Half Stator and Half Rotor Being Lowered into "Canberra."

inductance is measured with a self-balancing impedance bridge, excited from a 1,000 cycles per second motor-alternator set. The bridge is balanced by adjusting a variable resistor with a servo motor, the direction of motion of which is controlled by a transistor-assisted reversing relay, connected as a null detector. Indication and record of the clearance is given on moving-coil instruments. The meter circuit is driven through an output transistor from a potential divider ganged to the bridge balancing resistor. The inherent accuracy of measurement is high, as a bridge method is used, and the range is 0–200 mils (i.e., 0–0.2in.).

The eccentricity sensing head is identical to the differential expansion sensing head, and is fixed facing the shaft to be measured. The inductive coil inside the head is connected in series with a specifically designed "bucking" transformer across the 1,000 cycles per second supply, and the output voltage is modulated to a depth dependent on the amount of eccentricity. The range is 0–15 mils (i.e., 0–0.015in.).

For measuring the vibration at various points along the machine, a number of vibration detectors are used. Normally, one detector is fitted transversely or vertically on each bearing pedestal. The detectors are seismic devices, having an inertia-controlled moving coil, lightly held by springs in the air gap of a fixed permanent magnet. Above about 12 cycles per second, a voltage proportional to the vibration velocity is induced in the coil.

Alternators—

A bellows coupling connects the turbine and alternator rotors. Alternator design varies very little from land practice for a two-pole cylindrical rotor machine. A higher short-circuit ratio, of the order of 1.2 against 0.5, is adopted so that the alternator is a "stiffer" machine and more able to

Fig. 91.—One of the Condensers Being Lifted on Board.

Fig. 92.—Preparing One of the Shaft Intermediate Steady Bearings.

cope with load swings at sea. The air gap between stator and rotor is 2½in.

Fans on the alternator rotor circulate ventilating air, in a closed system, through sea-water cooled air coolers contained in an air chamber below the machine. The alternator neutral is permanently earthed through a high resistance located in the air chamber. All turbine and alternator bearings are forced lubricated by motor-driven pumps.

Propulsion Motors—

Each 42-pole synchronous propeller motor has a closed-air circuit and is rated at 42,500 S.H.P., 6,000 volts, 3-phase, 51.5 cycles at 147 r.p.m. on two units. Fig. 89 shows a rotor being entered into the stator, and Fig. 90 shows a half stator and half rotor being lowered into the *Canberra*. Fig. 91 shows one of the condensers being shipped. A fabricated drum carries the two spiders to which are bolted the rotor poles. The drum is supported between forged-steel stub shafts. Embedded in the faces of the rotor poles, are the squirrel-cage bars. The field coils are strip-on-edge wound.

During the starting period, when the propeller motor is operating as a squirrel-cage induction motor, its field is switched across a resistance mounted in the air trunking. The induction pull-out torque on boost excitation during starting is 67 per cent. full-load torque. When the motor has been synchronized at quarter full speed, the synchronous pull-out torque is 130 per cent. of full-load torque. At full power—85,000 S.H.P. on two screws—the synchronous pull-out torque is 200 per cent. of full-load torque.

Whereas, with a geared-turbine installation, the braking power during a reversal is dissipated in the astern turbine, with an A.C. electric drive the braking power is dissipated in the squirrel-cage winding and field circuit, completed by the discharge resistance, of the propeller motor.

Mention has been made of the flexibility in engine-room arrangement of propelling machinery possible with an electric drive and which, in the *Canberra* has enabled the owners to take the best advantage of an aft engine room. Not only can the motors be placed well aft to reduce shafting, but the turbines can be positioned independently to reduce the length of steam piping.

The flexibility of operation has also been referred to, whereby, for economical cruising, both the propeller motors can be powered by one turbo-alternator with the other set shut down. Also, the propellers can be synchronized to reduce hull vibration.

With uni-directional turbines, the advantages of high steam conditions may be gained without complication and without the possibility of troubles, or losses, in the astern turbines.

Fig. 93.—One of the Working Propellers.

These turbines can be run without the propellers rotating. They can, therefore, be warmed through, ensuring that power can be applied instantly on bridge orders being received. The fear of turbine shaft distortion with high steam conditions due to stopping on bridge instructions does not apply.

With electric transmission no "running-in" period at reduced power is required and, because it enables the same turbine to be used for ahead and astern operation, the full ahead power is always available astern. From the point of view of the passengers, electric propulsion machinery is noted for freedom from vibration and for quiet running.

It was decided by the owners to fit the Deutsche Werft Simplex tailshaft bearing, as it had proved, over twelve years in some thousand ships of all types, to be most reliable in service, with an annual wear-down of the order of two-thousandths of an inch. It had also been demonstrated in service that it possessed the most desirable feature of inherent damping, preventing a build-up of appreciable transverse tailshaft vibration normally excited by propeller-blade impulses. The two after "A" brackets each carry a pair of gun-metal bushes into which the white metal was centrifugally cast by Lagersmit. The tailshafts themselves are of bare steel in way of these bearings—but, where exposed to the sea, they are covered with several layers of glass-fibre tape impregnated with Araldite cement to provide the necessary protection.

The lower arm of the "A" bracket has a welded-on nosing, the two ducts of which connect the bearing with an oil supply from a small header tank housed within the ship. The height of the tank is arranged to provide a static head of about 12ft. above the deep load water line. The ends of the "A" bracket bosses are fitted with the Simplex oil gland which comprises a set of three special rubber labyrinth rings, located independently of the bossing by a white-metal lined carrier ring—but are also flexibly connected to the bossing. The labyrinth rings bear on to a polished stainless-steel sleeve which is solid with the closing ring and this compresses the propeller hub rubber sealing ring. At the forward end of the "A" bracket bosses,

similar glands are fitted, but in this case the stainless-steel sleeve is attached to a heavy split ring which clamps onto the shaft, at the same time sealing off the Araldite/glass-fibre liner by means of rubber rings. The shaft enters the hull through short stub bossings and here again Simplex gland and white metal lined bearings are used.

Owing to the long length—over 70ft. of unsupported shafting between the after "A" bracket bearing and the hull bossing—it was considered that the shaft might be vulnerable to serious damage in the event of picking up a wire at its mid-length. For this reason, an intermediate steady bracket was installed and fitted with a water-lubricated Tufnol-lined bearing working on a short bronze liner shrunk on to the shaft. This bearing will not normally carry any load but merely acts as a support in the event of the emergency to which reference has been made. The steady bracket bossing is split vertically to facilitate removal of the 40-ton, 40-ft. tailshaft to the half coupling which attaches to the tube shaft. Fig. 92 shows these bearings being prepared.

An interesting feature of the shafting alignment is that the bearing housings are all slope bored, to line of sight, to improve the load distribution along the bearings which are shorter in length than the 4D normally required for a lignum-vitae lined bearing. Appreciable economics in time and cost of maintenance and survey are expected during the life of these bearings which should last the life of the ship.

For the main thrust blocks, Michell type AR/1440 units have been chosen, and for trial and voyage data purposes, they are fitted with Michell propeller-thrust meters. Michell pivoted journal-pad type units have been selected for the six plummer bearings. All covers are hinged to facilitate overhauling, and two of the bearings have trailing faces incorporated.

The working propellers have been manufactured by the Manganese Bronze & Brass Co., Ltd., who have, of course, extensive experience in the marine propeller field and have supplied their propellers to most of the Naval and Mercantile fleets of the world since 1876. In recent years the company have developed a new alloy called Nikalium—nickel-aluminium-bronze. This alloy is considerably stronger than manganese-bronze, and even more resistant to corrosion.

Fig. 94.—One of the Spare Propellers Being Weighed.

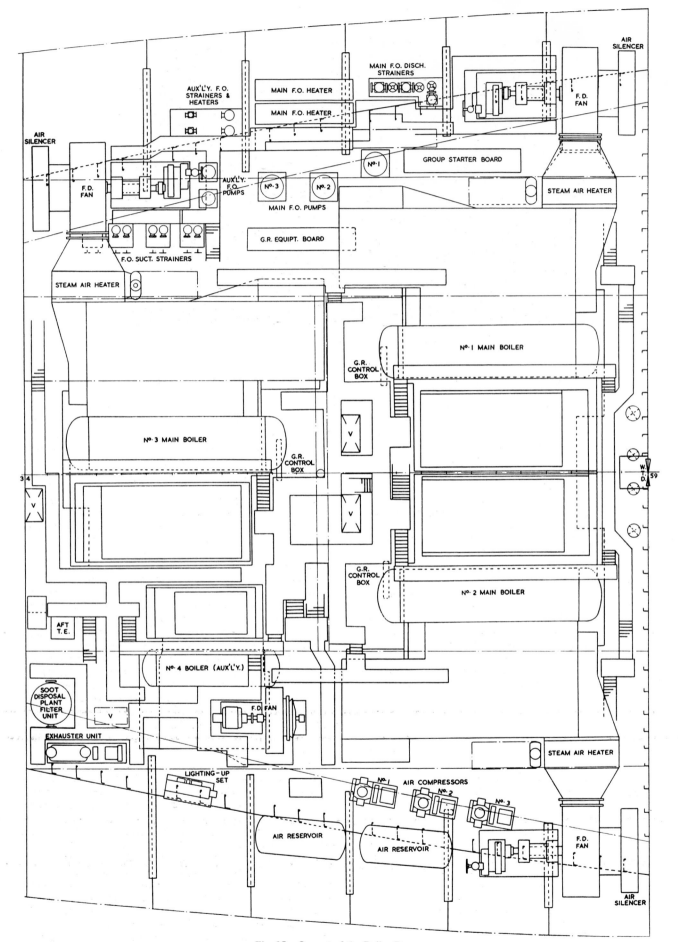

Fig. 95.—Layout of the Boiler Room.

Fig. 96.—Boilers Under Construction.

It is not surprising, therefore, that Nikalium has been chosen for the *Canberra's* working propellers which are of the Scimitar design.

In designing these propellers, exhaustive theoretical investigations were carried out to reach the best solution both from the propulsion and vibration points of view. Extensive vortex-momentum theory calculations were made for three, four and five-blade propellers to determine the most efficient blade form and to achieve the smallest hydrodynamic unbalance in the varying wake stream behind the hull designed for the *Canberra*. Model propeller experiments were conducted in open water as well as behind a self-propelled model of the vessel and a number of alternative designs were tested in the cavitation tunnel. The final Scimitar Nikalium design was considered the best to satisfy all the exacting conditions required to propel the vessel economically and efficiently at a service speed of 27½ knots.

Two working propellers have been supplied by the company and they each weigh 30 tons and have a diameter of 20ft. 6in. The photograph reproduced in Fig. 93 shows one of the propellers machined and ready for despatch.

Two reserve propellers, of Heliston design, have been constructed in high-tensile Novoston by Bull's Metal and Marine, Ltd. Each of these propellers weighs 29 tons and has been machined from a 40-ton Novoston casting (see Fig. 94).

STEAM RAISING PLANT

To generate the steam conditions of 750 lb per sq. in. at a temperature of 960 deg. F., the *Canberra* has been provided with what are probably the largest steam-raising units to be fitted into a British ship. The drawing reproduced in Fig. 95 shows the layout of the boiler room while Fig. 96 shows the boilers under construction, and a diagram showing the steam flow is given in Fig. 97.

The *Canberra* has three main boilers and one auxiliary unit, all four being located aft on a boiler flat. The main boilers have been designed with full air casings to suit operation with forced draught only, using steam-driven fans, the auxiliary boiler having a forced-draught motor-driven fan. All four boilers have been built under licence by Messrs. Harland & Wolff, Ltd. Photographs of one of the boilers being transported from the boiler shop to the ship are reproduced in Figs. 98, 99 and 100.

The plant includes the Foster Wheeler external-superheater D-type (E.S.D.) boiler, which has the superheater located in the gas flow after the boiler so that it receives heat by convection. This arrangement was first developed ten years ago for marine machinery operating at 950 deg. F., and has proved to be very successful in minimising superheater maintenance by reducing the working temperature of the tubes and their supports and by eliminating the slagging associated with partly radiant superheaters. A cut-away illustration of an E.S.D. boiler is reproduced in Fig. 101.

Control of the superheat is effected by an air attemperator comprising extended-surface tubing through which the steam flows continuously on its way between the first and second passes of the superheater. Combustion air is adopted as the cooling medium and the proportion needed for attemporation is regulated by dampers.

The Foster marine economisers have been built by Messrs. E. Green & Son, Ltd., and consist of a cast-iron extended surface and a steel base section. Soot blowers and fitments for water washing the gas side of the unit are included, with adequate access spaces provided throughout, Bled steam air-heaters are used for pre-heating the combustion air.

Each of the three main boilers has a normal evaporation of 175,000 lb per hour and a maximum evaporation of 260,000 lb per hour. The steam pressure is 750 lb per sq. in. at a temperature of 960 deg. F. with a feed temperature of 240 deg. F. The same pressure and temperature are available from the auxiliary boiler but this unit has a normal evaporation of 40,000 lb per hour and a maximum evaporation of 50,000 lb per hour.

Each main boiler is fitted with a Wellington steam air heater which, under normal duty, is designed to raise the temperature of 223,000 lb of combustion air per hour from 80 deg. F. to 232 deg. F. using steam at a pressure of 20 lb per sq. in. (gauge) and a temperature of 600 deg. F.

Complete Plibrico monolithic refractory linings are installed in all four boilers. The front burner wall lining consists of Plibrico super "X" plastic refractory as the hot-face refractory, backed by a jointless monolithic insulation of Plisulate Verilite 20. A further back-up of Plisulate Airlite castable insulation is fitted behind the generator tube bank front wall. The lining is securely anchored back by means of high-temperature alloy-steel Flexo-Anchors and sectionally supported by Taperlok wall seats, arranged so as to support

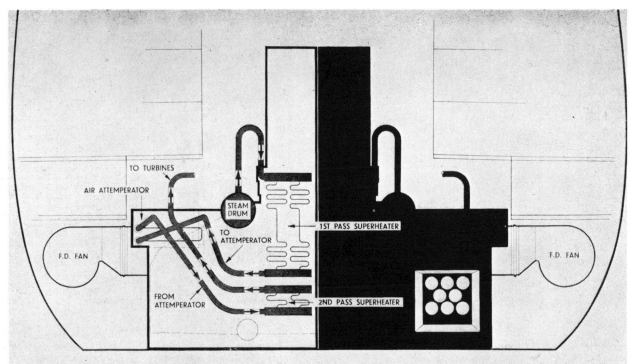

ELEVATION OF PORT AND STARBOARD MAIN BOILERS SHOWING
STEAM FLOW THROUGH SUPERHEATER AND AIR ATTEMPERATOR

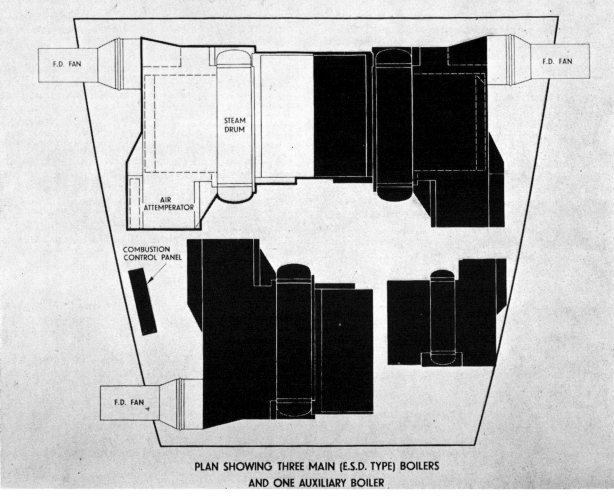

PLAN SHOWING THREE MAIN (E.S.D. TYPE) BOILERS
AND ONE AUXILIARY BOILER

Fig. 97.—Diagrams Showing Steam Flow.

Fig. 98.—One of the Boilers Leaving the Boiler Shop.

the weight of the lining from the steel casing, thus eliminating any tendency to overstress the lower sections of the refractory.

A similar construction in Plibrico super "X" and Plisulate Verilite is used for the furnace hearth. The furnace side, as well as the rear walls and roof, which are protected by tubes, are lined with Plicasto super castable refractory backed by Plisulate Verilite 20 and Plisulate Airlite castable insulation. Once again the anchorage is arranged so that the refractory is sectionally supported, and the weight is transmitted to the steel casing. The superheater hearth is constructed with Plisulate L.W.I. castable insulation as the hot face insulation and backed by Plisulate Verilite. Plisulate Airlite is used as additional back-up insulation in the front, side and rear superheater walls. The baffle is cast monolithically in Plisulate L.W.I. A total of 194 tons of Plibrico refractory and insulating products has been installed in the four boilers. Designed by the Plibrico company in co-operation with Messrs. Foster Wheeler, Ltd., the linings were installed by shipyard labour under the supervision of Plibrico staff.

Air for combustion for the main boilers is supplied by three Howden Z design single-inlet, forced-draught fans each having the open inlet fitted with a silencer and being capable of supplying 88,000 cu. ft. of air per min. against a pressure of 39in. w.g. when driven at 1,445 r.p.m. by a Weir 690 H.P. turbine. For the auxiliary boiler, air for combustion is supplied by Howden P3A single-inlet, forced-draught fans fitted with inlet vane control and capable of supplying 17,000 cu. ft. of air per min. against a pressure of 17in. w.g. when driven at 1,160 r.p.m. by a G.E.C. 65 H.P. motor.

Combustion equipment has been provided by Associated British Combustion, Ltd. The register is of the latest pattern, the design of which has, contrary to past practice, been evolved in accordance with aero-dynamic considerations. The main function of the primary swirler, in association with the secondary swirler, is to produce a series of controlled reversals in air flow. These, in turn, produce a large number of troidal vortices into which the atomiser injects the fuel. The effect is a very short and compact flame, the dimensions of which can

be trimmed by a variation in the sizes of both primary and secondary swirlers. It is possible to produce a flame to suit any shape or size combustion chamber. By virtue of the strong controlled air pattern, and the nature of the flame produced, the register is known as the "Suspended Flame" type—a very well-formed primary flame established some three to four inches in front of the primary swirler. The secondary flame is well matched to the primary flame forming, as a whole, a very stable flame, easy to ignite and to give trouble free burning over long periods.

The quarl serves the purpose of an air director and the flame has no contact whatsoever with it, thus ensuring very long life for the refractory wall. Providing the boiler front wall refractory is set properly and the combustion equipment used correctly, there is no reason why the setting should not last some years.

For the purpose of ensuring rapid combustion, the oil is sprayed into the furnace as a fine mist. This process is referred to as "atomisation." A feature of this burner is that there are two methods by which this can be effected. A change from one system to the other may be quickly carried out by merely changing the oil nozzles. Pressure-jet or mechanical atomisation is carried out by means of a conventional swirl-type nozzle. Here, the energy of the oil is used to break up the oil into fine particles. The alternative method utilises the energy of steam for this purpose.

A pressure-jet nozzle has limitations, as its output varies as the square root of the oil pressure and it is normally found that, below 150 lb per sq. in., the average size of the oil particles increases appreciably with a consequent deterioration of combustion. Fuel-pump design, design stresses and other factors impose a practical upper limit on fuel pressure and, therefore, the range of output for control purposes on any particular size of nozzle is very limited. For example, with a pump pressure of 400 lb per sq. in. essential system losses reduce the pressure at the burners to 320 lb per sq. in. and with an oil-pressure variation of 320 to 150 lb per sq. in., the range of output will be in the ratio of 1·5 : 1. Wide ranges of

Fig. 99.—Boiler Being Lifted from Transporter.

power must, therefore, be covered by varying the number of burners in use. With steam as the atomising medium the oil pressure can be reduced considerably, as the steam and not the oil pressure then provides the required energy. This increases the control range and provides easier manoeuvring as burners have not to be put on or off so frequently to maintain a constant steam pressure.

Fig. 100.—Boiler Being Lowered into "Canberra."

"Turn down" ratios in excess of 10 : 1 can be achieved on the oil discharge rate of the nozzle, but for the *Canberra* it has been decided to limit this, for practical reasons, to 3 : 1, as this covers most of the normal requirements. This output range is obtained by using a fuel-pressure variation of from 35 to 320 lb per sq. in. It is of interest to note from output/pressure curves that both types of atomiser have almost identical characteristics. This has been specially arranged so that the change from one system to the other may be made without making any adjustments to the air/fuel ratio controller of combustion control equipment. In fact, it would even be possible to operate with different types of atomisers in use on the same boiler at the same time, when supplied with oil at the same pressure.

The use of steam as an atomising medium has further advantages in that much "cleaner" combustion may be obtained, particularly in the lower output ranges and further, when a great deal of excess air may inadvertently be used at these ranges it is found that a steam-atomised jet is much more stable and preserves its entity while a pressure-jet flame is broken up, throwing oil all over the furnace, Boiler surfaces, therefore, stay cleaner for longer periods and boiler maintenance is minimised. The inherent features of design of this particular type of atomiser also results in longer periods of use without attention than might be expected from the pressure-jet atomiser. Against these advantages must be set the amount of steam consumed which, of course, comes from fresh-water that must be made by ship evaporators.

The mechanical or pressure-jet system will be used when fresh-water is in short supply or when the boiler can be set, on some voyages, to operate for long periods at a steady load; under these conditions very satisfactory combustion conditions can be obtained as high oil pressures can be used. The air register is also then operating near its maximum rating, a condition when it may be expected to give the best results. When fresh water is readily available, and when manoeuvring for comparatively short periods at fluctuating loads, the steam-atomised burners will be used. As water consumption,

Fig. 101.—Cut-away View of E.S.D. Boiler.

stated as a percentage of total boiler evaporation at full load, is rather less than 1 per cent., it will probably be possible to make extensive use of steam atomisers on many other occasions.

In accordance with the instructions of the builders, Messrs. Aiton & Co., Ltd., have designed and carried out a full stress analysis of the main steam, auxiliary steam and feed systems. The same firm have also fabricated the 10in. bore by 0·913in. minimum thickness main steam leads, in a cold drawn one per cent. Cr. ½ per cent. Mo. alloy-steel, from the superheater outlet to a common manifold, together with 6½in. bore by ⅝in. thick leads from this manifold to the main turbo alternator sets.

The 8in. bore by 0·76in. minimum thickness feed system operating at 1,150 ℔ per sq. in. gauge and 240 deg. F., has been manufactured by Aiton & Co., Ltd., from cold drawn carbon steel tube, as were the large bore auxiliary services including a 7¼in. bore by 0·67in. minimum thickness ring main. The same firm have also welded valve clusters, and they have been responsible for the design and manufacture of bulkhead expansion fittings in stainless steel. A number of intermediate pipe joints were butt welded at the firm's Derby works using the E.B. root insert method, flanged joints being provided at valves and terminal points.

High-capacity safety valves, manufactured by Dewrance and Co., Ltd., are fitted to the boilers. These safety valves are of the Dewrance-Consolidated full-lift type, which have been specially constructed for marine service. They have a high discharge capacity and, by means of an adjusting screw on the bush seating, the blow-down may be controlled to within 1 to 4 per cent. of the set pressure. A padlocked pin holds the adjusting ring in its correct setting. Positive and precise closing is obtained by a booster reseating feature. When the valve discharges, the escaping steam has access to

the chamber, the overlap collar rising to a predetermined position. The consequent increased area between a floating washer and the overlap collar permits steam in the chamber to escape to atmosphere. At the instant of closing, the overlap collar moves down, restricting the area between the floating washer and the overlap collar, thus effectively reducing the escape of steam from the chamber. The resultant momentary build-up of pressure produces a downward thrust which, combined with the spring loading, results in positive pressure closing without damage to the seat faces. The valve head includes a Thermodise, a special feature designed to permit rapid equalisation of temperature differential between disc and seat. Leakage due to distortion of the seat faces is, therefore, prevented. An easing lever is fitted to the valve, and unauthorised interference with the spring adjustment is prevented by a padlocked cap. The spring is enclosed in a sealed case and the body is provided with a box for draining the exhaust side of the valve.

These Dewrance-Consolidated safety valves have been supplied with a cast-steel body and cover, stainless-steel valve-head assembly and seat, and Dewrancalloy non-corrodible blow-down adjusting ring. The flanged connections conform to the appropriate British Standard Tables, and the valves have been approved by the Ministry of Transport and Lloyd's Register of Shipping.

A powerful B.V.C. vacuum plant is installed for boiler cleaning purposes, the primary function of which is the cleaning of the air heaters and economiser ducts while tube brushing is taking place. It can also be employed for cleaning the outside of the boiler casings and uptakes where soot is likely to lodge during the brushing operations. Previously these operations necessitated the use of pan and brush.

The suction unit comprises a primary container, a vertical fabric filter and a T8 type of air exhauster driven by a 3 H.P.

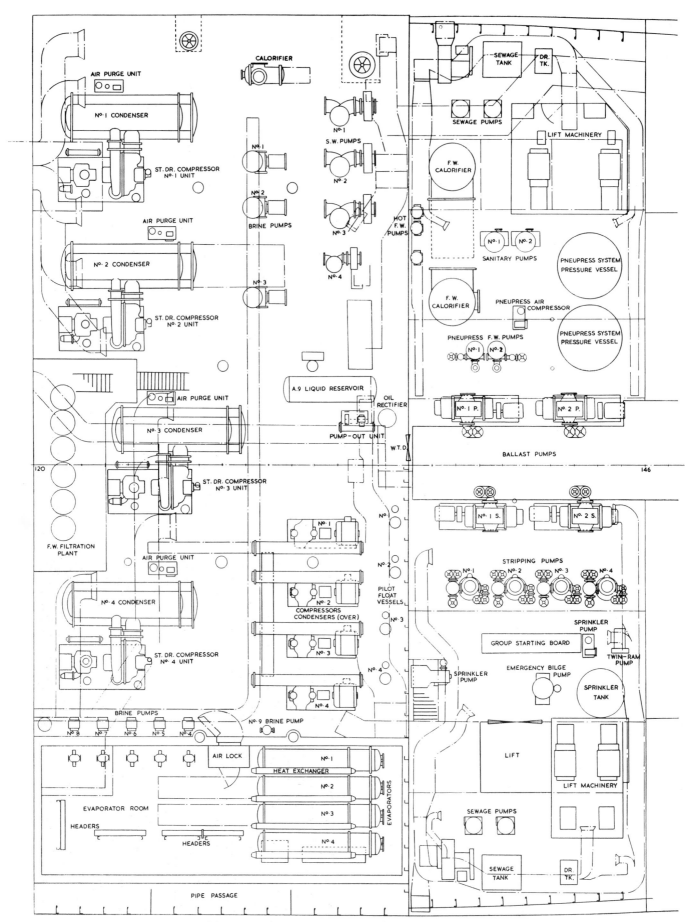

Fig. 102.—Layout of Pump Room and Refrigerating Machinery Room.

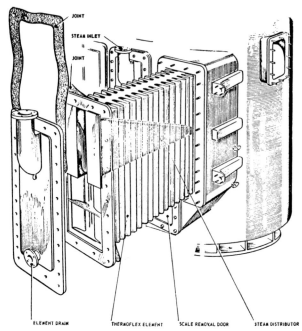

Fig. 103.—Weir Thermoflex Heating Unit.

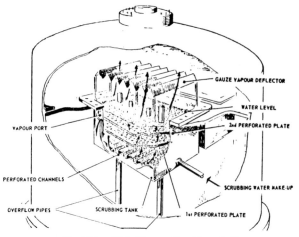

Fig. 104.—Weir Vapour Scrubber Unit.

motor. This compact unit stands in the engine-room and is connected to a pipe line by a short length of 2in.-bore flexible rubber hose. The pipe line consists of approximately 150ft. of 2½in.-bore steel piping which rises to the various levels to be cleaned. Hose connection points are positioned to use, conveniently, 25ft. of 1½in.-bore flexible rubber hose, to which can be attached a variety of tools for various cleaning operations. A further use to which the plant may be put is that of boiler-tube cleaning. This is accomplished by the use of a steel tube cleaning brush, of standard design, which is attached to the end of a special heat-resisting hose. The unit is pushed through the tube, and the brush displaces the soot which is collected by the tube and is then conveyed direct to the primary container.

AUXILIARY MACHINERY

With the exception of the air ejectors and the main turbo-feed pumps, one harbour feed pump, the large boiler forced-draught fans and the air-conditioning compressors, which are steam-turbine driven, the auxiliary machinery is all electrically driven. The drawing reproduced in Fig. 102 shows the layout of the pump room and the refrigerating machinery room.

The Weir sea water distillation plant consists of six vertical evaporator shells, each having a heating surface of 1,050 sq. ft. The installation is capable of providing all the fresh-water required by the ship for domestic, culinary and boiler-feed purposes, the total output being 750 tons. To ensure a very high degree of purity of vapour leaving the evaporator shell the heating elements are of the Weir Thermoflex design, and the Weir patent vapour scrubber is employed.

The Weir Thermoflex heating element, Fig. 103, is the result of extensive research into the problem of scale removal. Constructed in block form, the element has corrugated sides which, in addition to providing an extensive heating surface, expand and contract in response to even slight variations in temperature and pressure. At first, a slight but critical layer of scale is deposited when the plant is put into operation and the flexing of the element flakes-off the excess scale, which then falls to the bottom of the shell, from where it may be raked out periodically through the access door below the

steam manifold. In all, five elements have been provided for each of the six distillation units, and they are constructed from phosphor bronze.

Two Weir patent vapour scrubbers (Fig. 104) are fitted in each of the distillation units. Vapour rising within the shell of the unit passes through slots at the top of opposite sides of each scrubber tank, descends in the vapour port and enters the perforated channels at the base of the tank. These channels are submerged in scrubbing water, the level of which is controlled by two overflow pipes. The vapour bubbles through the holes and rises through the distilled water and two further perforated plates, giving a scrubbing action which removes a large percentage of any solids carried over with the vapour. Water particles that remain in the vapour on emerging from the scrubbing water are arrested by the gauze vapour-deflector screen. The scrubbing water is replenished by water from the discharge branch of the distilled water pump, and the replenishment quantity is approximately 2 per cent. of distillate output.

In addition to these items, Messrs. G. & J. Weir, Ltd., have supplied a large number of power plant auxiliaries,

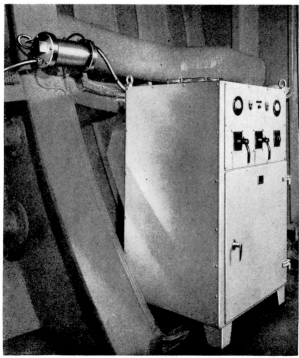

Fig. 105.—Clorocel Equipment in Position.

Fig. 106.—Clorocel Type CF/T.

including three sets of high- and low-level emergency gear, which incorporate a 2½-in. fuel-oil valve, and one set of high- and low-level emergency gear with a 1½-in. fuel-oil valve.

The make-up sea-water distillation plant comprises one vertical evaporator of 870 sq. ft. and one 500-sq. ft. distilling condenser, together with an electrically-driven evaporator feed pump with a discharge of 1,800 gallons per hour against a pressure of 45 ℔ per sq. in.

The two main condensers each have a surface area of 35,000 sq. ft. and are of the Weir regenerative type.

Included in the main de-aerating closed-feed system are four electrically-driven main extraction pumps, two steam-jet air ejectors, one 3,000-sq. ft. distiller, three flash chambers, one 760-sq. ft. drain cooler, one Weir concentric de-aerator, one 250-sq. ft. de-vapouriser, two electrically-driven de-aerator extraction pumps with non-return valves, one Kinghom valve, one de-aerator water inlet control valve, one change-over valve, one overflow valve and two closed-feed control valves.

The two turbine-driven main feed pumps, size T.M.F.P. 75, are of the three-stage type and are equipped with non-return valves and automatic cut-in gear.

Patterson Clorocel electrolytic chlorinating equipment has been installed for the prevention of adhesive marine organisms in the sea-water circulating systems. The four main services concerned are the auxiliary turbo-generator sea-water circulating systems, the air-conditioning and refrigeration circulating system, and the engine-room sea-water supply and sanitary system. A Patterson Clorocel as installed in *Canberra* is illustrated in Fig. 105. while a photograph of a Patterson Clorocel type CF/T is reproduced in Fig. 106.

Operation of each of these Clorocel plants is normally only needed for the period commencing from 6 to 12 hours before reaching port and is maintained continuously during docking and up to 6 to 12 hours after sailing.

The Clorocel electrolytic cells produce sodium hypochlorite by electrolysis of the sea water. This is taken on a by-pass across the pressure to suction sides of the main circulating pumps through the Clorocel units. Since the quantity of chlorine generated is directly proportional to the electric current applied, adjustment of the current is effected by tapping switches on the rectifier units which are installed for the provision of the necessary direct current. Production of the equivalent of 1 ℔ of chlorine by the Clorocel involves an electrical consumption of approximately 4 kW. hours and a by-pass flow of 75 to 80 gallons of sea water. This quantity will treat 230 tons per hour at 2 p.p.m. available chlorine which is needed to inhibit the formation of adhesive fouling organisms as well as being sufficient to prevent any other kind of marine growth formation.

With the installation of the Clorocel electrolytic chlorinating equipment there is no need for the carriage of any commercial hypochlorite as a more active solution is manufactured *in situ* as and when required by the simple opening of the appropriate valves across the sea-water pumps in operation, and the switching on of the rectifier adjusted to give the required current for effective chlorination treatment.

For harbour service there is a de-aerating plant comprising one harbour-service de-aerator, one 25-sq. ft. de-vapouriser, two electrically-driven de-aerator extraction pumps with non-return valves, one water inlet control valve, one Kinghom valve, one overflow valve and one change-over valve.

Two specially designed 750-tons per hour capacity Victor oily-water separating tanks are installed. This arrangement is in line with the modern trend towards specially designed built-in equipment where large quantities of oily-ballast water are to be handled in the shortest possible time to assist speedy turn-round bunkerings. As existing tanks are used for separating purposes, this method is economical in space.

Victor separating systems, as fitted in the *Canberra* are of the gravity-flow type and are fully automatic in operation. A novel feature is the multi-probe dual lever controllers which, by permutation of numbers of probes, regulate the discharge of oil or water, and maintain the oil/water interface between fixed limits, taking into account the effects of roll. In addition, an over-ride alarm probe is fitted, which will arrest the flow of fluid to the tanks if the oil reaches an excessively low level.

Fomescol, the British chemical discovery designed to overcome furnace corrosion in ships, is being used in the *Canberra*. It is a surface active agent which has been specially developed by research scientists of the Department of Scientific and Industrial Research and Glovers (Chemicals), Ltd.

The agent is being used in the vessel's sludge tanks to break down the water-in-oil emulsion collected from the oily-water separators. This is a particularly important application, as the double-bottom fuel tanks in the *Canberra* will be filled with sea water as ballast when the fuel oil has been used up.

Inevitably, the sea water used as ballast in dual purpose fuel tanks becomes contaminated with fuel oil which must be separated before the water is discharged ready to take in a fresh supply of fuel oil when the ship reaches a bunkering port. Under international convention it is an offence to discharge contaminated ballast water in a harbour as, obviously, severe pollution could result.

The ballast water has, therefore, to be stripped of oil contamination by the oily-water separators. The oil collected in the separators is drawn into the sludge tank but cannot be used as fuel as it still contains some salt water. The great advantage of Fomescol is that it enables the oil to be stripped of this salt water and the dry oil recovered to be used as fuel. Another advantage is that more than 80 per cent. of the agent itself can be recovered for re-use.

Six galvanised mild, steel, vertical-pattern calorifiers, have been manufactured by Messrs. Archibald Low & Sons, Ltd. These units are complete with rectangular heating batteries, thermostatic and relief valves, and are insulated with 2½-in. Stillite and galvanised-steel sheets. Two of the units have dimensions of 5ft. 6in. in height by 5ft. 0in. in diameter, a capacity of 650 gallons, and an output of 5,000 gallons per hour. They have a temperature range of 50 to 180 deg. F. with a steam supply at a pressure of 15 ℔ per sq. in. at a temperature of 300 deg. F. Two further units have similar dimensions and operate in the same temperature range with similar steam conditions but have an output of 1,500 gallons per hour.

The remaining two calorifiers each have a capacity of 950 gallons with dimensions of 6ft. 0in. in height by 5ft. 9in. in diameter. They operate in the temperature range of 50 to

180 deg. F. with a steam supply of 15 ℔ per sq. in. at a temperature of 300 deg. F. Also supplied by Messrs. Archibald Low are four galvanised mild-steel sewage tanks each with a capacity of 518 gallons and with dimensions of 4ft. 6in. by 4ft. 0in. by ½in. in thickness, and one mild-steel sewage tank of 982 gallons capacity which has dimensions of 8ft. 0in. by 3ft. 0in. by 7ft. 0in. by ½in. in thickness.

For the main engines there is an Auto-Klean oil-discharge filter. This is a 5in.-bore duplex unit incorporating four 5ft. 7in. diameter elements and fitted with magnetic units. Also installed are an Auto-Klean bearing lubricating-oil discharge filter with a 2in. bore and a 5ft. 7in. diameter single element, in addition to an Auto-Klean emergency lubricating-oil filter with a 3in. bore and twin elements 5ft. 7in. in diameter.

As already mentioned, all domestic fresh-water for drinking and washing purpose is produced by the ship's own evaporating plant. This water, unless correctly treated would be unpalatable and highly corrosive to the piping system. To obviate this, therefore, special treatment arrangements have been made by United Filters & Engineering, Ltd. This method of treatment consists of the addition of appropriate chemicals to the water to neutralise the natural acidity and to re-mineralise with desirable mineral salts. Chlorination is also incorporated to ensure sterility. The resultant treated water is thus non-aggressive to metals, palatable because of the re-introduction of mineral salts and of potable quality as it has been sterilised. The chemicals are added to the water by means of Variflo solution-injection metering pumps, drawing from appropriate glass-fibre lined preparation and storage tanks, and treated water is distributed to the services by the domestic-service pumps which have a capacity of 120 tons per hour.

A battery of six Fisto-type marine filters is fitted between the domestic service pumps and the pressure tank to ensure that all water pumped is filtered free of suspended matter. The filters have solid compressed porous carbon filter elements. Filtration is followed by the injection of further chemicals to de-chlorinate the water so that there will be no possibility of chlorine taint in the water used for drinking, cooking, tea making, etc., and to form a microscopic, glass-like protective film within the distribution pipelines. This chemical is prepared and stored in a glass-fibre lined tank and is injected into the rising main by Variflo metering pumps, actuated by the starting mechanism of the domestic service pumps.

The hot water services receive further protection by the addition of a compound producing the hard durable microscopic protective film, already referred to, which is supplementary to the treatment received after filtration.

When in harbour, fresh-water is taken from shore supplies, and this water, before reaching the storage tanks is sterilized by automatic displacement dosers which inject chlorine in proportion to the rate of filling. Shore water on being distributed is filtered and de-chlorinated.

The equipment provided ensures that all domestic water distributed is of the finest quality at all times, whether it be of shore or evaporated origin. Full control of the results is achieved by the use of a comprehensive testing set, and all tests are carefully logged.

Also incorporated in the evaporating plant is a 4in. Helix interchangeable-mechanism pattern marine meter, which has been provided by Messrs. Reginald Christie & Dickinson, Ltd. This firm also supplied a 10in. meter of special manufacture together with a small rotary meter and steam meter for the trials.

An Alcon cylinder servo-operated pilot control valve has been supplied by Alexander Controls, Ltd. Servo operation is from a three-way solenoid pilot valve.

The pressure in the exhaust main is controlled by Drayton Dialset controllers operating Drayton diaphragm valves. Bleed steam from the turbo-generators is metered into the main so as to maintain a pressure of 18 ℔ per sq. in. At sea, under full load conditions, pass-out steam from the main turbines is used to supply the exhaust main. In the event of the exhaust pressure exceeding 20 ℔ per sq. in. a Drayton pressure controller and control valve is applied to dump steam to an auxiliary condenser.

Cockburns, Ltd., have supplied valves and boiler mountings including main and auxiliary stop valves as well as boiler and economiser feed check isolating valves. These valves are all designed for a steam pressure of of 750 ℔ per sq. in. and a total temperature of 960 deg. F. and have a feed pressure of 940 ℔ per sq. in gauge.

Fig. 107.—One of the 1,500-kW. Turbo-alternator Sets Being Shipped on Board "Canberra."

Fig. 108.—Paxman Vega 12-cylinder Air-cooled Diesel Engine.

ELECTRICAL INSTALLATION

THE extensive electrical installation has been arranged on the most modern lines, to comply fully with the requirements of the owners, the classification societies and the Ministry of Transport. The generating plant comprises four A.E.I. 1,500 kW. turbo alternators. There are also two, 200 kW., 440 volt, three-phase, 60 cycles Diesel-driven alternators and these sets comprise Paxman air-cooled Vega engines driving G.E.C. alternators.

Electrical power is distributed from the main switchboard to masterboards which are positioned throughout the ship and an interconnector is fitted between the main and emergency switchboards. Auxiliary motors in the machinery spaces are controlled from five group starter switchboards situated in the engine-room, boiler room and auxiliary machinery rooms. Power is supplied for engine and deck auxiliaries, steering gear, refrigerating plant, galley and pantry equipment, air-conditioning plant ventilation fans, lifts and lighting.

The lighting installation is extremely extensive and in the public rooms, full use of fluorescent tubes has been made as an adjunct to the design features. Special floodlighting is installed for the Games deck and swimming pool, and illuminated signs are provided wherever necessary.

The four geared pass-out turbo-alternator sets—each of which has a combined condenser—are individually rated at 1,500 kW., 440 volts, three-phase, 60 cycles, 6,000/1,200 r.p.m. Steam conditions at the turbine inlet are 700 lb per sq. in. gauge, and 930 deg. F. The pass-out pressure is 70 lb per sq. in. and the quantity 15,000 lb per hour. The photograph reproduced in Fig. 107 shows one of the 1,500 kW. sets being shipped on board the *Canberra*.

The alternator has a closed air circuit with two sea-water circulated air-coolers. Voltage control is by a Magnestat automatic voltage regulator.

Tandem driven from the alternator is the 300 kW. normal propulsion main exciter. Exciters for the auxiliary alternator and propulsion main exciter are Vee-rope driven from the propulsion main exciter.

The low-power system is normally supplied from one of two motor generators (one being a standby). In case of failure of the ship's main supply, a 24-volt Nife battery automatically comes into operation. Provision is also made for the trickle charging of this battery through a trans-

rectifier or a quick-change arrangement through the standby motor generator. The luminous call system, loudspeaking telephones, manual fire alarms, lifebuoy release, etc., are supplied from this source. The automatic and manual telephones, as well as the electric clocks, each have their independent battery supply.

The Paxman Vega engines (Fig. 108) are 12-cylinder units and are mounted at the upper deck level. The engines are completely self-contained, requiring only an external fuel supply, and installation, therefore, is much easier than with water-cooled engines by virtue of the fact that the necessity for external cooling equipment is obviated. The absence of cooling water requirements makes them admirably suitable for operating in extremes of ambient temperature.

In the construction of these engines, individual cylinder assemblies are mounted on the cast-iron crankcase, an underslung crankshaft being used. The camshaft is positioned centrally above the crankshaft, within the crankcase. A light alloy sump enclosed the underside of the crankcase. The cooling fan is chain-driven from the crankshaft and is located within the 90 deg. Vee, together with the fuel-injection equipment. Forged steel is used for the crankshaft, which has a solid flange at the drive end. A tapered fitting coupling is assembled to the free end of the shaft and the coupling carries the viscous torsional vibration damper and take-off pulleys. The crankshafts are fully balanced by fitted weights.

A total of 48 transformers, covering a range from 20 kVA. to 75 kVA. have been provided by the English Electric Co., Ltd., who have also supplied the main A.C. distribution switchboard. The transformers are single-phase, 440/230 volt lighting units, and they are connected in three-phase banks, each bank having a separate unit mounted alongside. All units are carried on resilient mountings to keep noise and vibration down to a minimum. They are air-cooled, class-B, insulated, suitable for 60 cycles ship supply or 50 cycles shore supply and have been manufactured in accordance with the rules and regulations of Lloyd's Register of Shipping.

The switchboard consists of the latest high-breaking capacity, 440-volt, air-circuit breakers and is an outstanding example of the growing use of A.C. in ships. The 38-circuit switchboard—some 70ft. in length—is arranged with circuit-

Fig. 109.—Allen West Control Panel for Bow Thrust Propeller Unit.

breakers in double-tier formation and comprises four 3,000 amp. type OB 24 circuit-breaker incomers from the four 1,500 kW., 60-cycle alternators; four alternator excitation control panels; one synchronising control panel; and 28 type OB 23 circuit-breakers controlling outgoing loads of up to 1,600 amps. for various main auxiliaries.

The equipment is fitted with a full complement of protective and metering devices and a system of preferential tripping has also been incorporated to isolate selected non-essential services in the event of sustained overload.

Electric motor control gear, manufactured in Brighton by Allen West & Co., Ltd., is much in evidence aboard the *Canberra*. In all, more than 250 starters, apart from push-buttons, limit switches and ancillary items, have been provided for a wide range, from the largest to the smallest, of the motors installed.

The largest motor is the 800 H.P. bow-thrust propeller unit which, as previously mentioned, is mounted in an open transverse tunnel in the bows. Control is from the bridge and the Allen West contactor equipment, consists of a rotor control panel (Fig. 109) and an isolator for the 3·3 kV. stator supply. The smallest starters are for the $\frac{1}{6}$ H.P. motors used in the water treatment by chemical injection plant.

For the new type davits, Allen West A.31 direct-switching starters, watertight for deck mounting, have been provided and, for the 31 motors involved in the baggage and stores conveyor system, Allen West starting equipment has been supplied and includes 4 four-motor and 3 three-motor control panels together with a two-motor panel.

Allen West type ZB.5 drum controllers and circuit breakers, with D.C. injection braking for the hoist motor in each unit, have been supplied for the transporter installation.

Allen West equipment also includes starters for motors controlling the ship's powerful capstans and windlasses, the hydraulically-operated watertight doors, the Arena deck screens and partition, heaters and ventilating fans, sewage discharge pumps, lubricating oil pump, lathes, grinder and drilling machine, tube cleaning equipment, stores hoist, and engine turning gear.

Among the kitchen equipment for which Allen West control gear has been provided, are 26 starters for food preparing machinery, dough mixers, bakery ovens and machines and a bread buttering and slicing machine. Other Allen West starters are in the laundry and printing room and they are also employed for the revolving doors between the first-class and tourist-class dining rooms and galley.

All the main propulsion cables for the turbo-electric installation have been provided by Johnson & Phillips, Ltd. Due to the extremely heavy load to be carried by the cables, two single-bore cables per phase, operating in parallel, are installed to supply each of the four half motors which comprise the port and starboard engines. This involves two runs of 12 cables each, while a further run of 24 cables interconnects the vessel's two 32 MW. alternators.

The cables installed are 1·25in. sq., single-bore, paper insulated, lead-alloy sheathed and cotton braided and they are finished with a fire-resistant compound. They are of the mass impregnated, non-draining type, with a nominal overall diameter of 2·08in. and owing to the vital role they play in the operation of the ship, Johnson & Phillips were called upon to make the joints. Cables of similar construction and finish, for 3,000 volts, were also supplied and jointed by Johnson and Phillips for the transmission of power to the docking propeller.

Firms Associated with the Building of "Canberra"

Abboflex, Ltd., Guildford, Surrey .. Flexible metal tube for Diesel exhausts.
Accles & Pollock, Ltd., Birmingham .. Steel tubing.
Accordo Blinds, Ltd., West Bromwich .. First-class window units.
Acme Domestic Equipment, Ltd., Glasgow .. Combined washers and tumbler dryers.
Acoustical Investigation & Research Organisation, Ltd., Hemel Hempstead, Herts. .. Design of sound-resistant cabin bulkheads.
Adams & Co. (West Drayton), Ltd., West Drayton, Middlesex .. Gaboon plywood.
Addis, Ltd., Hertford .. Lavatory brushes.
Airscrew Company & Jicwood, Ltd., Weybridge, Surrey .. Meldec panel.
Aiton & Co., Ltd., Derby .. Welded valve assemblies and fabrication of steel pipes.
Alcan Industries, Ltd., London .. Aluminium plates and sections.
Alfa-Laval Co., Ltd., Cwmbran, Mon. .. Stainless-steel galley equipment.
Alexander Controls, Ltd., Sutton Coldfield .. Alcon control valve.
W. H. Allen, Sons & Co., Ltd., Bedford .. Pumping machinery and electrical equipment.
I. R. Amis, Ltd., London .. Exhibition model.
Anchor Insulating Co., Ltd., London .. Insulation of air-conditioning brine pipes.
Andersons Insulation Co., Ltd., Liverpool .. Insulation.
George Angus & Co., Ltd., Newcastle upon Tyne .. Oil relief valves, leather jointing and fibre ferrules.
Arabol Manufacturing Co., Ltd., London .. Perflex adhesive.
Arlington Plastics Development, Ltd., Harlow, Essex .. Mural Texturide.
James Armstrong & Co., Ltd., London .. Marking machine accessories.
Arnoplast, Ltd., Glasgow .. P.V.C. tubes.
Artic Fuse & Electrical Manufacturing Co., Ltd., Birtley, Co. Durham .. Electric lanterns, sockets and fuses.
Artofex Engineering Works, Ltd., Enfield, Middlesex .. Dough mixer.
George L. Ashworth & Brothers, Ltd., Hanley, Stoke-on-Trent .. Crockery.
Associated British Combustion, Ltd., Porchester, Hants. .. Combustion equipment and suspended flame register.
Associated Electrical Industries, Ltd., Cable Division, London .. Butyl rubber insulated cable.
Associated Electrical Industries, Ltd., Electronic Apparatus Division, London .. Turbine supervisory equipment.
Associated Electrical Industries, Ltd., Heavy Plant Division, London .. Machinery control system.
Associated Electrical Industries (Rugby), Ltd., Rugby .. Auxiliary turbo generator sets, revolution indicators, air-conditioning turbo compressors and sub-switchboards.
Associated Electrical Industries (Woolwich), Ltd., London .. Projectors and electric telegraphs.
Associated Metal Works (Glasgow), Ltd., Glasgow .. Stainless-steel sliding cereal bins and sinks.
Atlas Preservative Co., Ltd., Erith, Kent .. Aluminium high-temperature paint.
David Auld & Sons, Ltd., Glasgow .. Standard and Quietite valves for auxiliary saturated steam lines.

Auto-Klean Strainers, Ltd., Hounslow, Middlesex .. Filters.
Avamore Engineering Co., Ltd., Denham, Uxbridge .. Wicksteed bread buttering and slicing machines.
W. T. Avery, Ltd., Birmingham .. Weighing machines.

B.B. Chemical Co., Ltd., Leicester .. Bostik caulking compound and Prestik sealing strip.
Babcock & Wilcox, Ltd., London .. Expansion joints for uptakes.
Barlow & Jones, Ltd., London .. Bath towels for crew.
Barr & Stroud, Ltd., Glasgow .. Smoke observation fittings for boilers.
Barry, Ostlere & Shepherd, Ltd., Kirkcaldy, Fife .. Linoleum.
Baxenden Chemical Co., Ltd., London .. Spandoplast solid-buoyancy material for Viking lifeboats.
Baxter Brothers, Ltd., London .. Linen bags.
Bayham, Ltd., London .. Direct-reading contents gauges.
William Beardmore & Co., Ltd., Glasgow .. Castings and forgings.
Beldam Asbestos Co., Ltd., London .. Lascar Asbestos products.
Belfast Ropework Co., Ltd., Belfast .. Safety nets for swimming pools.
Bell & Hull, Ltd., Belfast .. Electric signs.
Belling & Co., Ltd., Enfield, Middlesex .. Table cooker.
Bell's Asbestos & Engineering, Ltd., Slough, Bucks. .. Bestobell J.6 Rubesto asbestos joints.
F. Bender & Co., Ltd., London .. Paper ware.
Berkel & Parnell's Slicing Machine Co., Ltd., Enfield, Middlesex .. Electric bacon slicer.
Bettles & Sons, Ltd., Wolverhampton .. Open-steel flooring panels in turbo-alternator and propulsion motor rooms.
Birmingham Battery & Metal Co., Ltd., Birmingham .. Tube plates for main condenser.
Thomas Bishop, Ltd., Glasgow .. Cereal bins and sinks.
C. H. Blackburn & Co., Ltd., London .. Stellex electrically-heated food conveyors.
R. Blackett Charlton & Co., Ltd., Newcastle upon Tyne .. Plumbing, pipework and voice pipe installation.
J. Blakeborough & Sons, Ltd., Brighouse, Yorks. .. Valves.
Bochumer Verin A.G., Bochum, Germany (through the Stahlunian Co., Ltd., London) .. Propeller brackets, stem and stern castings.
Bolivar Stamping Co., Ltd., Keighley, Yorks. .. Copper clips.
James Booth & Co., Ltd., Birmingham .. Aluminium/brass piping for hot and cold salt-water services, copper piping for hot and cold fresh-water services.
J. Boustead, Belfast .. Supply of Paraflor.
Robert Bowran & Co., Ltd., Gateshead, Co. Durham .. Maxoid bedding compound.
F. Braby & Company, Crayford, Kent .. Ash containers.
Brady & Martin, Ltd., Newcastle upon Tyne .. Kentometer for auxiliary turbo alternators and condensers.
S. Brannan & Sons, Ltd., Cleator Moor, Cumberland .. Distant-reading thermometers.
Isaac Braithwaite & Son, Engineers, Ltd., Kendal, Westmorland .. Laundry equipment.

W. I. Brine & Sons, Ltd., London .. Various special veneers.
Bristol Aeroplane Plastics, Ltd., Bristol .. Glass-fibre ceiling panels, lampshades and decorative pillar casings.
British Aluminium Co., Ltd., London .. Aluminium plates and sections.
British Electric Resistance Co., Ltd., Enfield, Middlesex .. Resistors for masterboards.
British Ermeto Corporation, Ltd., Maidenhead, Berks. .. Ermeto couplings and pipe fittings.
British Insulated Callender's Cables, Ltd., London .. P.C.P. fully-guarded overhead current collection equipment for transporters.
British Oxygen Co., Ltd. (Welding Division), Bilston, Staffs .. Electric arc-welding equipment.
British Paints, Ltd., Newcastle upon Tyne .. Lignolac fire-retarding wood finishes and caulking compound.
British Petroleum Co., Ltd., London .. Lubricants.
British Ropes, Ltd., Balby, Doncaster .. Coir matting.
British Rototherm Co., Ltd., London .. Rototherm gauges.
British Steam Specialties, Ltd., Leicester .. Velan steam traps, piping units and valves.
British Tubular Manufacturing Co., Ltd., Gateshead, Co. Durham .. Tubular armchairs and easy chairs for crew accommodation.
British Vacuum Cleaner & Engineering Co., Ltd., Leatherhead .. Dust removing plant for boiler cleaning.
British Vulcanized Fibre, Ltd., Hadfield, near Manchester .. Fibre washers.
J. Broadwood & Sons, Ltd., London .. Crew pianos.
Brookhirst Igranic, Ltd., London .. Start-stop push buttons.
Brown Brothers & Co., Ltd., Edinburgh .. Bow propeller, Denny-Brown stabilisers and steering gear.
S. G. Brown, Ltd., Watford, Herts. .. Gyro compass equipment and auto-electric steering control system.
Brownings Electric Co., Ltd., London .. Automatic valves for oily-water separator.
Buchanan Brothers, Ltd., Glasgow .. Thermometers.
Bull's Metal & Marine, Ltd., Glasgow .. Heliston spare propeller, metal windows and glazed screens.
Buncher & Haseler, Ltd., Birmingham .. Aluminium dish covers.
Burgess Products Co., Ltd., Hinckley, Leics. .. Acousti-Booths.

C.I.B.A. (A.R.L.), Ltd., Duxford, Cambridge .. Araldite epoxy resin for propeller shafting.
Cabinet Makers Supply Co. (N.I.), Ltd., Belfast .. Brummer stopper (polishing).
Caird & Rayner, Ltd., London .. Drain filters.
Calomax (Engineers), Ltd., Leeds .. Water boilers in galley.
Campbell Brothers (Glass Paints), Ltd., Belfast .. Frameless mirrors and obscured sheet glass.
Cape Asbestos Co., Ltd., London .. Caposite Amosite asbestos Rocksil for insulation.
Carntyne Steel Castings Co., Ltd., Renfrew .. Steel castings.
Carpet Manufacturing Co., Ltd., London .. Carpet for first-class restaurant.
Carpet Trades, Ltd., Kidderminster .. Carpet for first-class Lido lounge.
Carron Company, Carron, Falkirk .. Transporters, sidelights and galley equipment.
J. H. Carruthers & Co., Ltd., East Kilbride, Glasgow .. Drain tank pumps.
Cartem Engineering Co., Ltd., London .. Disposal unit sack holders.
Sir Hugh Casson, Neville Conder & Partners, London .. Decorative designs.
Caston Barber, Ltd., London .. Fire-resisting doors.
A. de Cecco, Ltd., Glasgow .. Terrazzo work.
Cellon, Ltd., Kingston-on-Thames .. Cellulose white undercoating.
Andrew Chalmers & Mitchell, Ltd., Glasgow .. Leven bulkhead multiple cable.
Chatwood-Milner, Ltd., Bristol .. Safes.
Chesterfield Tube Co., Ltd., Chesterfield .. Steel tubes for main steam pipes.
Chiesemans, Ltd., London .. Display items for tourist-class bar.
Chilton Electric Products, Ltd., Hungerford, Berks. .. Razor sockets.
Reginald Christie & Dickinson, Ltd., London .. Water meters.
Chubb & Son's Lock and Safe Co., Ltd., London .. Safes.
John Clarke & Co., Ltd., Belfast .. Furnace glasses.
Clarke, Chapman & Co., Ltd., Gateshead, Co. Durham .. Capstans and windlasses.
Clifford & Snell, Ltd., Sutton, Surrey .. Wheelhouse console for sundry instrumentation.
Clyde Alloy Steel Co., Ltd., Motherwell .. Refuse chutes and eyeplates.
Clyde Blowers, Ltd., Clydebank .. Air scavenge valves and soot blowers for boilers.
Clyde Rubber Works Co., Ltd., Renfrew .. Neoprene washers and ferrules.
Cockburns, Ltd., Cardonald, Glasgow .. Boiler stop and feed valves and turbine regulating and emergency shut-off valves.
Coles & Son, Ltd., London .. Plastic paper sheet.
J. Collins & Son, Ltd., London .. Fruit baskets.
J. Collis & Sons, Ltd., London .. Baggage and stores conveyors.
Colvilles, Ltd., Glasgow .. Steel plates and sections.
Commercial Marble & Tiles, Ltd., Newcastle upon Tyne .. Italian glass mosaic wall facings.
Cona Coffee Machine Company, London .. Coffee-making equipment.
Concquerels Sundries, Ltd., London .. Florapack.
Conex-Tern, Ltd., Tipton, Staffs. .. Pipe fittings.
Connolly Brothers (Curriers), Ltd., London .. Vaumol upholstery leather.
Conran Fabrics, Ltd., London .. Fabrics in first-class lounge and small dining room.
Conran & Co., Ltd., Furniture Division, London .. Chairs and stools.
Cope & Timmins (London) 1911, Ltd., London .. Gliss Rod.
Cork Insulation & Asbestos Co., Ltd., London .. Insulation of ventilation trunking.
James P. Corry & Co., Ltd., Belfast .. Douglas Fir logs, Oregon pine, whitewood, mahogany, teak, beech and plywood.
William Cory & Son, Ltd., London .. Fuel.
County Water Softner Co., Ltd., Mitcham, Surrey .. Ion-exchange water treatment plant for boiler feed air conditioning and laundry recovery processes
Eric Cowpe, Ltd., Hapton, near Burnley, Lancs. .. Candlewick lavatory seat covers.
J. A. Crabtree & Co., Ltd., Walsall, Staffs. .. Electric fittings.
Crane Packing, Ltd., Slough, Bucks. .. Mechanical shaft seals and gland packings.
Crater Products, Ltd., Woking, Surrey .. Electric switches.
J. Crisp & Son, London .. Leather for furniture.
William Crockatt & Sons, Ltd., Glasgow .. Boiler density outfit.
Crofts (Engineers), Ltd., Bradford .. Internal gear-type couplings in connection with bow propeller mechanism.
Crompton Parkinson, Ltd., London .. Nelson stud welding material, electric meters, and motors for conveyors.
Cronite Foundry Co., Ltd., London .. Heat-resisting steel for boilers.
Crumpsall Packing Co., Ltd., Manchester .. Fibre distance pieces.
Crypto, Ltd., London .. Galley equipment.
J. H. Cunliffe, Ltd., Rochdale .. Mattress covers.
William Cunningham & Co. (Dunfermline), Ltd., London .. Napery.

Davey, Paxman & Co., Ltd., Colchester .. Vega Diesel engines for emergency auxiliary services.
Denny, Mott & Dickson, Ltd., London .. French beech, teak decks, Douglas Fir logs and staging planks.
Derek Products, Ltd., Portsmouth .. Folding high chairs.
Deutsche Werft A.G., Hamburg (through Simplex-Turbulo Marine Co., Ltd., London) .. Simplex glands for stern tubes.
Dewhurst & Partners, Hounslow, Middlesex .. Brakes for cargo transporters.
Dewrance & Co., Ltd., London .. Boiler safety valves and mufflers.
Dexine Rubber Co., Ltd., Rochdale, Lancs. .. Dexine strip, washers and manhole joints.
J. Dickinson & Co., Ltd., London .. Paper ware.
Digby & Nelson, Ltd., Farnham, Surrey .. Handee cheese cutters.
Ditchburn Equipment, Ltd., Lytham, Lancs. .. Juke box, Hotopa and Coldspa drink dispensers.
E. Doherty & Sons, Ltd., London .. Bed trays.
Donald Brothers, Ltd., London .. Fabrics in veranda suites.
James T. Donald & Co., Ltd., Glasgow .. Stainless steel.
Donaldson Wireless Electric Irons, Ltd., Leith .. Cordless electric irons.
Doulton Industrial Porcelains, Ltd., Tamworth, Staffs. .. Ash holders.
Drayton Regulator & Instrument Co., Ltd., West Drayton .. Dialset controllers and diaphragm valves.
Drysdale & Co., Ltd., Glasgow .. Pumps and sewage plant.
James Duff & Sons, Ltd., Lisburn, Northern Ireland .. Pullman beds and chests.
Dunlop & Hamilton, Ltd., Belfast .. Bulkhead fittings.
Dunlop Rubber Co., Ltd., London .. Mattresses.
Dupont Co. (United Kingdom), Ltd., London .. Neoprene.
Duprint, Ltd., Chorleywood, Herts. .. Melamine veneer.
Durastic, Ltd., London .. Deck covering.

Eclab, Ltd., London .. Detergents for glass-washing machines.
Econasign, Ltd., London .. Stencils.
Edgar Brothers, Ltd., London .. Siamese silk and grass wallpaper.
Edinburgh Weavers, Carlisle .. Curtains in tourist-class restaurant, lounge, library, reading room and writing rooms.
Edmonton Panel Co., Ltd., London .. Tables and chairs in tourist-class ballroom.
Ekco Plastics, Ltd., Southend-on-Sea .. Babies' baths.
Electrical Apparatus Co., Ltd., St. Albans, Herts. .. Preventers for protecting electric motors.
Electrical Equipment Co., Ltd., Belfast .. P.V.C. cable conduit and fittings.
Electronic Switchgear, Ltd., Letchworth, Herts. .. Salinity indicator, pH meters and brine density indicator for evaporators.
Elkington & Co., Ltd., Walsall, Staffs. .. Wine coolers, condiment sets, sauce boats, lobster picks, grape scissors and ice tongs.
Elliot Equipment, Ltd., Lisburn, Northern Ireland .. Seiner inflatable liferaft.
Enfield-Standard Power Cables, Ltd., London .. Electric cables.
English Electric Co., Ltd., London .. A.C. distribution switchboard and lighting transformers.
W. Erskine Mayne (Sound), Ltd., Belfast .. Public address system for launch.
Escare Art Metal Co., Ltd., London .. Art metalwork.
Esso Petroleum Co., Ltd., London .. Esso Rust-Ban 339.
Euk Catering Machinery, Ltd., Oldham, Lancs. .. Butter pat machine.
Evershed & Vignoles, Ltd., London .. Recorders.
William Ewart & Son, Ltd., London .. Napery.
Extrudex, Ltd., Bracknell, Berks. .. P.V.C. tubing.
Eyre & Spottiswood (Publishers), Ltd., London .. Bibles, hymn and prayer books.

Federated Paints, Ltd., Glasgow .. Strathclyde etching primer for aluminium structures.
S. J. & E. Fellows, Ltd., Wolverhampton .. Stainless-steel galley equipment.
Alexander Ferguson (Engineers and Brassfounders), Ltd., Glasgow .. Domestic steam heating fittings.
Ferguson Shaw & Sons, Ltd., Glasgow .. Launching tallene and launching soap.
Ferguson & Timpson, Ltd., Glasgow .. Oil purifiers and insulation for pipe hangers.
Ferodo, Ltd., Chapel-en-le-Frith, Stockport .. Twin-channel stairtreads.
Fibreglass, Ltd., St. Helens, Lancs. .. Fibreglass insulation.
James Finlay & Co., Ltd., Catrine, Ayrshire .. Napery.
Finmar, Ltd., London .. Teak chairs in first-class Lido café.
Firth-Vickers Stainless Steels, Ltd., Sheffield .. Staybrite stainless steel.
Fisher Governor Co., Ltd., Rochester, Kent .. Fuel control valves.
Flexible Duction, Ltd., Glasgow .. Flexible sleeves for emergency Diesel alternator.
Foamite, Ltd., London .. Boiler-room fire extinguishers.
Formica, Ltd., London .. Formica.
Fosbery & Co., Ltd., Barking, Essex .. Valves.
Foster Transformers, Ltd., London .. Transformers.
Foster Wheeler, Ltd., London .. Boilers and economisers.
C. W. F. France & Son, Ltd., London .. Chairs and settees.
E. H. Frisby & Company, Maidenhead, Berks. .. Stainless-steel buckets.

G. & E. Equipment & Contracts, Ltd., New Milton, Hants. .. Lavatory brush holders.
Garage & Engineering Supplies, Ltd., Belfast .. Engine-room workshop tools.
Gaskell & Chambers (Scotland), Ltd., Glasgow .. Bar sundries.
General Electric Co., Ltd., London .. Boiler-room starter board, emergency switchboard, lighting fittings, ventilation fans, telephones, luminous call and fire alarm equipment.
General Regulator Corporation, New York, U.S.A. .. Automatic combustion control equipment.
Gent & Co., Ltd., Leicester .. Electric bells for passenger and crew alarms.
A. F. Genton & Sons (Hockley), Ltd., Birmingham .. Aluminium scoops.
G. & R. Gilbert, Ltd., Wallington, Surrey .. Galley equipment.
Glasgow Scientific Instrument Co., Ltd., Glasgow .. Thermometers and fuel-oil flash point testing apparatus.
Glenfield & Kennedy, Ltd., Kilmarnock .. Valves.
Glovers (Chemicals), Ltd., Leeds .. Fomescol corrosion inhibitor.
James Gordon & Co., Ltd., Stanmore, Middlesex .. Steam flow meters, valves, water-level indicators and desuperheating equipment.
James Gordon Valves, Ltd., Rochester, Kent .. Pilgrim ballast valves.
Goudie & Whittet, Ltd., Glasgow .. Globe wheel valves.
Gourock Ropework Co., Ltd., Glasgow .. Spindle cord for caulking wood deck.
Gravity Ladders, Ltd., Birmingham .. Light-alloy berth ladders.
Greaves & Co. (Art Metal Work), Ltd., Sheffield .. Stainless-steel sections.
E. Green & Son, Ltd., Wakefield .. Economisers.
R. & H. Green & Silley Weir, Ltd., London .. Crockery stowage frames.
Greengate & Irwell Rubber Co., Ltd., Manchester .. Electric cable and shower bath mats.
Grundy (Teddington), Ltd., Teddington, Middlesex .. Aluminium Grundycans.

Guest, Keen & Nettlefolds, Ltd., Smethwick, Staffs. .. Screws.
A. W. Gunton, London .. Bread tins.

Hadfields, Ltd., Sheffield .. Heat-resisting and stainless steels.
Haida, Ltd., London .. Stainless-steel cooking utensils.
J. & E. Hall, Ltd., Dartford, Kent .. Lifts and refrigeration plant.
Halex, Ltd., London .. Plastic measures.
Halpin & Hayward, Ltd., Belfast .. CO_2 portable recorder.
James Halstead, Ltd., Whitefield, near Manchester .. Poly-flor vinyl flooring.
Hangers Paints, Ltd., Hull .. Epoxide paints for hull.
F. C. Harbott Asbestos, Ltd., London .. Non-slip bath mats.
G. A. Harvey (London), Ltd., London .. Perforated plates for boiler steam drum.
William Harvie & Co., Ltd., Birmingham .. Electric and oil navigation lanterns and signals.
Heal's Contracts, Ltd., London .. Decoration in public rooms.
Heal's Fabrics, Ltd., London .. Curtains in crew's recreation room.
Heaton Tabb & Co., Ltd., London .. Combined glass-fibre w.c. and shower compartments, plastic window boxes, Perstorp glass-fibre shower trays, wash-stand basin recess, berth bottom, table pedestal and window lining.
W. T. Henley's Telegraph Works Co., Ltd., London .. Electric Cable.
Richard Henry, Ltd., London .. Backwash chains.
Heyes & Co., Ltd., Wigan, Lancs. .. Lighting fittings and Fluolacent fluorescent bulkhead fitting.
W. H. Heywood & Company, Huddersfield .. Acoustic ceilings.
Hille of London, Ltd., London .. Settees in first-class Lido café.
Hobart Manufacturing Co., Ltd., London .. Galley equipment (60 machines).
Hoffman Manufacturing Co., Ltd., Chelmsford, Essex .. Ball bearings.
Holoplast, Ltd., London .. Decorplast.
Honeywell Controls, Ltd., Perivale, Middlesex .. Flow measurement and ratio control gear.
Hoover, Ltd., Greenford, Middlesex .. Vacuum cleaners.
Hopkinsons, Ltd., Huddersfield .. Ferranti stop valves and Tread and Stamsel valves.
Horne Engineering Co., Ltd., Glasgow .. Thermostatic control valves for calorifier.
Horsley, Smith & Co. (Hayes), Ltd., Hayes, Middlesex .. Venetian blinds for Court alleyways.
Horton Manufacturing Co., Ltd., Rickmansworth, Herts. .. Liquid soap dispensers.
Hoskins & Sewell, Ltd., Birmingham .. Berths and mattresses.
Houseman & Thompson, Ltd., Burnham, Bucks. .. Pre-commission cleaning of boilers and steam lines.
Howard Brothers (Woodware Manufacturers), Ltd., Chesham, Bucks. .. Rolling pins.
James Howden & Co., Ltd., Glasgow .. Forced-draught fans and Instanter sluice valves.
J. & R. Howie, Ltd., Kilmarnock .. Arrondo shower control unit and baths.
W. J. Hubbard & Sons, Ltd., London .. Stainless-steel thermal urns in galley
Hudson & Wright, Ltd., Glasgow .. Copper piping.
F. A. Hughes & Co., Ltd., London .. Toxion anti-fouling system.
Hull Traders, Ltd., London .. Curtains, back cushions, pillow covers and bedspreads.
Humasco, Ltd., London .. Amtico vinyl tiles.
A. V. Humphries, Ltd., London .. Veranda suites.
Alfred E. J. Hurst, Ltd., Belfast .. Pyrotenax cables.

T. & W. Ide, Ltd., London .. Frameless mirrors.
Imperial Chemical Industries, Ltd., Hyde, Cheshire .. Vynide.
Imperial Chemical Industries, Ltd. .. Boiler water testing apparatus.
Imperial Machine Company, London .. Mora silver burnishing machines.
Industrial Tapes, Ltd., London .. Cellulose and Bondex tapes for electrical wiring identification.
International Nickel Company (Mond), Ltd., London .. Nickel.
Albert Isherwood and Co., Ltd., Wem, Shropshire .. Cutting boards and chopping blocks.
Irvin & Sellars, Ltd., Liverpool .. Teak decking.
W. D. Irwin & Sons, Ltd., Portadown, Northern Ireland .. Coarse sand.

Alfred Jeffery & Company, London .. Polycast caulking.
Jeyes-Ibco (Sales), Ltd., Barking, Essex .. Toilet paper and holders, paper towels, dispensers, and disinfectant.
Johnson & Phillips, Ltd., London .. Main propulsion cables.
Samuel Jones & Co., Ltd., London .. Wrapping papers and dispensers.
Jones, Stroud & Co., Ltd., Nottingham .. Yellow cotton Flexotube.

K.D.G. Instruments, Ltd., Crawley, Essex .. Contents gauge.
G. Kay, Ltd., Rugely, Staffs. .. Duffle coats.
Kay & Co. (Engineers), Ltd., Bolton, Lancs. .. Couplings.
Kelvin & Hughes (Marine), Ltd., London .. Wheelhouse navigating console, radar equipment, magnetic compass, Sal log and sundry nautical instruments.
Kennedy & Morrison, Ltd., Belfast .. Lifting gear.
G. B. Kent & Sons, Ltd., London .. Hair brushes.
George Kent, Ltd., Luton, Beds. .. Clear view screen.
Kentish Electrical Engineering Company, London .. Razor socket fittings.
Walter Kidde Co., Ltd., Greenford, Middlesex .. Smoke-detecting and CO_2 equipment.
Kings Langley Engineering Co., Ltd., Kings Langley, Herts. .. Kingsley copper tube fittings.
Kinnis & Brown, Ltd., London .. Aqua-Clear installation.
Robert Kirk, Ltd., Belfast .. Deck covering tiles.
Kiwi Polish Co. (Pty.), Ltd., London .. Kiwi groomers.
Richard Klinger, Ltd., Sidcup, Kent .. Graphite Klingerit for main steam lines and Klinger-Oilit for fuel-oil lines.
Kockums Mekaniska Verkstad A/B., Malmö (through Industrial & Mining Supplies Co., Ltd., London .. Tyfon steam whistle.
Korkoid Decorative Floors, Glasgow .. Flooring in teenagers' room.

Lagersmit Metsalgieterij en Lager Fabriek, Kinderdijk, Holland .. White-metal linings for stern bushes.
Samuel Lamont & Sons, Ltd., Belfast .. Table cloths.
Lamson Engineering Co., Ltd., London .. Tube message system.
Laurence Scott & Electromotors, Ltd., Norwich .. Motors and Pitt-Scott mooring winches.
Laycock's (Ashton-under-Lyne), Ltd., Ashton-under-Lyne .. Liquid glue.
Le Bas Tube Co., Ltd., London .. Steel tubes and pipe fittings.
Leyland & Birmingham Rubber Co., Ltd., Leyland, Lancs. .. Rubber flooring.
Lexington Products, Ltd., London .. Nenette polishers.
William Liddell & Co., Ltd., London .. Napery.
Lightfoot Refrigeration Co., Ltd., Wembley, Middlesex .. Metalshelves in veranda suites.
Linkleters Patent Ship Fittings Co., Ltd., North Shields .. Buoyancy apparatus.
Linoleum Manufacturing Co., Ltd., London .. Linoleum in first-class accommodation.
Liverpool Patents Co., Ltd., Liverpool .. Boiler tube-cleaning machines.

Locker Industries, Ltd., Warrington, Lancs. .. Perforated cable trays.
London Coathanger, Ltd., London .. Wooden coathangers.
Joseph Long, Ltd., Harrow, Middlesex .. Hydrometers.
Lorant & Co., Ltd., London .. Diros electric hand tool.
Archibald Low & Sons, Ltd., Kirkintillock .. Calorifiers, sewage tanks and boat winch platform steel piping.
W. Lumsden & Son, Ltd., Kirkcaldy, Fife .. Napery.
Lurashell, Ltd., Ware, Herts. .. Chairs, settees and tables.
Lytle & Pollock, Ltd., Belfast .. Masonite peg board and plywood.

McAlpine & Co., Ltd., Glasgow .. Lead-resealing traps and plastic bottle traps.
Robert McArd & Co., Ltd., Manchester .. Plastic toilet seats and covers.
A. M. Macdougall & Son, Ltd., Glasgow .. Dance floor, Burma teak strip and Canadian hardrock maple strip.
McEwan Insulators, Ltd., Clydebank .. Insulation of refrigerated provision rooms.
William McGeoch & Co., Ltd., Glasgow .. Door hooks and hardware.
James McGregor & Sons, Ltd., Belfast .. Native oak for the manufacture of bilge beds.
Hugh MacKay & Co., Ltd., Durham City .. Carpet in cardroom.
George MacLellan & Co., Ltd., Glasgow .. Casting pieces.
McMordie Brothers, Belfast .. Perspex.
McMurdo Instrument Co., Ltd., Ashtead, Surrey .. Aqualites lifebuoy marker lights.
A. Macnair & Co., Ltd., Manchester .. Jacobean oak Naphtha stain and thinners.
Macnaughton & Watson, Ltd., Glasgow .. Stainless-steel tracking for cold rooms and stainless-steel rails.
Charles McNeil, Ltd., Glasgow .. Manhole doors.
William Mallinson & Sons, Ltd., London .. Decorative hardwoods, decorative veneers and Mallite ceiling panel.
Malone Instrument Co., Ltd., North Shields .. Draught indicator and depth gauge.
Manganese Bronze & Brass Co., Ltd., Birkenhead .. Scimitar Nikalium working propellers.
Mappin & Webb, Ltd., London .. Cutlery.
Marconi International Marine Communication Co., Ltd., Chelmsford .. Radio equipment.
Marconi Wireless Telegraph Co., Ltd., London .. Television.
Marinite, Ltd., London .. Marinite panels.
Marley Rail & Cole Co., Ltd., Mallusk, Co. Antrim .. Marley handrail.
Marmet (Sales), Ltd., Letchworth, Herts. .. Hi-Lux children's chairs.
C. & C. Marshall, Ltd., St. Leonards, Sussex .. P.V.C. cable sleeving.
H. & J. Martin, Ltd., Belfast .. Marble slabs for bakery and confectioners' shop.
Martindale Electric Co., Ltd., London .. Prufrex A.6 armature and stator tester.
Mather & Platt, Ltd., Manchester .. Grinnell automatic sprinkler and fire alarm system and compressor.
Mawdsley's, Ltd., Dursley, Glos. .. Electric motors.
Medway Paper Sacks, Ltd., Maidstone, Kent .. Paper sacks for disposal unit.
Thomas Mercer, Ltd., St. Albans, Herts. .. Electric clocks.
Mersey Insulation Co., Ltd., Bootle, Lancs. .. Insulation work.
Metallic Manufacturing Co., Ltd., Ardrossan, Ayrshire .. Copper and asbestos joints.
Michell Bearings, Ltd., Newcastle upon Tyne .. Thrust blocks and plumber bearings.
W. Miller (London), Ltd., London .. Terrazzite flooring.
Miller, Rayner & Haysom, Ltd., London .. Stewards' badges.
Miller's Timber Trust Co., Ltd., Barking, Essex .. Rellim Gaboon plywood.
Mills Moore & Co., Ltd., London .. Table notices.
Minerva Mouldings, Ltd., Amersham, Bucks. .. Electric fittings.
Mirrlees (Engineers), Ltd., Glasgow .. Fuel-oil pressure pumps and lubricating-oil and jacking pumps for main motors.
Mitchells, Ashworth, Stansfield & Co., Ltd., Rossendale, Lancs. .. Mascolite for machinery space ventilation.
Paul Mitton & Co., Ltd., London .. Cooks' knives.
Modern Tool & Equipment Co., Ltd., Belfast .. Workshop machinery.
Modern Wheel Drive, Ltd., Slough, Bucks. .. Reverse-reduction gearbox in connection with bow propeller mechanism.
Monington & Weston, London .. Piano and duet stool.
Monitor Patent Safety Devices, Ltd., Wallsend, Northumberland .. Monitor pressure alarms.
Mono Containers, Ltd., London .. Plastic drinking cups.
Charles P. Moody, Ltd., London .. Fibre drawer slides.
F. D. T. Moore & Co., Ltd., Rickmansworth, Herts. .. Royal ironing boards.
Morphy-Richards (Installations), Ltd., London .. Silavent ventilation system in w.c.'s.
Herbert Morris, Ltd., Loughborough .. Worm-gear pulley blocks.
F. Mountford (Birmingham), Ltd., Birmingham .. Aluminium bolts.
Muirhead & Co., Ltd., Beckenham, Kent .. Control equipment for variable-delivery pump.
Munro & Miller, Ltd., Edinburgh .. Expansion joints.
Murray (Scientific Instruments), Ltd., Liverpool .. Oil detectors for auxiliary salt-water circulating system.
Murray, McVinnie, Ltd., Glasgow .. Fog gong with striker.
Nathan's Equipment, Ltd., London .. Defiance emulsifiers in milk room and stainless-steel ice-cream moulds.

Negretti & Zambra, Ltd., London .. Thermometers and pressure gauges.
W. J. Nelson & Co., Ltd., Belfast .. Neoprene sheet.
Nettlefold & Moser, Ltd., London .. Cash boxes.
Newalls Insulation Co., Ltd., Washington, Co. Durham .. Insulation.
Newman & Field, Ltd., Birmingham .. Padlock plates.
Nife Batteries, Ltd., Redditch, Worcester .. Electrical storage batteries.
North British Rubber Co., Ltd., Edinburgh .. Paraflor for table tops.
Samuel Nye & Company, London .. Galley equipment.

O.C.M. (London), Ltd., London .. Carpets in tourist-class ballroom.
Oakley & de Broen, Ltd., London .. Decorative designs.
Fred Olsen Aviation Maintenance Norsk Slyindustri A/S (through John Burnham, Ltd., London) .. Aluminium signal mast.

William Page, Ltd., London .. Galley equipment.
J. Pallee & Lake, London .. Wall curtains.
Paterson Engineering Co., Ltd., London .. Clorocel electrolytic chlorinating equipment for sea-water circulating systems.
Robert Patterson & Sons, Ltd., Belfast .. Brass screws.
Bruce Peebles & Co., Ltd., Edinburgh .. Motors for cargo transporter.
Peerless & Ericsson, London .. Pie and pastry machines.
Andrew Pegram, Ltd., London .. Basket work panels in stewards' messroom.
Peradin & Watercraft, Ltd., Bath .. Paint and Peratol primer for main inlets.
Perfonit, Ltd., St. Neots, Huntingdonshire .. Acoustic panels.
Phoenix Rubber Co., Ltd., Slough, Bucks. .. P.V.C. flooring.

Phosphor Bronze Co., Ltd., Birmingham .. Valve discs.
Pilkington Brothers, Ltd., St. Helens, Lancs. .. Glass.
Plastics by Denbar, Ltd., London .. Plastic aprons.
Plibrico, Ltd., London .. Monolithic refractory linings for boilers.
E. Pollard & Co., Ltd., London .. Haskins steel roller shutters.
Poulton & Nicholson, Ltd., London .. Texturide for captain and senior officers' accommodation.
Power Equipment Co., Ltd., London .. Rotary switches.
Power Petroleum Co., Ltd., London .. B.P. Energol lubricants.
Priestley Brothers (Blankets), Ltd., Halifax, Yorks. .. Blankets.
Primavera Contracts Department, London .. Wallpaper in veranda suites.
Process Units (Halifax), Ltd., Halifax, Yorks. .. Automatic controls in laundry.
Propert, Ltd., London .. White shoe cleaner.
Puritan Feather Co., Ltd., London .. Pillows.
Pyrotenax, Ltd., Hebburn, Co. Durham .. Cables.

Qualart, London .. Art metalwork.

Ernest Race, Ltd., London .. Tripos chairs and footstools.
Rae Stage Equipment, Ltd., London .. Seats.
N. R. Ramsay & Co., Ltd., Newcastle upon Tyne .. Master key system and Marinalium alloy hardware.
James H. Randall & Son, Ltd., London .. Planstore unit.
E. Reader & Sons, Ltd., Nottingham .. Cathodic protection of underwater hull.
Redifon, Ltd., London .. Communal aerial system.
Reditune, Ltd., Croydon, Surrey .. Taped background music.
Frederick Restall, Ltd., Birmingham .. Folding beds.
Revo Electric Co., Ltd., London .. Floodlight fittings.
A. Richards (Metal Workers), Ltd., London .. Stainless-steel trays for galley.
Charles Richards & Sons, Ltd., Darlaston, Staffs. .. Mild-steel welding studs.
J. N. Richardson Sons & Owden, Ltd., London .. Napery.
Richardson & Sheeres, Ltd., Greenford, Middlesex .. Laundry felt and sheeting.
E. M. Richford, Ltd., London .. Metal stencils.
Roanoid, Ltd., Glasgow .. Ring towel holders, bathroom cabinets, towel rails, drip-dry rails and door furniture.
Robb, Moore & Neill, Ltd., Glasgow .. Pyrotechnic outfits, gear tools and furnishings, and vices.
D. R. Robertson, Ltd., Rainham, Essex .. Controllers for bunkering and ballasting.
A. Robinson & Co., Ltd., Bootle, Lancs. .. Installation of pneumatic control equipment.
J. Robinson & Sons, Belfast .. Marble slabs for bakery and confectioners' shop.
John Roby, Ltd., Rainhill, near Liverpool .. Bell.
Rollo Industries, Ltd., Bonnybridge, Stirlingshire .. Workshop machinery.
Rotoflex, Ltd., London .. Special table lamps.
Rotolift Manufacturing Co., Ltd., Newcastle upon Tyne .. Rotolift flexible link chain tools.
Rowan & Boden, Ltd., Glasgow .. Aranbee and Neodek compositions.
Martin Rubeck, Ltd., Redhill, Surrey .. Wire wool.
Runnymede Rubber Co., Ltd., London .. Rubber flooring in first-class restaurant.

Safety Automatic Fire Escapes, Ltd., Layburn, Blackpool .. Automatic fire escapes.
Fred. Sage & Co., Ltd., London .. Public room decoration.
Arthur Sanderson & Sons, Ltd., Uxbridge, Middlesex .. Washbasin curtains.
Sandersons, Ltd., London .. Blinds for first-class Lido café.
Saro (Anglesey), Ltd., Beaumaris, Anglesey .. Welded aluminium hatchboards.
Savage Transformers, Ltd., Devises, Wilts. .. Electric transformers.
Schat Davits, Ltd., London Colney, Herts. .. Baggage davits.
Schermuly Pistol Rocket Apparatus, Ltd., Dorking, Surrey .. Quick-release link for inflatable liferaft.
A. Schrader's Son, Birmingham .. Pneumatic air controls.
G. W. Scott & Sons, Ltd., London .. Cane furniture.
Scott Bader & Co., Ltd., Wellingborough, Northants. .. Cryptic 189 polyester resin for lifeboats.
Henri Selmer & Co., Ltd., London .. Claviolines, cinema organ and stool.
Semtex, Ltd., London .. Vinylex tiles and underlay.
Service Electric Co., Ltd., London .. Secomak electric whistle.
Shanks & Co., Ltd., Barrhead, near Glasgow .. Sanitary outfit.
Shapland & Potter, Ltd., Barnstaple, Devon .. Set of drawers for sample cabin.
Shardlow Micrometers, Ltd., Sheffield .. Micrometer wear-down gauge.
Shaw-Petrie, Ltd., Glasgow .. Mild-steel heating coils in double-bottom tanks.
Shell-Mex & B.P., Ltd., London .. Bituminous solution for rudder and Epikote epoxy resins.
Harry Shimeild & Sons, Ltd., London .. Pewter panel for bar back.
Alexander Shimwell & Company, London .. Floodlight and electrical fittings.
Short Brothers & Harland, Ltd., Belfast .. Manual hydraulic systems for hatch covers and side doors.
Siddall & Hilton, Ltd., Sowerby Bridge, Yorks. .. Berths for Asian crew.
Siebe Gorman & Co., Ltd., Surbiton, Surrey .. Breathing apparatus and fire-fighting gear.
Simms Motor Electronics Corporation, London .. Inertia starters for lifeboat engines.
Skilbeck Brothers, Ltd., London .. Laundry sundries.
Silent Gliss, Ltd., London .. Curtain rails.
Simplex Electric Co., Ltd., Birmingham .. Switches.
Simplex-Turbulo Marine Co., Ltd., London .. Deutsche Werft Simplex tail-shaft bearing.
Skanska Attikfabriken A/B., Perstorp, Sweden .. Perstorp plastic laminates.
Sydney Smith & Sons (Nottingham), Ltd., Nottingham .. Steel valves and pressure gauges.
Smith Brothers & Co. (Hyson), Ltd., Nottingham .. Pressure gauges.
Sound Control, Ltd., West Drayton, Middlesex .. Sound-resistant bulkheads and cabin doors.
Spirax-Sarco, Ltd., Cheltenham, Glos. .. Steam traps.
Splintex, Ltd., London .. Plastic tableware.
Springfield Steel Co., Ltd., Glasgow .. Bollards, roller fairleads and deck castings.
Stafford Furniture, Ltd., London .. Stacking chairs.
Staines Kitchen Equipment Co., Ltd., London .. Steak tongs.
H. M. Stanley (Scales and Weights), Ltd., Burgess Hill, Surrey .. Letter scales and weights.
H. H. Stark, Ltd., London .. Trucks and trolleys.
Steele's (Contractors), Ltd., London .. Steelplate doors.
Steiner Co., Ltd., London .. Streamliners towel dispenser cabinets.
Steven & Struthers, Ltd., Glasgow .. Laminised weathertight doors.
Stevenson & Turner, Ltd., Belfast .. Instantor fittings.
Stewarts and Lloyds, Ltd. .. Steel tubes and derricks.
W. M. Still & Sons, Ltd., London .. Galley equipment.

Stillite Products, Ltd., London .. Stillite mineral wool for noise-insulation of first-class staterooms.
S. J. Stockwell & Co. (Carpets), Ltd., London .. Carpet for cinema.
J. Stone & Co. (Deptford), Ltd., Deptford .. Aluminium rivets.
J. Stone & Co. (Propellers), Ltd., Charlton .. Watertight doors.
Stothert & Pitt, Ltd., Bath .. Ballast and stripping pumps.
Sunderland Forge & Engineering Co., Ltd., London .. Cargo hold light fittings and electrical fittings.
Swindens Patents, Ltd., London .. Vice in engine-room workshop.

Talbot Stead Tube Co., Ltd., Walsall .. Steel tubing.
Tangyes, Ltd., Birmingham .. Hand pumps for hydraulic rams.
Tannoy Products, Ltd., London .. Sound reproduction equipment.
Taw Manufacturing Co., Ltd., London .. Stainless-steel galley utensils.
C. F. Taylor (Plastics), Ltd., Crowthorne, Bucks. .. Plastic tidy bins.
Samuel Taylor & Sons (Brierley Hill), Ltd., Brierley Hill .. Anchors and cables.
Taylor, Pallister & Co., Ltd., Dunston, Gateshead .. Dunstos warping guides, blocks and shackles.
Taylor Rustless Fittings Co., Ltd., Leeds .. Stainless-steel galley utensils.
Telephone Manufacturing Co., Ltd., London .. Telephones.
Tempered Spring Co., Ltd., Sheffield .. Springs.
James Templeton & Co., Ltd., Glasgow .. Carpets in tourist-class lounge, library, reading and writing rooms.
Thermo Plastics, Ltd., Dunstable, Beds. .. Perspex baths.
Thermotank, Ltd., Glasgow .. Air-conditioning and ventilation.
E. H. Thew, Ltd., Gateshead .. Nameplates.
F. Thomas & Co., Ltd., London (through Electrical & Allied Distributors (N.I.), Ltd., Belfast) .. Lighting fittings and quick-start control gear and batterns for fluorescent lighting.
William Thomson & Co. (Kinning Park), Ltd., Glasgow .. Chain blocks and electric hoist.
Thornton & Co., Ltd., Belfast .. Rubber hose and black rubber washers and valves.
Tidmarsh & Sons, London .. Pinoleum cane blinds in first-class restaurant.
F. S. Tolliday & Partners, London .. Viscotherm continuous and direct-reading viscosity meter.
Tough Ropes, Ltd., Greenock .. Steel wire ropes.
Triangle Valve Co., Ltd., Wigan, Lancs. .. Valves.
Ronald Trist & Co., Ltd., Slough, Bucks. .. Level alarms for lubricating oil tanks, and Mobrey magnetic level switch.
Tubes, Ltd., Birmingham .. Steel tubes.
Tufnol, Ltd., London .. Tufnol rudder bearings.

United Filters & Engineering, Ltd., London .. Water filtration plant.
United London Workshops for the Blind (Sales), Ltd., London .. Basket ware.
United States Metallic Packing Co., Ltd., Bradford .. Pump traps.
United Yeast Co., Ltd., London .. Icing turntables.
Universal Office Appliance Co., Ltd., Belfast .. Suppliers of planstore unit.

Varilectric, Ltd., London .. Switch fuse units.
Varley-FMC, Ltd., Brentford, Middlesex .. Oil pumps.
Vent-Axia, Ltd., London .. Ventilating units.
Verplast, Ltd., London .. Glass-fibre decorative panels.
Victaulic Co., Ltd., Hitchin, Herts. .. Victaulic joints.
Victor Engineering Works Company, London .. Automatic ballast and fuel-oil valves.
Victor Oily Water Separators, London .. Victor oily-water separating tanks.
Vigers Brothers, Ltd., London .. Teak parquetry flooring.
Viking Marine Co., Ltd., Ashford, Middlesex .. Lifeboats.
Vokes Genspring, Ltd., Guildford, Surrey .. Variable support hangers for steam piping.
Vono, Ltd., London .. Vono table.

Waeco, Ltd., Salisbury, Wilts. .. Wessex Manoverboard lifebuoy marker signals.
Wailes Dove Bitumastic, Ltd., Hebburn, Co. Durham .. Bituminous work.
James Walker & Co., Ltd., Woking, Surrey .. Treadmaster mats.
Thomas Walker & Son, Ltd., Birmingham .. Commodore log.
Walker & Hall, Ltd., Sheffield .. Silver-plated holloware.
Duncan Wallet & Co., Ltd., London .. Lifebuoys, lights, and supply of galley equipment.
F. E. Ward (Hammersmith), Ltd., London .. Music stands.
Bernard Wardle (Everflex), Ltd., Caernarvon, North Wales .. Everflex P.V.C.-coated fabrics.
Wardle Engineering Co., Ltd., Manchester .. Drying-room tubular heaters.
A. E. Warner (London), Ltd., London .. Infra grills in galley.
James Warnock & Son, Belfast .. Canvas.
G. & J. Weir, Ltd., Glasgow .. Fresh and salt-water evaporating and distilling plant and high and low-level alarms for boilers.
Weir-Pacific Valves, Ltd., Glasgow .. Cast-steel valves for fuel oil discharges, bled-steam drain and exhaust systems.
Welin-Maclachlan Davits, Ltd. London .. Davits and accommodation ladders.
Wellington Tube Works, Ltd., Tipton, Staffs. .. Steam air heaters for main boiler.
A. C. Wells & Co., Ltd., Hyde, Cheshire .. Waste oil filters.
A. West & Partners, Ltd., London .. U.N.O. stencils.
Allen West & Co., Ltd., Brighton .. Starters and control equipment.
Westinghouse Brake & Signal Co., Ltd., London .. Rectifier unit.
W. H. Wheatley & G. E. Dyer, Ltd., London .. Pilgrim valve control console.
Whitby & Chandler, Ltd., Sheffield .. Asbestos tape.
White Allom, Ltd., London .. Public-room decoration.
Whites-Nunan, Ltd., Manchester .. Hose connections.
J. Whitehead & Sons, Ltd., London .. Marble facings for bar counter.
Whittingham & Mitchel, Ltd., Byfleet, Surrey .. Ola Pac insulated containers.
A. Withers, Ltd., London .. Twine and string.
Wolstenholmes (Radcliffe), Ltd., Manchester .. Sluice valves.
E. Wood, Ltd., Ware, Herts. .. Paint.
Wood Brothers (Furniture), Ltd., Ware, Herts. .. Tables and chairs.
Woods of Colchester, Ltd., Colchester, Essex .. Aerofoil Maccess ventilation fans.
Worcester Royal Porcelain Co., Ltd., London .. Heat-proof oven ware.
Worthington-Simpson, Ltd., Newark-on-Trent .. Air compressors and circulating pumps.
John Wright & Sons (Veneers), Ltd., London .. Veneer.
Wright, Layman & Umney, Ltd., London .. Commodes.
J. Wuidart & Co., Ltd., London .. Table glassware.
Wynstruments, Ltd., Staverton Aerodrome, Gloucester .. Straight-Line window wiper.

James Young & Co. (Metals), Ltd., Glasgow .. Fullway gate valves.
James Young & Cunningham, Ltd., Glasgow .. Expansion glands and hand pump.
Yorkshire Imperial Metals, Ltd., Leeds .. Kunifer cupro-nickel main condenser tubes.

THE COMPLETION AND DELIVERY OF "CANBERRA"

THE completion of the *Canberra* has aroused widespread interest not only in Britain but throughout the world. Built at a cost of about £16,000,000 and having the distinction of being the largest passenger liner to be built in Britain since the *Queen Elizabeth*, it was natural that her performance should be anticipated with acute expectancy. The technical staffs were confident that the results of their work would be shown in a highly satisfactory trial performance, and they were not to be disappointed, for the meticulous care which had been taken by the owners and builders alike had put the issue beyond doubt.

Leaving Belfast on the 29th April for dry-docking at Southampton, the ship then proceeded to the Clyde where a most comprehensive series of tests were completed in a highly satisfactory manner and a trial speed of 29·27 knots was recorded. The official handing-over ceremony took place on the 19th May, and the *Canberra* set out on her maiden voyage on the 2nd June. She left Southampton at 4 p.m. on a three-month journey that will take her through the Mediterranean to Australia, New Zealand, and the Pacific coast of North America, and she is scheduled to return to Southampton on the 1st September.

She has joined a fleet which already consisted of 17 liners, including 10 ships of post-war construction. Until the handing over of the *Canberra*, the largest liner in this fleet was the 42,000-ton *Oriana*, another great ship which entered service on the 3rd December, 1960. This fleet of 18 liners, totalling 463,313 tons gross, is the largest passenger fleet being operated in the world.

Built at a total cost of some £30,000,000, the *Canberra* and *Oriana* both use Southampton as their terminal port in the United Kingdom.

Apart from being the most modern passenger ship in the world, the *Canberra* also has the distinction of being the largest passenger-carrying ship in the world, the maximum number of passengers she can carry being 2,238, and it augurs well for her future that for her maiden voyage she is fully booked. Among the passengers are 750 emigrants for Australia and another 120 going to New Zealand. Some of the others are making a short voyage to Gibraltar and Naples, but the great majority are going all the way to the Antipodes.

During the two days prior to the maiden voyage parties of distinguished visitors were entertained on board, including the new Minister for Shipping and Shipbuilding, Vice-Admiral Hughes-Hallet, and British and foreign shipowners. The P. & O.-Orient Lines have made arrangements to take every opportunity of demonstrating the vessel to as many people as possible during this memorable maiden voyage. A series of luncheons and cocktail parties have been arranged for government and civic leaders, shippers, travel agents and journalists and it is fully expected that more than 20,000 people will inspect the ship at various ports of call, before her return to Southampton.

The *Canberra* is under the command of Captain G. A. Wild who was appointed Commodore of the P. & O. fleet the day before the maiden voyage. Captain Wild is the son of a Lancashire clergyman and he was born in February, 1904. He served his early apprenticeship at the Nautical College,

Fig. 110.—"Canberra" Entering the Dry Dock at Southampton.

Fig. 112.—On Trial.

Fig. 111.—"Canberra" in Dry Dock.

Fig. 113.—Captain Geoffrey Alan Wild.

Pangbourne, from 1918 to 1919, being one of the second entry at Pangbourne which had been formed in 1917. Following a year as a cadet on the barquentine *St. George*, he completed his apprenticeship with two years in the New Zealand Shipping Company. He joined the P. & O. Steam Navigation Company as fourth officer in the *Novara* in 1923 and obtained his master's certificate in 1929. During the war, Captain Wild served in troopships, commencing in the 22,270-ton *Strathnaver* on the long voyages, in convoy, round the Cape to Suez, and he also served as first officer in the *Ile de France*, of 44,356 tons, when she was a troopship operated by the P. & O. Company. In 1944, Captain Wild went to the United States of America, to take over as chief officer of the 15,100-ton *Chitral*, which had, until then, been operated by the Royal Navy as an armed merchant cruiser, and he stood by this ship while she was being converted into a troopship at Baltimore. He served in the *Chitral* during the landing in Malaya a few days after V.J. Day and later brought home British ex-prisoners of war from Rangoon.

Captain Wild was promoted Staff Captain of the *Stratheden* in 1949 and in the following year was appointed Staff Captain of the *Chusan*. His first regular command was in 1951 as the Captain of the *Shillong*, in which vessel he stayed for over four years. After relieving voyages as commander of the *Iberia* and *Strathnaver* in 1956, Captain Wild flew to Cape Town in 1957 to command the *Canton*. Since then he has commanded the *Corfu, Chusan, Strathaird* and *Arcadia*.

In October, 1960, Captain Wild was relieved of the command of the *Arcadia* to enable him to stand by the *Canberra*. In March this year he flew to Naples where he joined the *Oriana*, for the final stages of her maiden voyage. By observation and discussion with the captain of the *Oriana*, Captain Clifford Edgecombe, he familiarised himself with the ports and problems which will be encountered during the *Canberra's* maiden voyage.

Staff Captain Michael Prowse has been appointed Staff Captain of the *Canberra*. Born in October, 1915, Staff Captain Prowse did his early training as a *Worcester* cadet prior to serving an apprenticeship with the P. & O. Company. His first ship was the *Maldavia*, which he joined as fourth officer in December, 1936. While serving in the *Strathaird* in 1942, on trooping operations, he was promoted to second

officer, and later in the war he transferred to the *Maloja*, the *Strathmore* and then the *Ranchi*.

In November, 1950, he was appointed chief officer of the *Mooltan*, after having served as second officer in several of the company's ships. He stood by the *Iberia* during the latter stages of her building and was appointed first officer when she was commissioned in July, 1954, and then in March, 1955, he was promoted to chief officer while still serving in the *Iberia*. Promotion to Staff Captain came in April, 1958, when he was transferred to the *Strathnaver* in which he served for two years. Staff Captain Prowse joined the *Arcadia* in February, 1960, and he remained in this vessel until he was appointed to the *Canberra*.

After serving an apprenticeship with Messrs. R. & H. Green and Silley Weir, Ltd., the chief engineer of *Canberra*, Mr. John A. Shakle, joined the P. & O. Steam Navigation Company in 1931 as assistant engineer. His first ship was the *Naldera*, in which he remained for three years. After serving in the *Viceroy of India* he joined the *Carthage* later in 1934, and the next year, while still serving in her, obtained his second class certificate. He has served as chief engineer of the *Iberia* and the *Strathmore*, and was appointed to the *Canberra* in January, 1960, and has been standing by during her construction at Belfast since then.

Mr. Leonard Samuel Warran is the *Canberra's* purser. His first appointment as purser was made in March, 1932, when he served in the *Mantua*. During the last war he served in the Royal Naval Reserve, returning to the Company in March, 1944. Mr. Warren was purser of the *Strathaird* for nearly three years until February, 1949, while she was engaged in trooping, after which he did a series of voyages in the *Mooltan* and the *Canton*. He joined the *Strathmore* early in 1952 and was with her until 1956. He transferred to the *Iberia* for one voyage and then, during 1957, joined the *Arcadia*. From December, 1957, until July, 1960, he was purser of the *Chusan*. Mr. Warren left the *Chusan* on being appointed purser of the *Canberra*.

Fig. 114.—An Impressive Bow View of "Canberra."

EPILOGUE
By Neil McCart

1961

THE beginning of 1961 saw *Canberra* only a few months away from completion. On April 29 she left the builder's yard for Southampton, where she was to be dry-docked for the final stages of fitting out, for, surprising as it may seem, Harland & Wolff did not have a dry-dock large enough to take her. It was while these final touches were being made at Southampton, that HRH Prince Philip visited the ship. He was shown round by Sir Donald Anderson and Sir Hugh Casson, and met most of the personalities who had been responsible for the design and building of the vessel. After this period of docking was over the ship went north again for her trials off the Isle of Arran. She was handed over to the P&O company on May 19 at Greenock, and was now ready to make her debut and to show herself off to the nation prior to her maiden voyage.

It had been planned that she would make a two-day cruise from Greenock to Southampton, carrying several hundred special guests, and hugging the coast for most of the voyage. By 8.45pm on May 20, embarkation was completed and she weighed anchor and set a course south into the Irish Sea. All the public rooms were open throughout this voyage, but service and bars were only available in the first class part of the ship. Sir Donald Anderson held a cocktail party on board, and it is significant that he was asked whether he had ever considered making *Canberra* a one class ship. He replied to the effect that this had been considered, but in his opinion a vessel of that size would not be economical if it were one class. He pointed out that *Canberra* had over twice as many tourist class berths as there had been in previous vessels, whereas there were only a dozen or so more first class passengers. It is obvious from these remarks that the vessel was to be engaged primarily on the liner voyage, and cruising was only thought of as a minor part of her role. It was also significant that the increase in tourist class berths was to cater for the huge number of emigrants to Australia from the United Kingdom.

Although the airlines were making big inroads into the trans-atlantic routes, the longer routes to Australia which carried thousands of emigrants were as yet more or less untouched, and the liners were still sailing with full passenger lists.

Still, none of the implications of air travel can have been in the minds of any of the guests on board *Canberra* on that Whitsun bank holiday weekend as she steamed south. At 7am on Whit Sunday, as her passengers started to filter up on deck, she passed by Douglas, Isle of Man. All that afternoon she steamed down the Welsh coast, and at 5 pm she was off St Anne's Head, and ready to navigate the Bristol Channel. That evening the holidaymakers of Minehead and Ilfracombe had their opportunity to see the blaze of lights as *Canberra* passed by both towns. She must have slowed down considerably that night, for at dawn the next day she was off Penzance. By mid-morning on a beautiful sunny day *Canberra* was in Torbay, and she must have been a magnificent sight from the heights of Berry Head. A small ceremony was held on board at this point, when Sir Donald Anderson presented the BEM to *Canberra*'s chief engine room serang, to whom it had been awarded earlier in the year. All that day *Canberra* steamed along the south coast until, at 11.10 pm, she reached Dover. There she turned round to head back to Southampton, where at dawn on Tuesday May 23, she tied up alongside 106 berth in the Western Docks. The new terminal at 106 berth had been built specially for *Canberra* and *Oriana* at a cost of some £300,000. It would, of course, be used in the future by other company vessels, as in 1969 P&O took the decision to base their whole passenger fleet at the port, giving a welcome boost to Southampton's passenger and tonnage figures.

On June 2 everything was ready for her maiden voyage to Australia, and from there to the Pacific and west coast of the United States. She sailed at 4.50 pm that day amid a blaze of publicity, and took P&O's traditional route to Australia, calling at Gibraltar and Naples. On June 8, what was probably

Canberra about to dock at Southampton Docks after her two day cruise from Greenock *(F.R. Sherlock)*.

Passing the ferry terminal San Francisco (P&O).

the most nostalgic and dramatic meeting of the whole voyage took place, in the Mediterranean, not far from Port Said. She sailed passed the 'old lady' of the P&O fleet *Strathaird*, which was homeward bound on her last voyage before going on to Hong Kong to be broken up. *Canberra* was in fact taking the place of *Strathaird*, and the sirens blew on both ships as they passed close by. *Strathaird* was flying her 30 ft (9.14 m) paying off pennant, and Captain A.E. Clay in command sent the following signal to Commodore Wild in *Canberra*, 'You look magnificent, and all in *Strathaird* wish you a happy and successful voyage, and from the old to the new, *Strathaird* bids you farewell'. Commodore Wild replied, 'You too look magnificent with your paying off pennant flying gaily. You look a gracious and not too elderly lady. All well here.' It was a very moving experience for all on *Canberra*, but, contrary to Commodore Wild's optimistic signal, one problem had already arisen down below in the engine room. From very early on in the voyage there had been trouble with the leaky tubes in the port condenser. At Aden on June 12, the trouble became worse and resulted in a 14-hour delay in the port. In fact at one stage there was a loss of electrical power, and the air conditioning was out of use. Both passengers and crew sweltered in the stifling heat of South Arabia. There was a lot of publicity in the Press about the problem with the condenser, just as seven years later the trouble in *QE2*'s turbines on her maiden voyage made headlines. *Canberra*'s troubles were, however, far less drastic than *QE2*'s were to be, and as Sir Donald Anderson said, they were no more than a 'blistered heel on the foot of a great athlete'.

Twenty days after leaving Southampton *Canberra* arrived at Fremantle, Western Australia, and was given her first massive welcome in that country. The shore was lined with cheering crowds and well-wishers sounding their car horns as the ship passed by and came alongside her berth. A few days later she was given a similar welcome in Melbourne, and along with the rest of the well wishers was Dame Pattie Menzies. She was going to travel in 'her' ship to Sydney, where *Canberra* arrived on June 28. It was inevitable that Sydney would provide a tremendous welcome, and the crowds were literally hanging

from the bridge. From Sydney the vessel went on to call at Auckland, Honolulu, Vancouver, San Francisco and Los Angeles. At each port the welcome was just as enthusiastic, but perhaps the greatest welcome of all was in Vancouver, where the weather was perfect, hundreds of small boats turned out, and helicopters, light aeroplanes and even a jet fighter roared overhead. *Canberra* cleared the Lions Gate Bridge with only 10 ft to spare. In the street there were dozens of welcome banners, and the crowds were wearing 'Welcome *Canberra*' ribbons. From there she sailed to San Francisco, where she was given what had now become a routine welcome. The crowds packed on to piers 32 and 34 as she came alongside. The mayor, George Christopher, declared the day, July 20, '*Canberra* Day'. The celebrations went on for two days, until she finally sailed again.

Contrary to most reports, *Canberra* did not return via Panama, but followed her original route back to Sydney and then back to Southampton via the Suez Canal. On Friday September 1, she overhauled and passed the Italian liner *Leonardo da Vinci*, which had sailed from Naples several hours before *Canberra*. So she had a triumphant return to Southampton, having encountered every kind of weather, including force 12 winds off Wellington. She had cut the passage time from Southampton to Sydney by one week. Of course, it was not just her superior speed that had enabled her to do this, but the fact that she carried so little cargo, which meant that she could be handled quickly at each port. The statistics for her maiden voyage are impressive. She had steamed some 42,000 miles, and had carried 11,000 passengers, and more than 50,000 people had visited her at the ports of call during the voyage.

After a stay of two weeks in Southampton *Canberra* sailed once again for Sydney. This voyage took her along the same route as her previous journey, arriving in Sydney on October 14. After a month in the Pacific, she left Sydney for Southampton, sailing once again via Suez; and so ten days before Christmas she arrived back in England. Her first year in service had been a resounding success.

1962

BY the time her second year was under way *Canberra* was already a firm favourite with travellers. Her design had made her an easy vessel for the passengers to find their way around. The class barriers were amidships, just forward of the William Fawcett room on her Promenade Deck. For the first class passengers all the public rooms were either on that deck, or on the Games Deck, immediately below the Sun Deck. The layout for tourist class passengers was almost the same, except that the Alice Springs bar was situated on 'B' deck. The main tourist lounge, the William Fawcett room, had been so named after the first ship owned by the Peninsular Line (the forerunner of the P&O), from 1835 to 1838. What a difference between the *William Fawcett* and *Canberra*, 206 tons and 82 ft (24.99 m), against 45,000 tons and 818 ft 6 in (249.48 m). There was a small model of the *William Fawcett* in the foyer just forward of the lounge.

Unfortunately, *Canberra*'s fourth long voyage to Australia was not a happy one for her engineers. Trouble with her distilling plant, boilers and turbine, forced the company to bring her home direct from Australia via the West Coast of the USA and the Panama Canal. It was to be *Canberra*'s first transit of the Canal, and quite a tight squeeze it would prove to be. In parts the Canal locks are just 110 ft (33.52 m) wide, and as *Canberra*'s width is 102 ft 5 in (31.24 m), this gave a clearance on each side of just over 3 ft 6 in (1.06 m) . . . not much with a 45,000-ton vessel! It must have been quite a relief to Commodore Wild to bring her through virtually unscathed, with only one slight scrape. At the time *Canberra* paid £11,500 in dues to the Panama Canal Authority (a record for any single vessel then). She was also the widest commercial vessel to pass through the Canal up to that time. She arrived back in Southampton in June, where she spent 29 days in port, and received the necessary repairs to her machinery. She also received a very minor change to her profile, which was probably not even noticed by a lot of people, namely, extensions to her funnel uptakes. There is no doubt that this minor alteration made quite a considerable improvement to her general appearance. Somehow her slender twin uptakes had never looked properly finished before.

Canberra was ready to sail on Friday July 20. Her next voyage was a short cruise to the Atlantic island of Madeira and Gibraltar. It must have been a great success because 20 passengers stayed on for the next momentous cruise. This time

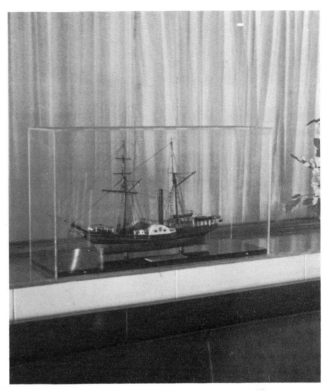

The model of P&O's first vessel the *William Fawcett* in the foyer outside the William Fawcett lounge *(Neil McCart)*.

the P&O company was entering the Cunard domain and running a cruise across the North Atlantic to New York. It would also be a milestone in company history, as the last time a P&O vessel had called there was exactly 100 years before in 1862, when the company's *Haddington* had called at the port. She had started her career in 1846 as a 1,847-ton paddle steamer, but had been converted to sail in 1854, and used to supply P&O stores in the East. So it could be said that in all its 127 years of history it was the first peacetime visit of a P&O steamship to the port. Of course, the North Atlantic is not a 'sunny' cruising area, and *Canberra*'s crossing was no exception, the siren being kept quite busy in the fog. On the first day out she passed the now elderly *Queen Mary* as she

Canberra **in the early 1960s, soon after she received her funnel extensions** *(F.R. Sherlock)*.

steamed eastwards bound for Southampton. The latter was nearing the end of her distinguished career, and the Cunard Line was going through a traumatic time with the changing role of the transatlantic liner and the building of a replacement for the two 'Queens'. However, it must have been a magnificent sight to see the two great liners pass at sea.

Canberra was given the traditional warm American welcome on her arrival at the Hudson River. All the fire floats came out, as did helicopters from the New York and New Jersey police forces, some flying extremely close to her. She berthed at pier 91. The ship was not a superliner by the transatlantic standards, but the welcome was certainly as big as those given to the 'Queens' themselves. President Kennedy had been in office for 18 months in the USA, and at 45 he was the youngest President to be elected. Many people in the United States and in the western world viewed his presence as being like a breath of fresh air, and supported his idea of increasing tourism to the USA. The United States Travel Service responded to his call, and a broadcaster from the NBC network had been filming on board *Canberra* during the outward voyage; his film went out in one of the USA's morning TV programmes, the 'Today' show, which was estimated to have at least 12 million viewers. Even the President himself was said to be an ardent fan. Telegrams of congratulation came in from all over the US, even one from Hollywood who wanted to replace Marlon Brando with Commodore Wild, for the part of Fletcher Christian in their epic movie, 'Mutiny on the *Bounty*'. A visit to the ship was made by Hermione Gingold, who called herself 'New York's unofficial ambassador'. A baseball star even donated an autographed baseball for the Cricketers' Tavern; perhaps it is still there, along with all the other trophies given by famous sportsmen. *Canberra*'s visit to New York lasted for four hectic days, before she sailed once again, this time eastwards and back to Southampton, from where she continued to be employed on her conventional route to Australia and the Pacific, for the rest of what was to be another successful year for her.

1963-64

1963 started very badly for *Canberra*. She had set sail from Southampton just before the New Year for her usual voyage to Australia and New Zealand and was in the Mediterranean, about 150 miles from Malta when, at 4 am on January 4, there was an explosion in the main switchboard. The resulting fire destroyed the whole of the starboard side of the switchboard, and many of the main electrical distribution cables were also damaged. It was several hours before make-shift leads could be rigged up, and until then the vessel was without lighting, ventilation, and power for the galley. Of course, being a turbo-electric powered ship, the main engines were out of action, which meant she was in fact lying totally helpless. Fortunately the company's liner *Stratheden* was not far away when the accident happened. She stood by *Canberra*, and both vessels made ready for a tow. *Canberra*'s crew were superb and, by giving frequent broadcasts about how the repair work was progressing, proved to be a great comfort to her passengers. Later in the day limited electrical services were restored, and in the evening one main engine was started. All that night she limped towards Malta, and was able to reach Grand Harbour by the next morning. Once in port special generator vessels could be brought alongside, and before long all the normal services were restored to the ship.

However, P&O had one enormous problem on their hands with over 2,000 passengers stranded in Malta. The Royal Rotterdam Lloyd liner *Willem Ruys* called into Malta and was able to take on board about 100 passengers, but it was quite obvious that the only way in which the problem could be solved was for the company to charter enough aircraft to fly everybody either on to their destination, or back to the UK. So began an operation which became known in the company as the 'Malta airlift' and in the course of one week P&O chartered some 14 large aircraft, and flew 1,700 passengers mostly to Australia and New Zealand. For anyone in the company who had the time to sit and think about it, this should have been a very ominous sign for the future.

Naturally, the news media soon got hold of the story and it was not long before graphic accounts appeared in the newspapers of passengers on 'sit down strikes', refusing to go by air, although most of the passengers did in fact accept the situation without complaint. There was even a touch of humour in the press when Carl Giles included a reference to *Canberra*'s plight in a cartoon about the annual boat show, but at least he did not strand his famous characters Chalkie and Grandma on the Promenade Deck for the P&O staff to deal with.

As the passengers were getting away to their destinations, the BI cargo ship *Woodarra* was sent to Malta to take on the baggage and cars. *Canberra* herself sailed on January 16, with 40 or so passengers still on board—those who had declared themselves unfit to fly. Arrangements had been made at Belfast for the necessary repairs, but it was to be a slow journey as she limped back home on one engine, encountering bad weather and having to battle through winds of up to 60 knots. It was March 17 before she arrived at the Harland & Wolff yards on the River Lagan, and it was almost two months before the repairs were completed and she was back in service once again. The accident had put *Canberra* out of action for nearly half of the year, but there was one ray of comfort in that the company had kept the goodwill of most of the passengers and many of them even expressed a preference to travel in her if and when they made the journey again. By the middle of May *Canberra* was back in service, and the rest of the year passed without any further mishaps.

Later in the year P&O withdrew the remaining pre-war ships *Strathmore* and *Stratheden* from service, two ships which in their day had been almost as revolutionary as *Canberra* herself. In fact with the five 'Straths' the company had first introduced the all-white livery and buff funnel into general use. The old Orient Line ship *Orion* was also taken out of service that year, and the withdrawal of these vessels resulted in the conversion of the next generation of P&O-Orient Line vessels, *Himalaya* and *Orcades*, to one class tourist-only ships.

1964 was a far less traumatic year for *Canberra*, and it was marked with another visit to New York. This time she berthed at pier 92, but her welcome to the city was just as warm as it had been on the first occasion. A Dixieland jazz band played her in, and her 1,700 cruise passengers were able to visit the New York World Fair. Another first for *Canberra* that year was her visit to Alexandria in Egypt, which coincided with the opening of a new passenger terminal at the port. She was the largest ship to call there, and careful planning was needed for her arrival, on account of her size and rather deep draught. A party was held in the Crow's Nest bar for the city dignitaries, and the manager of the Maritime Transport Shipping Agents presented a plaque to the ship to commemorate the visit, which proved to be a much needed boost to Anglo-Egyptian relations, which were not particularly good at the time. Clear evidence of Soviet influence could be seen in the port, in the large number of Russian and Polish vessels there. These were the early days of Russian-Egyptian co-operation, and it was only two months later than Mr Krushchev paid his first visit to Egypt to mark the completion of the first stage in the building of the Aswan Dam.

1964 had been a successful year for *Canberra*, but in December an important event took place, an event that could be said to have 'put one more nail in the coffin' of the liner voyage; it was the issuing of a certificate of airworthiness to the new Vickers Super VC 10. This aircraft could carry 163 passengers, 30 more in fact than the Boeing 707 and both these aircraft could fly at speeds in excess of 500 mph, with a range of over 4,000 miles. Soon both aircraft would be in service with BOAC as it was then called, and it was becoming increasingly obvious that not only were the transatlantic routes going to be taken over by air travel, but the long routes to the Far East and Australia were being increasingly threatened as well. Already the Atlantic liners were losing money at an alarming rate, and their owners were having great difficulty in finding alternative roles for their vessels.

1965-71

IN 1965 the P&O company acquired the remaining minority shareholdings in the Orient Line, and so set in motion the final stages in the integration of the two fleets and the final demise of the Orient Line as a separate company. However, this did not actually happen until later in 1966, and before then another incident occurred which seriously damaged the whole merchant service. This was the strike by seamen which lasted for 45 days from the middle of May to midnight on July 1 1966. It was the first seamen's strike for 55 years, and there is no doubt that it caused a lot of bitterness in the industry. Even a plea from the Prime Minister, Harold Wilson, failed to prevent it, so why did it happen? The seamen's union were demanding a 17 per cent increase in wages, and a shorter working week. As they had already received a 13 per cent rise in the previous year, the shipowners thought the seamen's demands were unreasonable; there was a stalemate as neither side would give ground, and meanwhile the ships which were in port lay idle. For many people memories of the strike will be of seeing both *Canberra* and the smaller *Arcadia* tied up alongside each other at 106 berth in Southampton Docks, as a way of making the best possible use of the limited space. The Union Castle Line also had three of its vessels tied up alongside each other, just forward of them.

As with all strikes the workers in the industry suffered as much as anyone else, and when it was all over Mr R.M. Thwaites, the chairman of the P&O-Orient Line, said that once strike action had seemed certain, the company had received numerous applications from seamen who wanted to go to sea before it all happened, thus, hopefully avoiding having to strike. The P&O-Orient Line had five liners idle in port, as in addition to *Canberra* and *Arcadia* in Southampton, there were *Orcades, Orsova* and *Himalaya* berthed at Tilbury. The disruption to the passenger ships' schedules meant the cancellation of both voyages and cruises. Several thousand passengers had their fares refunded, but others at various places in the world had to wait for a sailing. The direct cost to the company was substantial, and in addition there was the cost of implementing the final settlement. Once it was all over much hard work had to be done to get all the vessels back on to their normal programmes as soon as possible. All *Canberra*'s cruises from the UK were cancelled; one was a four-day cruise over the bank holiday and two were cruises to the Mediterranean. These last two were scheduled for after the strike ended, but had to be cancelled to get her away on a world voyage. So although the company had lost three cruises, it was fortunate for them that the strike ended when it did or they would have had to cancel the world voyage as well.

On the last day of September 1966 the Orient house flag was lowered for the last time, and the company ceased to exist; on the following day, October 1, the P&O-Orient Line company name was changed to P&O.

June 5 1967 saw the outbreak of war between Israel and Egypt. The rapid Israeli advances closed the Suez Canal for the second time in 11 years, and the P&O company suffered financially as a result. However, this time the Canal was closed

for eight years and so the routes were changed to sail via Cape Town on a permanent basis.

As the 1960s drew to a close another factor in the decline of the liner voyage was making itself apparent. Between 1947 and 1969 some five million people had emigrated to Australia; over half of them were of British origin, and of these 84 per cent had received assisted passages. There is no doubt that these places which were booked and paid for by the Australian government did much to keep the tourist class berths on *Canberra* and *Oriana* filled. By 1970 this had begun to slow down appreciably, and the assisted passages were not so easy to obtain, being kept more and more for people with the particular professions or trades which the Australian government needed. Then in 1970 came the most decisive factor yet in the decline of the liner voyage when, on January 12, Pan American Airlines *Clipper Constitution*, the first giant Boeing 747 jumbo jet, crossed the Atlantic and landed at Heathrow. Within half an hour 362 passengers had been disgorged and were dispersing to their various destinations. Six of these aircraft could carry as many passengers to Australia in one day, as *Canberra* could carry in three weeks. Once this high performance aircraft entered service and was flying to Australia, there was no hope that *Canberra* could survive as a viable economic unit employed on that route in her traditional role.

1972-73

1972 was not a particularly good year for the older P&O liners, as massive oil price rises were forcing up running costs quite dramatically. When the *Queen Elizabeth* sank in Hong Kong harbour at the start of the year, after being ravaged by fire, some people viewed the incident as a bad omen for all ocean liners. Cunard had already been forced to reduce their fleet, as had the Shaw Savill Line. However, one very hopeful event took place in 1972, which proved that P&O was not going to foresake its passenger division for the foreseeable future—the new cruise liner *Spirit of London* entered service. She had been laid down in an Italian shipyard for a Norwegian company, and was bought by P&O while still on the stocks. She was to be the first of a new generation of purpose-built cruise liners, with the emphasis on an extremely high standard of accommodation. She sailed on her maiden cruise from Southampton on November 11, and it was significant that only 180 berths were reserved for UK residents, the rest being sold in the USA and Canada. *Spirit of London* was to be based on the USA's west coast, and was P&O's first permanent foothold in that cruising area. By the end of 1972 it had become clear that P&O would have to reduce the passenger fleet, and find completely new roles for those vessels which remained.

So in January 1973, *Canberra* was sent over to New York, to be based in the port, and to begin cruising mainly to Caribbean ports. However, it soon became evident that many of her berths were not being filled on these cruises, and even the dropping of class divisions did not draw enough passengers to enable *Canberra* to pay her way. The answer which P&O came up with was quite an unusual one for the company. In February she was laid up for 20 days near Wilmington in the picturesque state of North Carolina. She was anchored at the mouth of the Cape Fear River, about 30 miles from the town of Wilmington, and some 5 miles from the nearest land. The closest settlement ashore was a small fishing town called Southport, nearly half an hour's journey away by the ship's launch. The main and rather tenuous link with the shore was in the form of a local fishing boat, which brought out mail and newspapers, except when an Atlantic gale blew up, or thick fog prevented it. Most of the crew were discouraged by these long distances from going ashore, and plenty of entertainment had

to be provided on board to while away the long hours of boredom.

Happily by mid-March *Canberra* was back in service once again, completing her New York cruise programme. Then, at the beginning of June, came the bombshell. At a Press Conference Mr Richard B. Adams, head of the passenger division, announced that *Canberra* was to be withdrawn from service when she returned to Britain on September 20, and sold. This announcement must have stunned all those present, for the ship was only 12 years old, and this was less than half of the average age of a liner which had reached the end of its service through old age. Mr Adams went on to explain that she had not been profitable for two years, and had lost half a million pounds between February and September 1972. In answer to a question as to what the chances were of adapting *Canberra* for a cruising role, he stated that in his opinion the chances were 'very poor'. Thank goodness he was soon to be proved totally wrong. One very valid point made by Mr Adams was that *Canberra*'s 35½ ft (10.82 m) draught meant that there were very few ports which she could get into for cruising, and this is still her greatest problem. He stated that it was possible she would be sold for further trading, but in this author's opinion that was very unlikely, because Mr Adams had assured the conference that P&O remained firmly committed to the passenger division; and if she had been sold for further trading it was inevitable she would end up in competition with P&O's other vessels. Furthermore, if her original owners could not make her pay, who could? Mr Adams replied to further questioning that *Oriana* would become the passenger division's new flagship and, indeed, plans were so far advanced that new radio equipment destined for *Canberra* was diverted to *Oriana*. So it seemed that *Canberra* was bound, prematurely, for the breaker's yard and there was an air of gloom and despondency among the many crew members on board both *Canberra* and *Oriana*.

Suddenly the decision to withdraw *Canberra* was reversed, and it was announced that she was to stay in service and would replace *Orsova* in the 1974 cruising programme. The official reason for this sudden alteration of plans was that there was a growing demand for 'open class' cruises and *Canberra* was more suitable for this type of operation. This was indeed a very valid point, but it was also known that some of *Orsova*'s steelwork was in a poor condition, and so for this reason as well the policy change made good sense. There were stories of a boardroom battle over the decision, and whether it is true or not, there must have been a lot of heart searching amongst the board of directors.

Mr Adams' remarks at the June Press conference about *Canberra*'s excessive draught were well and truly proved correct when, in July, she went aground at Grenada in the Windward Islands of the West Indies, and was stranded there for three days. In the following month she went aground once again, this time in St Thomas harbour in the US Virgin Islands, but she was, however, able to return to Southampton in September as planned.

By the end of 1973 the names of *Chusan, Iberia* and *Orcades* had disappeared from the fleet lists, and the ships themselves had gone to fuel the yards of the Kaohsiung shipbreakers. There had also been changes at board level in the company with Mr Ford Geddes relinquishing the chairmanship of the P&O group and being succeeded by the present chairman, Lord Inchcape, who was to lead the passenger division successfully into a new era.

In King George V dry dock at Southampton in the early 1970s *(British Transport Docks Board).*

1974-81

THE first major task which had to be undertaken by the passenger division, headed by Mr H.F. Spanton, was to adapt from sailing on the traditional liner voyages to operating profitable cruises. When Mr Spanton took over control of the division its operation was unprofitable, and there is no doubt that its future was uncertain. There was a strong body of opinion on the P&O board of management which thought the only feasible course was to dispose of the passenger fleet completely, and consequently morale among the crews was very low. However, no such drastic action was taken, and as the first stage in the changeover, all vestiges of the old liner voyage were removed and all the vessels of the fleet were converted to one class operation. The fleet was further reduced by the disposal of *Himalaya* and *Orsova*, both ships being sent to the breakers in Taiwan. There were to be three separate cruising areas; the UK with cruises from Southampton; Australia with a base at Sydney; and the West Coast of the USA. It was not long before P&O's share of the market on the Pacific west coast grew from owning just one ship, to being one of the biggest operators in that area, when they acquired the company called Princess Cruises from the industrialist Mr Stan McDonald. The two vessels belonging to the company were built in the early 1970s as *Sea Venture* and *Island Venture*. They were renamed *Pacific Princess* and *Island Princess* respectively, and were joined by *Spirit of London* which was renamed *Sun Princess*. At last, some 16 years after the formation of the Orient & Pacific line, P&O were now a major force in the Pacific cruise area.

Oriana had been converted to one class operation in 1973, and in 1974 *Canberra* followed suit. There is no doubt that her design lent itself for a conversion of this nature, and once the barriers had been removed, passengers on board *Canberra* could walk the full length of the ship without interruption, on each deck from the Sun Deck down to 'D' deck. There were also some changes made inside the ship to cater for her new role as a cruise liner. The Pop Inn, a popular rumpus room for teenagers, became the photographers' shop (which generated a lively business in its own right during cruises); the first class children's playroom, on the starboard side of the Games Deck, became the Card Room, and the tourist class playroom on the port side was kept for use by all the children. The Stadium which was forward on the Games Deck was converted from a dance floor to a theatre, and the moveable deckhead was welded down permanently. The tourist Letter Bureau on 'A' deck became a kiosk for the sale of everyday items, like sweets, postcards and toiletries, and the Writing Room on the starboard side of the Promenade Deck became the William Fawcett gift shop. *Canberra*'s open weather decks and wide open deck spaces (common to all P&O liners built for long voyages in tropical waters), were ideal for cruising holiday-makers. Her passenger capacity in this new role was cut to 1,737, achieved mainly by converting four berth cabins, in what used to be the tourist class, into two-bedded cabins. Top class entertainers were employed, and with 14 public rooms passengers were given plenty of choice, or they could just relax and do nothing at all. During the day all manner of activities were offered from flower arranging and ballroom dancing to keep fit classes. A whole new department of entertainments staff was formed, working under the cruise director. The whole ship was now run for sun and fun seeking holidaymakers, and not for the traveller going east.

No company was better placed than the P&O to run successful cruises, and it is generally accepted that they first arranged cruising as long ago as 1844; many of the routes covered then were much the same as those which *Canberra* plies today during the UK cruising season.

During the summer season *Canberra* was based at

At Circular Quay, Sydney in February 1975 *(New South Wales Government Offices).*

In Sydney *(P&O).*

In Sydney at night *(P&O).*

Southampton, sailing on mainly two or three week cruises in conjunction with *Oriana*. Each autumn she spent a short period in dry dock before setting out on a Christmas and New Year cruise, returning early in January. She then set sail on a three month world voyage, which as the years went by became almost a ritual. *Oriana* left the UK in the autumn to join *Arcadia*, based in Sydney. In October 1975 *Oronsay* was withdrawn from service and sold for breaking up.

It is interesting to compare the prices of cruises aboard *Canberra* in 1975, with those of 1981. For instance a 13-night cruise in a two-berth outside cabin in 1975 cost £268, and by 1981 the fare for a similar cruise had risen to £776. This reflects the enormous rises in the price of oil, and overall running costs in those six years. During this time many new types of cruising holiday were marketed; 'fly cruises' catered for those people who wanted instant sunshine, and also avoided a sometimes uncomfortable crossing of the Bay of Biscay, as did the 'coach cruises' introduced later. In an effort to encourage more passengers to sail as far as Australia on the world cruise, P&O offered free return flights back to the UK. In 1976, whilst on her world cruise, *Canberra* called at Hong Kong, and for the first time 431 passengers were able to enjoy a three-day excursion into the People's Republic of China. The tour was stage managed by the Chinese authorities, but it was nevertheless a great achievement to have been able to make the visit. Later in the year a fly link was arranged for *Canberra* passengers to fly from London to Rio de Janeiro in Concorde and cruise back, or vice versa. It was a good year for the passenger division, and early in 1977 Lord Inchcape was able to announce a profit of £4.1 million for 1976, as opposed to losses of £6.9 million in 1975. 1977 was another good year for *Canberra* as she consolidated her position in the cruising market, and when she sailed on her annual world cruise in

January 1978 she carried 1,700 passengers, most of whom were booked for the whole voyage. Among the famous names on the passenger list was that of Eleanor Hibbert, better known as authoress Jean Plaidy. She apparently took her typewriter along as well, in order to work on her next novel during the voyage.

Later in 1978 P&O took delivery of the 27,000-ton liner *Kungsholm*. She was renamed *Sea Princess* and took *Arcadia*'s place in Australia, the latter going on to Taiwan for breaking up. This did not affect *Canberra*'s cruising schedules for another two years.

In August 1979 *Canberra* received some unusual publicity, when two 15-year-old schoolboys managed to stow away at Southampton and remain undetected for 12 days. They even went ashore at several ports of call in the Mediterranean, being discovered only after they were reported missing from home, and the police asked P&O to carry out a search of the ship.

Once again in 1979 and 1980 large increases in the price of oil had to be absorbed, and a new factor was beginning to make itself felt. This was the world recession in the shipping industry, which had started in 1974 with tankers and bulk carriers being worst affected at first. Nevertheless, the chairman was once again able to announce that the passenger division had made a profit, and this time the pre-tax figure was £8.8 million.

In early 1981 *Canberra* was again in the news, when she returned to Southampton from the first cruise of the season, a three-week trip which had taken her to Haifa and Limassol among other Mediterranean ports. Unfortunately, the Southampton dockers were involved in an industrial dispute at that time and were not working at weekends. So on Saturday May 2, when she reached Southampton and had almost arrived alongside 106 berth, the dockers refused to berth her.

At 106 berth, Southampton Docks, in August 1981, shortly before departing on a Mediterranean cruise *(Neil McCart).*

After several hours of confusion *Canberra* was ordered to anchor at Spithead, where her passengers were disembarked by tender and taken to Portsmouth. Her evening departure was consequently delayed as the passengers for the next cruise were embarked in the same manner.

Later that month P&O announced that *Oriana* would be moved to Australia in November 1981 to take the place of *Sea Princess*, which would return to the UK in May 1982 to cruise from Southampton on a regular basis. She was scheduled to sail on a world cruise in January 1983, which up until then had always been *Canberra*'s role. In late November 1981 *Canberra* underwent her annual overhaul in Southampton's King George V dry dock, and in December sailed on her Christmas and New Year cruise to Florida and the West Indies. On her return in January 1982 she was all set to sail on what was to be almost certainly her last world cruise.

Leaving Southampton on a fjords cruise, June 19 1981 *(Neil McCart).*

1982

AT the beginning of 1982 *Canberra*'s schedule was to cruise as normal from Southampton, and then in the autumn to make a positioning voyage to Sydney to undertake a season of cruises from that port, *Sea Princess* having taken her place on the world cruise. So this fateful year started in a routine fashion, when on January 6 *Canberra* left Southampton. The first call on the 90-day voyage was Madeira, then it was on to Bermuda, Florida and into the Pacific Ocean. The brochures described it as 'the voyage of a lifetime', and none of her passengers could have imagined how true that would turn out to be. However, before the course of world events completely changed *Canberra*'s history, P&O itself took a step which without doubt will eventually affect the vessel's future.

On February 16, while the ship was at Sydney, the company announced that an order had been placed with the Wartsila shipyard at Helsinki for a new, luxury cruise ship of 40,000 tons. This ship, costing in excess of £80 million and designed to carry 1,200 passengers, would be the largest purpose-built cruise ship ever constructed. The vessel is due to enter service

The huge bow towers overhead. Southampton, August 15 1981 *(Neil McCart).*

with the company in late 1984; it confirms P&O's intention to remain firmly committed to the cruising industry, and to remain the world leader. The new ship, at present unromantically named 'yard number 464', will be only slightly smaller than *Canberra* and *Oriana*, which in 1984 will be 23 and 24 years old respectively. Undoubtedly the new ship will replace one of them. As soon as the announcement was made, controversy broke out as to why the order had not gone to a British company. Questions were asked in the House of Commons but, sadly, it soon became clear that no British shipbuilder could meet the delivery date. Harland & Wolff at Belfast did not tender for the contract, as they were now geared for building oil tankers and bulk carriers. It was a sad reflection on an industry that had built some of the world's greatest liners. However, the row over the building of the new liner was soon lost to events in the South Atlantic which were beginning to look more and more ominous.

It is not normally the custom of aggressor nations to proclaim their objectives from the housetops in advance. Observers usually have to piece together their conclusions on this score from a succession of episodes or incidents pointing in one direction or another. So it was in the case of Argentina's aggression in the Falkland Islands in April 1982, with the additional consideration in this case of the continual threats of invasion which had been forthcoming in recent years, but which have never materialised. British sovereignty over the Falkland Islands and their dependencies rests on a secure historical and legal foundation. The first British settlement was established in 1766 and, after a period of confusion up to 1833, the British possession and administrative control has been continuous since then. The residents of the islands are mainly descendents of Scots 'garrison colonists', and are fiercely loyal; the first British governor was appointed in 1866. Argentina's claim to the Falkland Islands is based on her being the successor to the Spanish Empire which governed most of South America, although a small Spanish presence on the Falklands lasted only a few years. The island of South Georgia, some 800 miles south-east of the Falklands, was discovered by Captain Cook in 1775 and until 1965 provided a centre for whaling. Argentina's claim to the island dates from as recently as 1927, and it is not altogether clear on what this claim is based.

Soon after *Canberra* sailed from Southampton in January the signals were coming from Argentina which gave clues about the Argentine junta's intentions. The newspapers in Argentina were openly proclaiming that the islands would be seized by force, and that Argentina would have sovereignty of the islands before 150 years of British rule there was celebrated in 1983. It is also now known that Argentina reduced her deposits in London banks by nearly half in the weeks before the invasion (so that the inevitable financial sanctions would not bite so hard). But they were signs which went virtually unreported, and so unnoticed in Britain. On the other hand some political decisions by the British government were totally misread by the Argentinian junta; the intention to withdraw the ice patrol ship HMS *Endurance*, and the continuing defence cuts are examples. The junta must have taken the view that Britain would not oppose any Argentine invasion of the islands, but would merely retaliate by breaking off diplomatic relations and imposing economic sanctions. They were obviously prepared to go along with that.

The incident which brought matters to a head seemed a most insignificant affair at the time. An Argentine entrepreneur, Constantino Davidoff, had arranged a deal involving scrap metal from the former whaling station at Leith, South Georgia, with the owners of the station, Christian Salveson of Edinburgh. However, on March 19, whilst *Canberra* was in the Indian Ocean and about to visit the sunshine islands of the Seychelles, an Argentine naval transport, the *Bahia Buen Suceso*, sailed into Leith and landed 43 of Davidoff's scrap metal merchants. The party had been told beforehand of the need to comply with the immigration procedures, but either accidentally, or as seems likely now, deliberately, they ignored these instructions. HMS *Endurance* was ordered to the area to assist the British administrator, who was a member of the British Antarctic Survey team. On March 25 the Argentine naval transport, the *Bahia Paraiso*, made further deliveries to the party on Leith, and the Argentine Foreign Minister stated publicly that the scrap merchants were on Argentine territory and would be given full protection by the Argentine government. The situation had now become a full diplomatic incident, and the world's Press started to take more and more interest. *Canberra* was now at Suez and only 13 days away from the completion of her world cruise. Five days later the British Foreign Secretary, Lord Carrington, who had also been in the Middle East, returned to Britain and spoke about 'the potential danger of the situation'. He also warned that Britain would defend the islands. This warning obviously fell on deaf ears, for the Argentine fleet, led by the aircraft carrier *Vienticinco De Mayo*, was already at sea, ostensibly for 'routine exercises', but the decision to invade had probably already been taken. Only two days before the invasion it became known for certain that the fleet was heading for the Falklands, where the defence force consisted of about 80 Royal Marines. Half of these had only recently arrived on the *John Biscoe*, another Antarctic survey vessel.

At 4 am on Friday April 2 the Argentine invasion fleet was sighted off Port Stanley. After heroic stands at the airport and the Governor's residence the small defence force was overwhelmed. For the British public it was a day of uncertainty with little official news, most of the details coming from a Falkland Islander who was a 'radio ham'. One thing was certain, there was a mood of anger throughout the country, that sovereign British territory had been invaded and nearly 2,000 British people subjected to an alien and undesirable rule. The mood of the whole nation was caught the next day when an emergency debate was called in the House of Commons. It was the first weekend sitting of parliament since the Suez Crisis in 1956. Mrs Thatcher gave a pledge to the nation that she would free the islands from the 'fascist junta', and spoke of a 'task force', the first units of which would sail for the South Atlantic on April 5, two days later.

At the time of the invasion *Canberra* was in Naples, the last port of call on her long voyage. She had arrived at 8 am, and was due to sail again at midnight, direct for Southampton. It was during the course of that Friday that P&O Cruises heard of the possibility that *Canberra* might be requisitioned. Next day while she was at sea it became even more likely to happen in the near future. On Sunday April 4, the possibility became a reality when the Queen signed a special 'Order in Council' enabling the government to requisition any vessels that might be needed under contingency plans to meet a national emergency. The following day, when the aircraft carriers HMS *Hermes* and *Invincible* sailed to spearhead the task force, *Canberra* was officially requisitioned by the government, and she was to sail as one of the first of over 100 ships which would eventually make up the task force. The move was announced in the House of Commons by Mr Biffen, the Trade Secretary, and it became clear that her primary role was to be that of a troop transport. Meanwhile *Canberra* was at sea, but fortunately about only one day's sailing from Southampton.

The requisitioning of its vessels, and their use as troopships is certainly nothing new to the P&O company, as throughout its history its ships have played a part in almost every national emergency. In 1848 the little 533-ton steamer *Lady Mary Wood* had carried troops from Madras in India to Ceylon to quell a rebellion there. In the Crimean War the company's *Himalaya* carried troops to Gallipoli, and throughout the First

The Crow's Nest bar is stripped of its luxuries as *Canberra* prepares to sail for the South Atlantic. Soon the bar would be festooned with scaffolding as the flight deck was built overhead *(P&O)*.

The Stadium is stripped in preparation for the journey to the South Atlantic *(P&O)*.

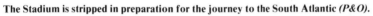

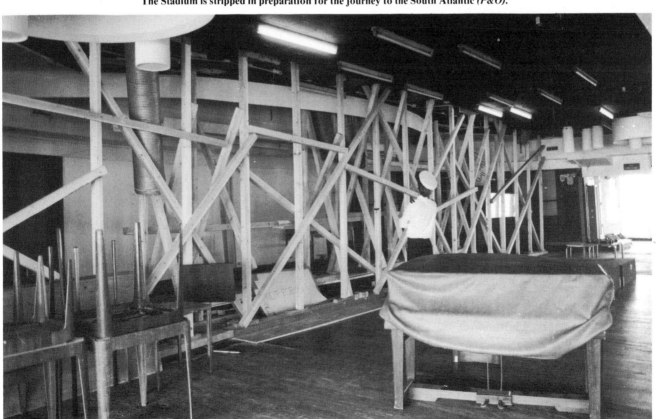

World War P&O ships had served as troopships, hospital ships and armed merchant cruisers. In August 1939, just before the outbreak of the Second World War, the P&O passenger liner *Rawalpindi* was one of the first ships to be requisitioned as an armed merchant cruiser. Three months later she fought a hopeless battle with the German battleships *Scharnhorst* and *Gneisenau*, and was sunk. *Canberra*'s predecessor *Strathaird* had served as a troopship throughout the war and her sister *Strathnaver* had been bombed at Bougie in 1942, whilst serving as a troopship in the North African landings. No one could have thought when *Canberra* was launched in 1961 that one day she would also sail in this role.

Canberra arrived back at 106 berth at 7.30 am on Wednesday April 7 as scheduled, and her world cruise passengers disembarked. Telegrams had already been sent out to would-be passengers, cancelling all cruises up to June 11; they were all offered alternative cruises, some on *Sea Princess*, or given a full refund of money paid. Meanwhile at Southampton the plans to get *Canberra* prepared for service with the task force were going ahead. Vosper Thorneycroft were working flat out removing guardrails and windshields on the Sun Deck, and building two helicopter landing pads. The midships one was built over the Bonito Pool, the other, on the Observation Deck, just forward of, and underneath, the bridge. The Crow's Nest bar became festooned with steel girders re-enforcing the landing pad. (The room was later used as an officers' mess.) Sheets of hardboard were laid over the fitted carpets throughout the ship in an effort to save them from the army boots. Special communications systems were installed on the compass platform, and the Stadium on the Games Deck was converted into a hospital unit. *Canberra* was to be set up with operating theatres and emergency wards, and would carry a large amount of medical equipment, along with a 120-strong team of surgeons, technicians and nursing staff. Casualties could be embarked by helicopter on to the forward flight deck,

and from there be transferred straight down into the hospital. *Canberra* could not sail under the protection of the Red Cross, as she was carrying troops, and so would be a legitimate target. Another important modification was made to the ship to enable her to refuel at sea from RFA tankers. She was re-stored and re-provisioned, and queues of military trucks lined up at 106 berth carrying ammunition and supplies. The deck tennis and quoits courts were soon stacked with containers of ammunition and anti-tank guns.

Half of *Canberra*'s crew were Asian, and the government had decided that no foreign nationals should be involved in operations in the South Atlantic; so all her Lascars and Goanese stewards were paid off. About 130 English seamen were temporarily employed for the duration of her government service. *Canberra* was commanded by Captain Dennis Scott-Masson from Ilminster, Somerset, who was an officer of the Royal Naval Reserve and so ideally suited to work with the Navy. He had joined Pangbourne Nautical College when he was 14 years old, and after service with Shaw Savill, joined P&O in 1950. Captain Scott-Masson's first command had been the 8,000-ton cargo ship *Pando Head*, and since then he had commanded most of the company's prestigious liners. His crew of 450, which included 15 women, were all volunteers and indeed many others, such as entertainment staff, had to be turned down.

All day on Wednesday *Canberra* embarked about 2,000 men of the 3rd Battalion, Parachute Regiment, 40 and 42 Commando, Royal Marines along with supporting personnel and nursing sisters from Queen Alexandra's Royal Nursing Service. Lord Inchcape sent the following message to the Prime Minister, 'I am pleased to report that the P&O ships SS *Canberra* and MV *Elk* are on station in Southampton and prepared to sail immediately under instructions from the MOD naval command. The P&O Board of Directors, and staff afloat and ashore, once again takes pride in supporting Her

April 9 1982, work goes on to complete the flight deck over the Bonito Pool *(Neil McCart).*

Captain Dennis Scott-Masson CBE, RD, RNR, the master of *Canberra* throughout the Falklands campaign. He soon got used to throwing 45,000 tons of ocean splendour around like a destroyer *(P&O).*

Royal Marine commandoes embark at Southampton on April 8 1982
(Southern Newspapers Ltd).

Majesty's Government in the pursuance of legitimate national policy and the rule of international law. We recognise clearly that the free flow of international commerce is dependent upon the worldwide acceptance of law and UN treaty obligations.' It was thought that she would sail the next day, but despite non-stop working, the flight decks being fitted by Vospers were not yet ready. Work had been hampered by 40-knot winds, which were so strong that it took six tugs to to pull Southampton's floating crane to *Canberra*'s starboard side to lift the huge pre-fabricated steel sections, which were designed to take a 15-ton load. Meanwhile the 8,000-ton ro-ro ferry *Elk* was berthed nearby and was loading armoured vehicles and mine clearing equipment.

By the time Good Friday arrived it was clear that *Canberra* would be able to sail that day. *Elk* was first to go as she slipped quietly and almost unnoticed down Southampton Water to play her part with the task force. All that afternoon work went on to complete the flight decks on *Canberra*. In Mayflower Park the crowds were gathering, and the cold, windy day could not dampen anyone's enthusiasm. At 4.30 pm the large floating crane was towed away from her starboard side; by 6 pm the park was packed full to capacity and still more people were coming. It seemed that the whole of Southampton and, indeed, the south of England had turned out to wave goodbye. At 7.30 pm the light was failing rapidly, when three tugs bedecked with good luck slogans appeared from the direction of the Eastern Docks, and went alongside *Canberra*. This was the sign that she would be sailing within minutes. At 8.15 pm the last link had been broken as the bow rope was let go, and slowly *Canberra* was pulled away from 106 berth. Ten minutes later she came level with Royal Pier, ablaze with lights, and the troops stood to attention, lining her decks. Her siren boomed out, the crowd replied with prolonged cheering, and hundreds of motorists answered with their car horns and headlights. The deep boom of *Canberra*'s siren could still be heard half an hour later as she turned into the Solent and prepared to join the task force. Lord Inchcape sent the following message to Captain Scott-Masson: 'As *Canberra* takes her place in the Falkland Islands task force, your colleagues elsewhere in the fleet, and ashore the world over, go with you in spirit. You and your ship's company may count upon our total support. Whatever its outcome, your present enterprise must take a prominent place in the annals of the company and, indeed, in

The Royal Marine band plays as *Canberra* prepares to sail, April 9 1982
(Southern Newspapers Ltd).

the history of the nation. With you, we pray that its progress may be peaceful, and its objectives successfully won. We, every one of us, wish you God Speed and safe return.' The thoughts of the whole nation were echoed in that message.

At dawn the next day *Canberra* rounded Ushant, and set a course across the Bay of Biscay. Her decks were soon resounding to the tread of army boots, and it was a very different kind of passenger who now mustered for boat drills. The midships flight deck over the Bonito Pool was tested very early on, when a Sea King helicopter landed on it. Work on the forward flight deck was continued by men from Vosper Thorneycroft, who had sailed with the ship in order to complete it. It was not long before *Canberra* was being shadowed by Soviet ships; a 3,400-ton 'Primorye' Class spy ship took up station about 10 miles astern of her. The Russian ship seemed particularly interested in *Canberra*'s refuelling at sea (RAS) exercises, which she had been carrying out with RFA *Plumleaf*. They must have been very impressed with *Canberra*'s station keeping, as the Soviet Navy does not have a good reputation for carrying out this particular manoeuvre. Training for the troops started immediately. The long and spacious Promenade Deck (four circuits of which equal 1 mile), proved to be ideal for route marching, or 'yomping' as it was soon to be known. Weapon practice was carried out on the Games Deck and PT on what was now the flight deck. Bofors guns had been rigged up, and as the ship made her way south she became more and more like a troopship and less like a luxury liner.

No sooner had the P&O staff got *Canberra* to sea, than the news came that the BI cruise liner *Uganda* had been requisitioned as a hospital ship. She was in the Mediterranean at the time, and put into Naples four days early to disembark her passengers, most of them schoolchildren. She then went to Gibraltar to be fitted out for her new role, before sailing for the South Atlantic.

The staff at P&O's offices and also at the MOD, were now presented with an unusual problem. The last time liners had been requisitioned was during the Second World War, and the rules which existed for compensating the shipowners were now unused and outdated. Nevertheless, negotiations with the government were successful and P&O were assured that all losses resulting from the cancellation of the cruises would be made good. One major worry for the company was that the Russian cruise operators would cash in on P&O's disappointed holidaymakers, but as events turned out there was to be no loss of public goodwill.

On April 17 *Canberra* berthed at Freetown in Sierra Leone, where she fuelled and took on more stores. The party from Vosper Thorneycroft were disembarked, having completed the work on the forward flight deck. This stop at Freetown was the first indication for people at home of her exact location, although Captain Scott-Masson kept in touch with the P&O company as and when he could. It was also the last time that *Canberra* was able to dock in a friendly country. The next time she was to go alongside would be in Argentina. These first few weeks were dominated by the diplomatic efforts which were being made to achieve a peaceful settlement. It was obvious that the Argentine invasion had been carefully planned, just before the winter set in down in the Southern Ocean. Britain had to set a definite time limit on any negotiations, for if they dragged on and on, the chance to land troops and liberate the islands could be lost for seven or eight months, or even longer. Britain's Foreign Secretary, Lord Carrington, resigned, for it seemed that the Foreign Office had blundered. The UN and countries of the Common Market supported Britain and condemned Argentina. On April 13 the US Secretary of State, Alexander Haig, began his terrific effort to achieve a diplomatic solution, but also on that day Britain announced that at least four nuclear powered hunter-killer submarines were in the Falklands area, and a 200-mile 'total exclusion zone' was to be enforced around the islands. There was a strong body of opinion at this time which favoured a long drawn out blockade of the islands, but events were to prove that this would have had little effect in removing the invaders.

In the meantime, however, *Canberra* had left Freetown bound for Ascension Island which was being used as the staging post for the task force. She was being escorted by the frigate HMS *Ardent*. Contrary to reports which appeared in the Press, Captain Scott-Masson's brief was to take *Canberra* down to the 'total exclusion zone', where the troops would be transferred to other ships. It was during this part of her voyage that *Canberra* was shadowed by an even more sinister vessel than the Soviet spy ships. The 10,409-ton Argentine cargo ship *Rio De La Plata* was spotted close by, and although she was in international waters, the vessel was well away from the recognised shipping lanes. The escorts were sent to clear her from the area, and divers inspected *Canberra*'s hull to ensure that no mines had been laid. The ship's carpenter, Mr R. Chessell, had a mammoth task making hundreds of window blackouts, for as she got nearer to the war zone *Canberra* would have to 'darken ship'. Meanwhile, in the galley, Chef Denis Rogers was well used to troopship routine, having started his career with P&O 31 years previously in 1951 on the troopship *Empire Fowey*, when troops were being carried to the Korean War. He and his staff, supplemented by naval cooks, worked non-stop to feed both ship's company and troops.

On April 20 *Canberra* arrived at Ascension Island to rendezvous with the rest of the task force. It was the first chance that the troops had had to conduct full scale battle exercises. It was only 18 days since the initial invasion of the Falklands, and the largest British military armada since the Second World War was poised to liberate the islands. There is no doubt that the speed with which the task force was assembled will give the Warsaw Pact countries plenty to think about. Meanwhile on the diplomatic front, despite the efforts of Mr Haig, it was clear that the Argentine troops were not going to withdraw and that they were playing for time. Five

An aerial view as *Canberra* refuels at sea from an RFA tanker. The Soviet spy ships showed great interest in this operation (*Crown Copyright, Central Office of Information*).

days later came the recapture of South Georgia; during the operation naval helicopters crippled the Argentine submarine *Santa Fe* which had been carrying reinforcements. The SAS and Royal Marines captured about 200 Argentine prisoners. This must have dispelled any thoughts there may have been in the minds of the junta that the task force was merely a bluff.

Back at Ascension Island Captain Scott-Masson broadcast the details of the battle for South Georgia to his ship. He was unable to say when they would leave and head south, but *Canberra* was under six hours' notice to sail. She was to stay at Ascension for another ten days, giving the troops more time for exercises and it was better that they were kept there, rather than at sea in the rough, icy waters of the Southern Ocean. At the end of April President Reagan came down firmly on Britain's side and strongly branded the Argentines as aggressors—it was clear that diplomacy had failed.

Almost at once the battle to liberate the Falklands began in earnest. On May 1 a lone Vulcan bomber made a 7,000-mile flight from Ascension Island to bomb the runway at Port Stanley. It was followed up with an attack by the Sea Harriers, which were beginning to prove their superiority over the Argentinian Mirage jets by shooting down two of them. At home in the Press the maps of the Falkland Islands, which had first been shown as small dots in the South Atlantic, were suddenly getting more detailed; Goose Green and Darwin were now becoming familiar names for the first time in most British households.

Then came the announcement that the *QE2* had been requisitioned at Southampton. She, too, was to be given a helicopter flight deck and, like *Canberra*, would be used as a troop transport. Work began immediately on the 67,000-ton liner, the main task being to fit the flight deck, and only minor conversions were made internally. Once again Vosper Thorneycroft worked flat out to get her ready.

Soon afterwards there came the news that the Argentine cruiser *General Belgrano* had been hit by two torpedoes from one of the nuclear powered hunter-killer submarines, HMS *Conqueror*. At first it was not clear what had happened to the cruiser, but gradually it became known that she had sunk with many casualties. Although she had been outside the 'total exclusion zone', she had been skirting the perimeter of it and heading in the direction of the task force. On May 4 came the stunning news that HMS *Sheffield* had been hit by an Exocet missle.

Two days later *Canberra* and the assault force sailed from Ascension Island, and it was now clear that an invasion was inevitable. A few days earlier Captain Scott-Masson had attended a meeting of the task force commanders on board HMS *Fearless*, and had been asked by Major General Moore whether he would be prepared to take *Canberra* right into the islands for the landing. His reply was that if it was required, then he would undertake it. This must have been the first indication for him that his ship would be going into the thick of the battle. The BBC news reporter Brian Hanrahan was with the task force throughout the campaign and, when interviewed on his return, in a Radio 4 programme on June 26, he said that the commanders found it difficult to decide whether *Canberra* should go in or not; the advantage of getting all the troops landed in one swift operation seemed to tip the balance. As *Canberra* steamed south the exercises and manoeuvres continued, and as Captain Scott-Masson said, he got used to 'throwing 45,000 tons of ocean splendour around like a destroyer'. At home there were many people who strongly believed that the Vulcans should bomb Argentine air bases. In an editorial, the *Daily Telegraph* spoke of keeping the option open. The uproar it would provoke in world opinion, it said, must be weighed against the 'possibility of the *Hermes* or even *Canberra* suffering the same fate as *Sheffield*'. There is no doubt that the ferocity and skill of the Argentine Air Force was a very worrying factor.

The Pacific Restaurant was used as the officers' dining room during the Falkland Islands operations (*Southern Newspapers Ltd*).

On May 12 there were detailed briefings on board *Canberra* for the troops who were to make the first landings. Two days later she and the assault force entered the 'total exclusion zone'. That same day *QE2* sailed from Southampton with about 3,000 troops of the 5th Infantry Brigade aboard, these being two battalions of Scots and Welsh Guards, and the 7th Ghurka Rifles. She set course for South Georgia where, in late May, she would rendezvous with *Canberra*. By May 19 the final briefings had been given and the landings were a certainty. Captain Scott-Masson broadcast to his crew and passengers, amongst whom a genuine mutual respect had grown up. He commended the exemplary conduct of the troops, and said he hoped that he would have the honour of returning them all safely to Southampton. The first landings of the liberation had been planned for the sheltered and deep waters of Port San Carlos, in the north-west of East Falkland. *Canberra* would have to navigate the northerly tip of Cape

Paratroops waiting half an hour before the first landings at San Carlos *(Crown Copyright, Central Office of Information).*

British and Argentine wounded are treated side by side in the hospital. On the left is Able Seaman J. Dillon from HMS *Ardent* **who was awarded the GM for his bravery** *(Crown Copyright, Central Office of Information).*

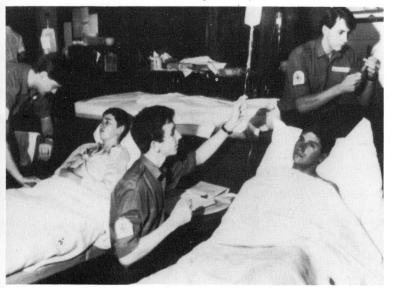

Dolphin, sail in to the Falkland Sound and then to San Carlos Bay. By now many anti-aircraft guns had been fitted on the Sun Deck, fixed to the guard-rails and to the containers of equipment. Soon they would all be needed as *Canberra* played her part in the stealthy landings which were to be made on May 21.

In the early hours of that Friday morning, the assault force led by HMS *Fearless* and *Intrepid* steamed into the natural anchorage of San Carlos Bay. *Canberra* was given one of the safest anchorages and, as the troops scrambled from her shell doors into the waiting landing craft, Admiral Woodward placed the escorting frigates and destroyers in a 'gun line' in Grantham Sound, to await the inevitable air attacks. Diversionary attacks were made in other parts of the Falklands to distract attention from the main landings. By the time dawn broke over San Carlos Bay, most of the troops were ashore and the British bridgehead had been established. But then the air attacks started. Wave after wave of Argentine jets swooped low over the ships anchored in the bay. At first they seemed to be concentrating on the line of escorts, and HMS *Ardent*, which had been escorting *Canberra* from very soon after she set sail, was hit and sunk. She was only 2 miles from *Canberra* at the time, and a close affiliation had grown up between the crews of the two ships. Twenty-two men died, and 30 were injured, many of the survivors being taken on board *Canberra.* It was not long before many of them set to work with a will, helping to prepare supplies for delivery by helicopter to the troops in the bridgehead. As the air attacks intensified many of the barmen, stewards and waiters on *Canberra* manned the machine-guns. They had been given some training by the troops, and now they volunteered to help beat off the attacking aircraft. One of these was Bernie Layfield, who manned a gun on the Games Deck. He and his colleagues took it in turns to feed the ammunition into the guns, and he later described the din of numerous machine-guns and Blow Pipe missiles.

In the hospital on board the medical staff were treating both British and Argentine wounded side by side. Back at home two photographs were published in the Press, which were the first indications the British public had received that *Canberra* was in the firing line. One photograph showed her lying close to shore with a Sea King helicopter in the foreground, and the other pictured Able Seaman John Dillon from the *Ardent* lying in the hospital on board next to an Argentine casualty. AB Dillon was later awarded the George Medal for his bravery on the stricken *Ardent.* As darkness came on that historic day, with her task completed, *Canberra* was ordered to leave the danger of the enclosed waters, and move to a safe area which had been set up to the east of the Falklands. She carried with her over 50 wounded men, both British and Argentine. The Captain's message to London as she left San Carlos Bay, read: 'Have survived our first prolonged air attacks and all ship's company still in good heart having delivered their passengers as required'. There is no doubt that her day under attack had endeared the *Canberra* to everybody in the task force and to the British public back at home.

On the next day the frigate *Antelope* was hit by a 500 lb bomb, which tragically blew up as the bomb disposal expert was attempting to defuse it. There were no other casualties, and *Antelope* broke her back and sank. The bomb disposal expert was posthumously awarded the Conspicuous Gallantry Medal for his bravery.

Meanwhile Argentine propaganda was claiming triumphantly that her air force had hit and seriously damaged *Canberra.* One can only imagine that they hoped seriously to undermine the morale of both the task force and the British public with this wild claim. In fact, *Canberra* sustained no damage at all and received the order to proceed to Grytviken in South Georgia, where she would embark the troops of 5

Brigade from *QE2*. It must have been a strange sight to see the 'Great White Whale', as she was affectionately known in the task force, sailing through the icebergs of that lonely part of the Southern Ocean.

On May 27 and 28, whilst the 2nd Battalion of the Parachute Regiment were fighting and winning their epic battle for Darwin and Goose Green, both *Canberra* and *QE2* were anchored off Grytviken. It was, indeed, the furthest south that both vessels had ever been, and hopefully were ever likely to go in the future. For two days the embarkation of the troops and loading of supplies went on, sometimes in the most appalling weather. Once the transfer was complete *Canberra* headed once more for the Falklands, while *QE2* headed back to Southampton, her mission completed. There can be no doubt that the MOD's decision to keep *QE2* away from the battle area was because, like the 'Queens' during the Second World War, she would have made a special target for enemy aircraft or submarines. Given the Argentine Air Force's skill and almost reckless bravery they may very well have got through with at least one bomb or Exocet missile. During the early morning of June 2, and under cover of darkness, *Canberra* once again sailed into San Carlos Bay, this time to disembark over 2,000 troops of 5 Brigade. The Guards and Ghurkas who had begun their journey in *QE2*, finished it in small landing craft as they were ferried ashore from *Canberra*. This time the weather was on their side, and for the two days she was anchored off San Carlos thick fog surrounded the area, and all was quiet. Once she had completed her task *Canberra* sailed for the loitering area which had been set aside east of the Falklands.

By now British paratroops and marines had 'yomped' (force marched) their way across 50 miles of appalling marshy and muddy terrain, a feat which the Argentines would not have believed possible. There were still the terrible tragedies of Bluff Cove, and the bloody battles on the mountains around Stanley to come, but the die was cast, and it was only a matter of time before the besieged Argentine garrison would have to surrender. The superior skill and physical fitness, the high morale and sheer guts of the British troops won the day and, on June 14, General Menendez and his garrison surrendered unconditionally to General Moore, commander of the British land forces. The Union flag was once again raised over the governor's residence by those same Royal Marines who had been forced to surrender just 74 days before. It was a remarkable feat of British arms, for against all odds a British force had sailed 8,000 miles, and defeated an Argentine garrison which heavily outnumbered them.

However, amid the euphoria of victory, a very real and massive problem confronted General Moore. Not only did he have the living conditions of the British troops (which had to take priority) to attend to, but also he had thousands of Argentine prisoners on his hands, and it was not even clear how many prisoners there were. The figure given to General Moore by the defeated Argentine commander was 15,000, but later, like most of their claims, this too was found to be false. The true number was in the region of 10,000; but one thing was certain, that most of them were in poor physical condition, some suffering from exposure and malnutrition. Thousands of tents which would have provided them with shelter had been lost when the *Atlantic Conveyer* was sunk by Exocet missiles on May 26. Another problem was the apparent lack of interest in their plight shown by the Argentine junta. Perhaps this was owing to internal power struggles developing in Buenos Aires, or perhaps they wanted to blame Britain for any deaths amongst the prisoners and thus save some face in international opinion.

Canberra **and other task force ships off Port Stanley** *(Crown Copyright, Central Office of Information).*

At Grytviken, South Georgia *(Press Association).*

Argentine prisoners of war eating a meal in the Atlantic Restaurant. All are wearing 'C' deck baggage labels tied to their uniforms for identification *(Crown Copyright, Central Office of Information)*.

A wounded Argentine soldier is carried ashore at Puerto Madryn, he is clutching a menu card usually used for the farewell dinner for cruise passengers, a memento of his voyage *(Press Association)*.

Whatever the reasons, General Moore had to act quickly and, once again, the answer came in the form of *Canberra* and her huge bulk. Captain Scott-Masson received orders to bring his ship back from the loitering area to San Carlos to take on the first 1,000 prisoners. He then took her round the coast and, guided by HMS *Andromeda*, navigated a partially uncharted Argentine minefield into Port Stanley. The prisoners ashore had been disarmed and herded into the area of the airport, where they had constructed their own makeshift shelters from any available material. The first prisoners to be processed and embarked on *Canberra* were the young conscripts, who seemed to be very glad it was all over. They were led from the airport in groups of 200 to be ferried out to *Canberra*, and the North Sea ferry *Norland*. There was one ugly incident when a group of the prisoners rioted in Stanley, but this was quickly brought under control by the British troops guarding them. Reports at the time suggested that a rumour was circulating among the prisoners that *Canberra* would be sailing without them. It was also suggested that their behaviour was a demonstration against their officers, who were greatly disliked; they certainly set fire to a building in which senior Argentine officers were billeted. Once on board the liner all the prisoners were given a bowl of soup and a roll. The chief steward John Murray recalls one young Argentine soldier who was so cold, that he just stood holding his soup bowl for warmth, and when the soup finally went cold he was given another. Many of the prisoners appeared to be little more than boys, and there were stories of a class of 14- and 15-year-old schoolboys amongst them. Nevertheless, they were all searched and given a shower, their clothes were washed, and a P&O baggage label was tied to each man to identify him. About 4,000 were taken on board altogether, and they were packed into the cabins and public rooms, many of them sleeping on the hardboard covered decks. Despite the hygiene precautions which were taken when they embarked, many of the prisoners were suffering from dysentery, and all the reports speak of fouled cabins and the terrible smell.

However, the problem was not solved yet. The Prime Minister had told the nation that no British ship would sail to repatriate the prisoners, until assurances of safe conduct had been received. No such assurance was forthcoming from the junta in Buenos Aires. But eventually, with the help of the International Red Cross, the impasse was broken and the safety of both *Canberra* and *Norland* was guaranteed. They did not sail to the nearest and most obvious port in Argentina, Commodoro Rivadavia, which would have been only one day's sailing away; instead the junta wanted the prisoners delivered to a small and remote fishing port in Patagonia, Puerto Madryn, some 300 miles further north. It had probably been chosen because it was so remote, and the prisoners could be landed there discreetly, far removed from the gaze of most of the Argentine population. Up to the very last the Argentine propaganda machine had fed the country with false reports of great victories, and now they wanted as few people as possible to witness this final humiliation. *Canberra*'s arrival at Puerto Madryn was graphically described by the BBC correspondent, Robert Fox, who was aboard the ship at the time. He recalled that as they approached Argentine territorial waters, the destroyer *Santisima-Trinidad* met them and, ironically, signalled that she was there to escort *Canberra* in, and to protect her. (The *Santisima-Trinidad* is of British design and identical to *Coventry* and *Sheffield*.) A pilot came aboard, and a second Argentine warship, the *Commodoro-Py* stood off in the distance. Robert Fox goes on to say how relieved the prisoners were to be home, and delegations of them had been thanking the British troops for the way they had been treated. *Canberra* berthed at an almost deserted quay, and was alongside for four hours whilst the Argentine troops disembarked. There were only a few military officials to greet them, and all the prisoners were quickly put into trucks and then driven away. It was the first time *Canberra* had been alongside since Freetown, 11 weeks before, and so much had happened since then. Once her strange passengers had left the ship, she set sail once more for the Falkland Islands where, on arrival at Port Stanley, she found the Royal Marines she had brought on the 8,000-mile journey south, waiting to embark once more to sail, this time for home. Towards the end of June, the P&O offices in London received confirmation that *Canberra* was about to set sail for Southampton, and would arrive on July 11.

As she left the South Atlantic for the last time, not only was she carrying her military passengers, but there was one very special civilian on board also. Mr Jack Abbott, a Falkland Islander, who had actually been about to take a holiday in Britain, travelling via Argentina in early April, but the invasion of the islands scotched his plans. Mr Abbott saw that *Canberra* was included in the task force and, having complete confidence in the British forces, he decided to try to book a passage with her once the battle was won. With help from the Army he was allocated a cabin, and he became *Canberra's* only truly civilian passenger during her war service. He was no newcomer to P&O though, having cruised before on *Sun Princess* in Canada. It was a happy coincidence that the master of *Sun Princess* on that occasion, Captain M.V. Bradford, was also the deputy captain on *Canberra* during her war service. Mr Abbott enjoyed his journey back to the UK and, even though the ship was still on a war footing, the return journey was a far more relaxed affair than the voyage south had been. He expressed the wish that perhaps one day *Canberra* could make another journey to the Falklands, but this time as a cruise ship! For the rest of the passengers and, for that matter, the crew, there was now just one event dominating their thoughts—their arrival home on Sunday July 11. But it did not prevent everyone from enjoying themselves in the meantime. The Lido swimming pool was filled, and contests and competitions such as kite flying from the Sun Deck were organised. As she came through the tropics and across the equator once again, *Canberra's* decks were crowded with sun-bronzed bodies. Parties were held for the officers in the Crow's Nest bar, amongst all the scaffolding, and there was even a story of one officer who could drink a gin and tonic whilst hanging upside down from it. When *Canberra* broke the journey with a call at Ascension Island, a team of officials from the MOD embarked to inspect the damage to fittings, and the wear and tear caused by her service in the South Atlantic.

Meanwhile, at home, the preparations for her return to Southampton were under way. All the indications were that it was going to be a day to remember. The *QE2* had already been given a tremendous welcome when she returned earlier in June, and she had not actually sailed into the war zone as *Canberra* had done. It was estimated that tens of thousands of people would line Southampton Water. Nobody could guess how many small boats might turn out to escort her in. There was some speculation that she might call into Plymouth to disembark the marines, but this hope was soon dispelled, as it was not a practical proposition, considering her deep draught.

At dawn on that historic Sunday of July 11, *Canberra* was off the Isle of Wight but hidden in the early morning mist. All that morning the crowds had been building up around the Solent. By 8.30 am there were queues of traffic on the approach roads to Southampton, and it was impossible to get through the crowds surrounding the dock gates. In the Solent itself, thousands of small craft had come out to greet the 'White Whale', most of them bedecked with bunting and messages of welcome. On board *Canberra* the Royal Marines were packed on to every available vantage point, including the lifeboats. The men had draped their own messages over the ship's side, one of them in friendly rivalry to *QE2*. It read

Argentine prisoners disembark to a cool reception at Puerto Madryn *(Press Association).*

Canberra's **great day; the whole of Southampton seemed to have turned out to welcome her home** *(Press Association).*

Canberra returns to her home port escorted by hundreds of small boats *(Neil McCart)*.

Canberra emerges from the mist as she nears her berth in the Western Docks *(Neil McCart)*.

Royal Marines pack every inch of available space, lifeboats as well, as they return from the South Atlantic *(Neil McCart).*

HRH Prince of Wales prepares to leave shortly before the ship docked; he was piloting a Wessex helicopter of the Queen's Flight *(Neil McCart).*

'*Canberra* cruises where *QE2* refuses'. Another was addressed to the striking railmen, 'Call off the rail strike, or we'll call an air strike'. Perhaps the one that said it all was, 'We came, we fought, we conquered', and there were many more expressing similar sentiments. At 9 am HRH The Prince of Wales landed on the midships flight deck in his scarlet Wessex helicopter of the Queen's flight, and was met by Captain Scott-Masson and Lord Inchcape (who had joined the ship the evening before). Also on board were Admiral Sir John Fieldhouse and General Sir Steuart Pringle of the Royal Marines. The Prince of Wales spoke with a good cross section of the crew and troops, as well as meeting the dignitaries.

The enormous procession of boats, yachts, ferries and even P&O's cross channel ferry *Dragon* made its way slowly through the Solent and into Southampton Water. There *Canberra* was met by the port's fireboats, and cascades of water joined the scene of gaily coloured flags and bunting. Every few minutes *Canberra*'s deep siren boomed out its reply to the shouts, cheers, and whistles from the small boats. A tide of emotion followed the 'White Whale, as she steamed proudly up towards her home port, her gleaming white hull streaked with dirty brown rust, her 'battle scars' from the South Atlantic. As she drew level with the Eastern Docks a squadron of Lynx helicopters trailing coloured smoke roared overhead. The ship seemed to come almost to a stop, almost as if she was unable to move for the masses of small boats gathered around her. She had, in fact, slowed down to allow the Prince of Wales' helicopter to get away before she berthed. At 106 berth the P&O staff had hung out dozens of banners and welcoming messages to decorate the quayside. As *Canberra*'s huge bulk was edged into the berth, the whole emotional welcome reached its climax. The Royal Marine band struck up 'Land of Hope and Glory' with the full accompaniment of the 2,500 marines on board and the huge crowds ashore. Thousands of coloured balloons were released, and the crowd surged past the barriers on to the dockside. Without a doubt, the sight of *Canberra* in the South Atlantic, a great liner lying virtually helpless, and at the mercy of the Argentine air force, had won the hearts of the whole nation.

As the gangways went down and the troops disembarked unit by unit, each man received a red rose, donated by a florist for him to give to a loved one. With their hands full of baggage, most of them could only carry the rose between their teeth. The miracle was that everyone was reunited with his family so quickly in the huge crowds. As Captain Scott-Masson came ashore he praised his crew, and described the ten hours of tension as *Canberra* had been on red alert all that dreadful day in 'Bomb Alley'. He probably summed up the feelings of all his crew when he said, 'Life is going to be delightfully dull after the South Atlantic'.

The statistics of *Canberra*'s 94 days with the task force make impressive reading. She steamed a total of 27,187 miles, and did not suffer a single mechanical failure of any major machinery. Her evaporators produced 39,522 tons of fresh water; the galley served 650,000 meals and produced over one million bread rolls. Perhaps one of the most impressive figures

was that of the 420,000 man miles that 3 Brigade had run around the Promenade Deck. It can be proudly claimed that *Canberra* landed most of the ground forces who went into action on the Falkland Islands and, as well as operating as a troopship, she acted as a hospital ship and prisoner transport, and provided much needed rest and recreation to hard pressed task force units.

Two days later the jubilation of her return was marred slightly when the 129 crewmen who had volunteered to sail with her were paid off, and the regular Asian crew were taken back. The criticism in the Press was somewhat unfair as, when the voyage started, the volunteers knowingly accepted it as a 'one off' job. P&O's Indian crews are not employed simply for convenience; their employment goes back into the company's history, and has been a tradition on all P&O ships since the 1800s. Over the years they have proved to be very loyal and efficient seamen.

However, this unfortunate criticism was soon forgotten, and work got under way to refit and refurbish her for cruising again. There was a lot to be done, and on August 1 she went into King George V dry dock. Apart from the obvious tasks such as removing the flight decks, large sections of wooden deck planking and the internal carpeting had to be replaced. In addition all the passenger accommodation needed to be thoroughly cleaned, and the hull of the ship re-painted. On September 2 she was refloated and moved back to 106 berth for the work to be completed. She was scheduled to start cruising again nine days later on September 11, the first in a series of three cruises, all of which were fully booked. When she left Southampton on the first of these, the port and city gave her a warm send off. Once again the fireboats came out and large crowds gathered. As *Canberra* pulled away it was fitting that she was saluted by the Antarctic survey vessel *John Biscoe* (registered in Port Stanley), which was berthed nearby. This time she was escorted down to the Solent by the training ship *Malcom Miller*, in addition to a number of small boats, but not quite as many as before.

On October 11 the Falkland Islands honours list was announced and, in recognition of his service and that of his ship, Captain Scott-Masson was awarded the CBE. Also honoured was Miss R.M. Elsdon, the senior nursing officer on *Canberra*'s medical staff. She was awarded the MBE in recognition of the vital work carried out by the medical teams on board. The next day at the victory parade in the City of London, one of the crew who represented *Canberra* was Assistant Purser Lois Wheeler, one of the 15 women who served throughout the campaign.

What lies ahead for *Canberra* now? With the new P&O cruise ship due to enter service in late 1984, her future looks uncertain. She will be 23 years old, a reasonable age for any passenger liner. Whenever she makes that final voyage to the ever hungry ship breaking yards, she will have had a full and successful career, serving the P&O company and, indeed, her country well. May 21 1982, will go down in her history as her 'finest hour'.

Refurbished and ready for cruising again: the new bar which has been added to the Island Room, the Crow's Nest bar and the William Fawcett lounge.

At 106 berth, refitted and ready to start cruising once again *(Neil McCart).*

Leaving on her first cruise following her release by the government, appropriately she passes the Antarctic ship *John Biscoe* registered in Port Stanley, Falkland Islands. Hundreds of balloons are released from the Sun Deck *(Neil McCart).*

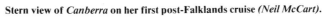

Stern view of *Canberra* on her first post-Falklands cruise *(Neil McCart).*

Q

What's so special about the Canberra's decks?

A

They're sealed with 'Bostik' Caulking Compound

As you might expect of the largest luxury liner produced in Britain over the last 20 years, the P & O Orient liner *S.S. Canberra*, built by Harland and Wolff Limited, has a full complement of up-to-date shipbuilding ideas. Included among these is the use of 'Bostik' Caulking Compound. Not only is this compound extremely easy to apply: it will stand years of exposure to all climatic conditions *with little or no maintenance.*

The word 'Bostik' is a trademark registered in the United Kingdom and many other countries. Manufactured by B.B. Chemical Co. Ltd (the 'Bostik' people), Leicester, England

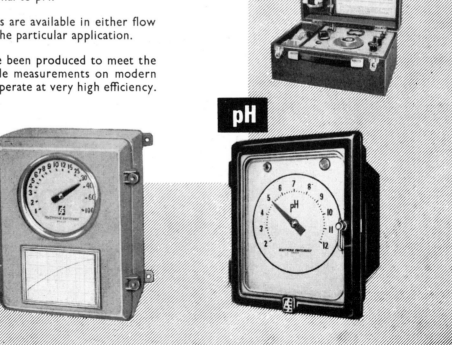

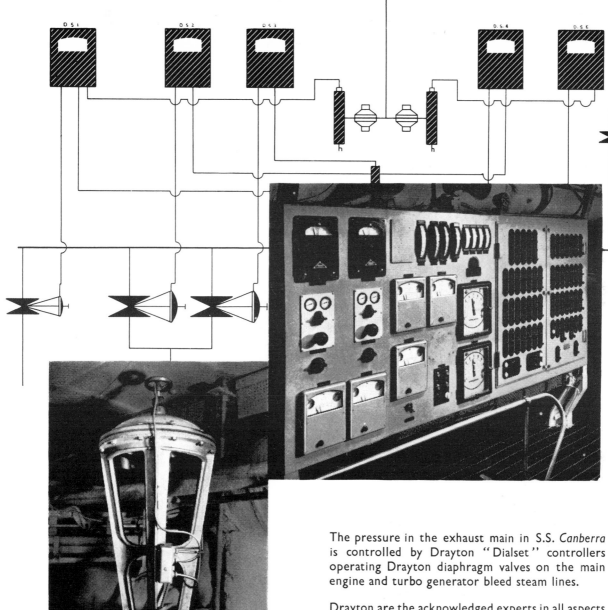

Stothert & Pitt pumps and deck machinery for s.s. "Canberra".

PUMPS

The ballast problems created by positioning the machinery aft in the new P & O Liner s.s. 'Canberra' placed greater importance than usual on the choice of pumps. To deal with oily ballast and for stripping, it was decided to install Stothert & Pitt screw pumps.

For oily ballast Stothert & Pitt built horizontal positive acting screw displacement pumps with external bearings. Of all round clearance design and fully self priming, each pump has a capacity of 250 tons per hour.

For stripping, the 'Canberra' uses S & P vertical screw displacement pumps, also of external bearing design; each is direct coupled to an electric motor and has a capacity of 75 tons per hour.

Both types are fitted with mechanical seals.

DECK MACHINERY

We also supplied for the s.s. 'Canberra' two 50 b.h.p. 'Pitt-Scott' Johnson type automatic mooring winches. These are fitted on the starboard side, one forward and the other aft, and hold the ship against a set tension on the mooring wire, heaving-in and paying-out as the pull on the wire varies.

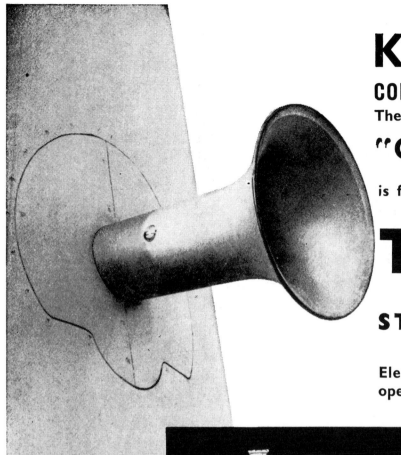
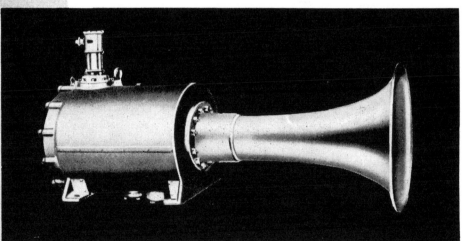

Setting completely new standards of speed, safety and passenger comfort and service, Canberra is a symbol of creative achievement. Throughout her construction, only the finest and most advanced materials have been used. Caposite amosite asbestos and Rocksil rock wool were both used extensively in two of the largest thermal insulation contracts in the ship. The work was carried out by Andersons Insulation Co. Ltd., and included the contracts for the 'A' Class Fire Insulation in the steel and aluminium structures, and the whole of the engine room and machinery insulation. This embraces such details as the crowns of the boiler room and engine room spaces, the majority of the entrance halls, stair-wells and lift-shafts; and the insulation of the boilers, engines, machinery, funnel uptakes and forced-draught fans.

welcome
to the new age
of luxury
ship travel!

another Cape insulated ship

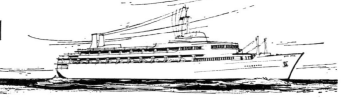

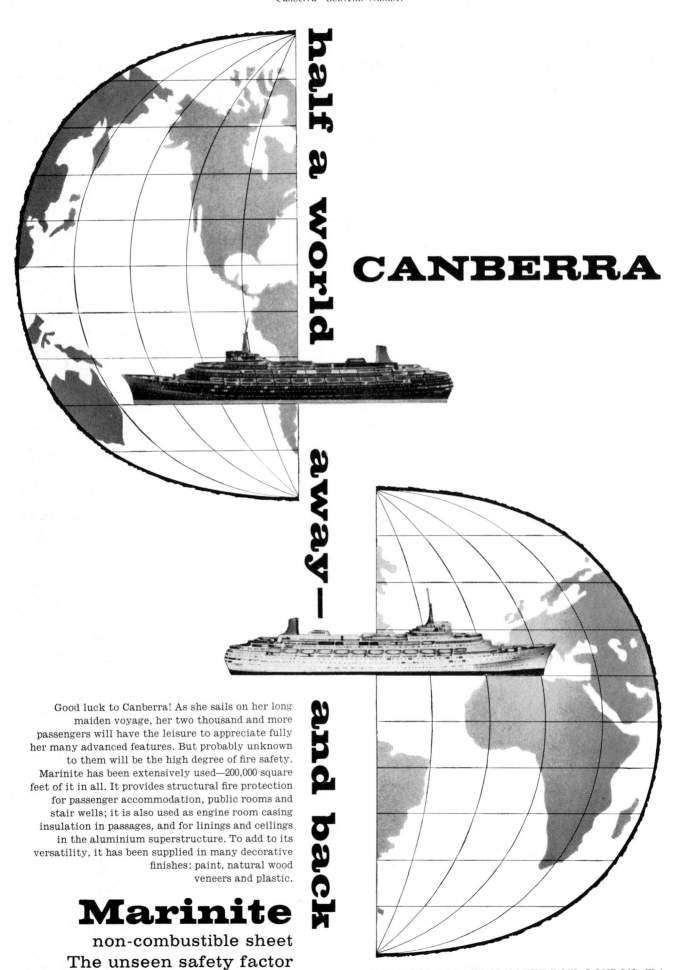

CASTODOR
AND
BARBADOR

Fire-resisting marine doors

CHOSEN FOR THE

CANBERRA

Built for P & O - Orient Lines by Harland & Wolff, Ltd.

Castodor and Barbador Marine Doors are fully approved by the Ministry of Transport as fulfilling the requirements for closing openings in "A" Class Fire-Resisting Divisions, including passenger and service lift shafts, in accordance with the International Convention for the Safety of Life at Sea 1948, and Merchant Shipping (Construction) Rules 1952.

Other well known ships fitted with doors by Caston Barber Ltd. include:

R.M.S. Queen Elizabeth	S.S. Pretoria Castle	S.S. Ocean Monarch
R.M.S. Queen Mary	S.S. Willem Ruys	S.S. Himalaya
R.M.S. Mauretania	S.S. Chusan	The Empire Fowey (M.O.T. Troop Ship)
S.S. Kenya Castle	S.S. President Peron	
M.S. Stirling Castle	S.S. Eva Peron	The Empire Orwell (M.O.T. Troop Ship)
M.S. Athlone Castle	S.S. 17de Octubre	
S.S. Dunnottar Castle	S.S. Ruahine	M.S. Cabo San Roque
S.S. Dunvegan Castle	S.S. Canton	S.S. Leonardo Da Vinci
S.S. Strathallen	M.V. Kungsholm	M.S. Arlanza
S.S. Empress of Britain	M.V. Gripsholm	M.S. Amazon
S.S. Empress of England	T.S.S. Saxonia	M.S. Aragon
M.V. Bergensfjord	T.S.S. Ivernia	S.S. Empress of Canada
M.V. Kanimbla	T.S.S. Carinthia	S.S. Oriana
S.S. Edinburgh Castle	T.S.S. Sylvania	T.S. Canberra

CASTON BARBER LTD., 47 TABARD STREET, LONDON S.E.1. TELEPHONE: HOP 1991

THE HARDEST WORKED DECKS ON THE 'CANBERRA'...

have been laid with POLY-FLOR P.V.C. Flooring

Nearly 5,000 square yards of Poly-Flor have been laid in the alleyways, stairways and crew's cabins on the five lower decks of the Canberra. For these all-important, ever busy floors, a smart, strong, long-lasting floor covering is essential — and Poly-Flor was the natural choice. With its quiet tread and non-slip surface, resistant to all grease, oil and acids, Poly-Flor is ideal for floors with a lot to stand up to. Poly-Flor was chosen for the Canberra — and we are proud to get under foot where quality and efficiency all count.

Photograph by courtesy of P & O-Orient Lines Ltd.

JAMES HALSTEAD LIMITED
P.O. BOX No. 3
CROW OAK WORKS
WHITEFIELD · MANCHESTER

Specialised
PIPEWORK
for T.E.V. Canberra

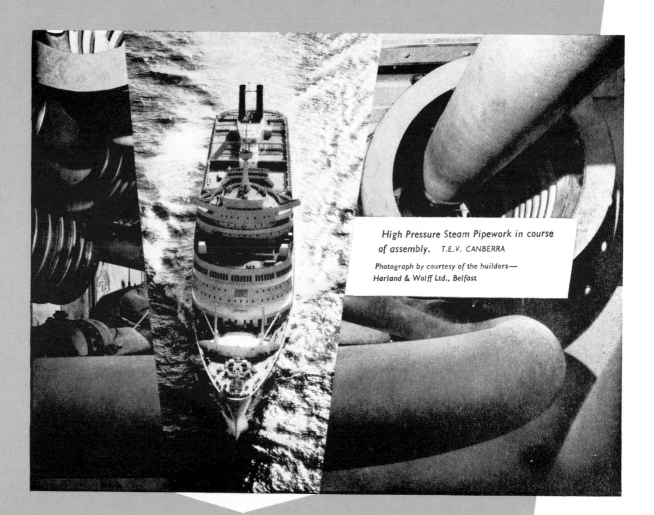

High Pressure Steam Pipework in course of assembly.   T.E.V. CANBERRA

Photograph by courtesy of the builders—
Harland & Wolff Ltd., Belfast

We record, with pride, our association with this new 45,270-ton P & O - Orient Passenger Liner

— FOR EXAMPLE —

★ **ALLOY STEEL MAIN STEAM PIPEWORK** (750 p.s.i. pressure) (960°F. temperature)
★ **WELDED VALVE ASSEMBLIES**
★ **MAIN FEED PIPEWORK** (1150 p.s.i. pressure)
★ **STAINLESS STEEL BULKHEAD FITTINGS**

HEAD OFFICE: DERBY, ENGLAND
WORKS: DERBY & SUNDERLAND
TELEPHONE: DERBY 47111 (10 lines)
TELEGRAMS: CHANNELED, DERBY

AITON
DERBY   & CO. LTD.
ESTABLISHED 1900

Aboard
the Canberra...

... there are over one million square feet of
Fibreglass thermal and acoustic insulation.
Thermal insulation ensuring the
comfort of cabins, public rooms, and
crew accommodation; insulating domestic piping,
air-conditioning ducts, and food storage chambers.
Acoustic insulation in the cabins and
on the engine-room casings, for
quiet and restful travel.
Fibreglass Reinforced Plastics also play a
leading part amongst the new structural
materials abounding in the Canberra.
The lifeboats, shower and toilet compartments,
decorative wall and ceiling panels,
table supports and many of
the chairs, are all in FRP.

FIBREGLASS
TRADE MARK

FIBREGLASS LTD., ST. HELENS, LANCS. ST. HELENS 4022

o

We
are
as
proud
as
a
peacock

De Luxe Veneers
in 'CANBERRA'

We are proud to have had the privilege of adding to the lengthy list of fine ships which carry our veneers, the P & O-Orient Lines' S.S. "CANBERRA"

In this outstanding ship, blue-dyed Bird's Eye Maple Veneer (in Peacock Room), Doreng Teak Veneer (1st class Bureau area, 1st class shop and Cinema Foyers) are practically unique, and others of our veneers used in the first-class and tourist accommodation spaces include Pine, Blackbean, Willow, Rio Rosewood, etc.

S.S. CANBERRA is fitted with THE DECCA

NAVIGATOR

S.S. Canberra

has fresh water pipe joints that will not pull-off or work loose

KINGLEY joints were selected for the fresh water installations in S.S. Canberra—already described as "the ship of the century." Kingley joints are also used by H.M. Dockyards for new shipbuilding and refitting, also by many private yards at home and abroad. Kingley are the ideal choice for hot and cold fresh water installations, compressed air and oil feed lines wherever B.S.S. 659 or B.S.S. 1386 tubing is used. Due to the patent swaging principle employed, KINGLEY joints are well able to withstand the stresses and strains to which they are likely to be subjected at sea.

A standard range of over 240 deck and bulkhead fittings is available, backed by a first-class delivery service.

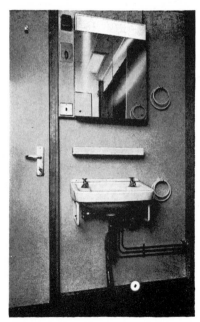

A bathroom in S.S. Canberra for which Kingley fittings were used, is shown by kind permission of P & O-ORIENT LINES and HARLAND & WOLFF LTD.

THE 100% EFFICIENT JOINT
KINGS LANGLEY ENGINEERING CO. LTD.
Kings Langley, Herts.   Tel: Kings Langley 4022

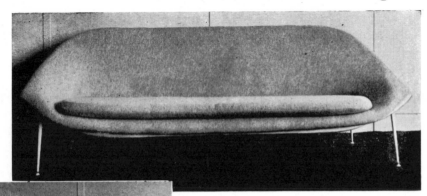

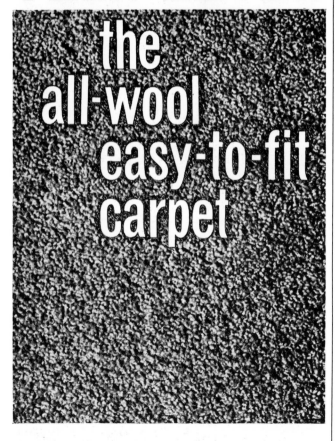
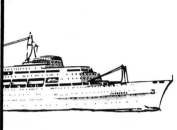
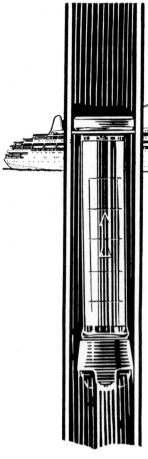

Fanfare by David Mellor

Chosen from the Fanfare range
for S.S. 'Canberra', this
magnificent new coffee service is in
silver-plate. Perfect spouts give superb
pouring and beautifully positioned black
nylon handles and knobs give absolutely cool
grip. A service to last a lifetime at least

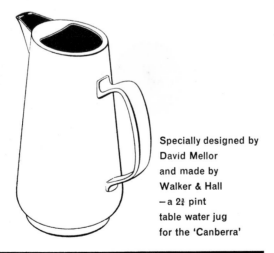

Specially designed by
David Mellor
and made by
Walker & Hall
— a 2¾ pint
table water jug
for the 'Canberra'

Walker and Hall
Sheffield cutlers and silversmiths since 1845

"CANBERRA"

is protected against fire

by the

GRINNELL

Automatic

Sprinkler

and

Fire Alarm

System

MATHER & PLATT LTD.
Park Works, Manchester, 10

A. 132a.

CANBERRA'S CURTAIN RAILS

are

. . . streamlined rails in harmony with modern decor. White Nylon Gliders slide noiselessly in anodised Aluminium channels which are siliconised for permanent lubrication.

Ocean-going LINERS

fit SILENT GLISS for RESISTANCE TO HUMID-ITY and SALT AIR, SILENT WORKING. Simplicity and clean lines.

AIR LINERS

fit SILENT GLISS for LIGHT WEIGHT SILENT WORKING. Simple lines and near invisibility.

HOSPITALS

fit SILENT GLISS for SILENT WORKING. HY-GIENIC—NO DUST TRAPS. Simplicity and strength with light-weight.

LEADING ARCHITECTS

have specified SILENT GLISS for many major or new buildings for MODERN STREAMLINED APPEAR-ANCE. SILENT WORKING Reasonable Cost.

For every curtain, from casement window to stage . . . for HAND-DRAWN and CORD-DRAWN operation . . . specify SILENT GLISS!

SILENT GLISS LTD. 29-30 WINDMILL STREET
(off Tottenham Ct. Rd.) LONDON W.I.
PHONE: MUSEUM 9484 (3 Lines)

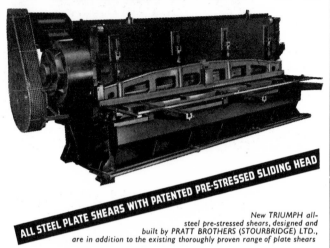

DOCTOR TAKEN OUT TO DUTCH TANKER

GREAT YARMOUTH & GORLESTON, NORFOLK. At 10.58 on the morning of the 24th March, 1960, Lloyd's agent at Great Yarmouth informed the honorary secretary that there was a sick man aboard the Dutch tanker Mare Novum, which was proceeding towards Yarmouth Roads. The master had asked for a life-boat to meet him with a doctor. The life-boat Louise Stephens, with a doctor on board, was launched at low water at 1.2. There was a fresh easterly wind with a heavy swell. The doctor boarded the tanker and found the patient lying in the engine room with severe internal injuries. He decided the man was in too bad a state to be landed by life-boat. The tanker entered the harbour, where the patient was taken by ambulance to hospital. The life-boat reached her station at 1.31.

This is another true story of the Life-Boat Service— typical of the work that is going on day and night, year in, year out.

An English Coxswain

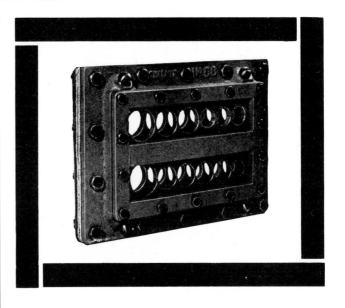

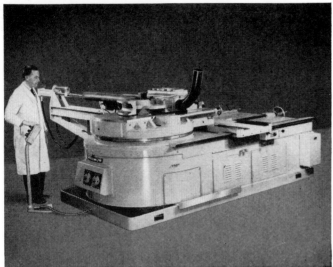
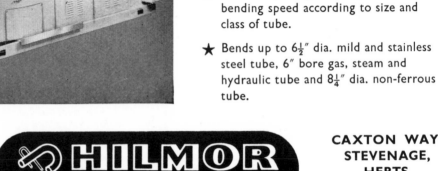
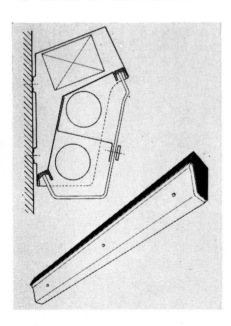

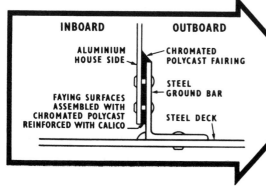

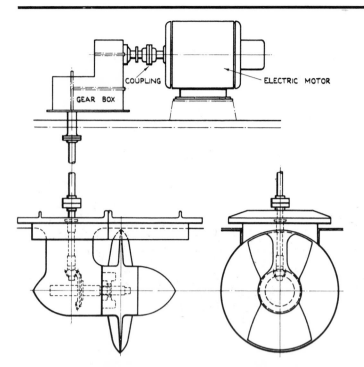

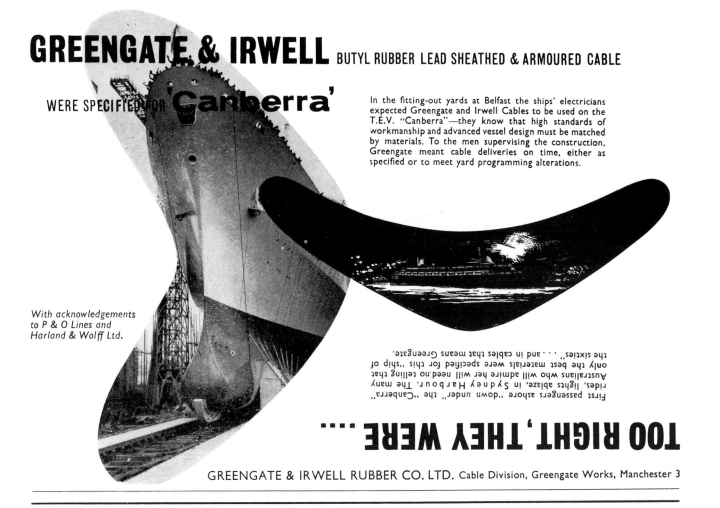

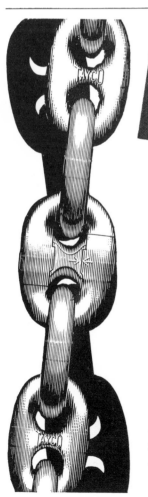
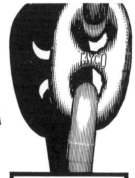

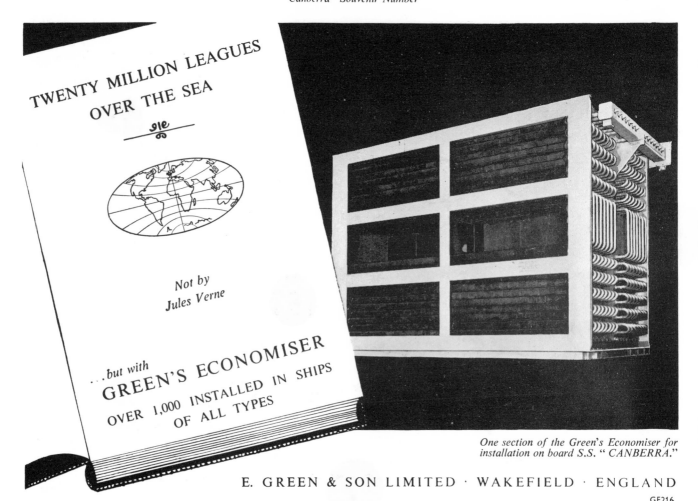
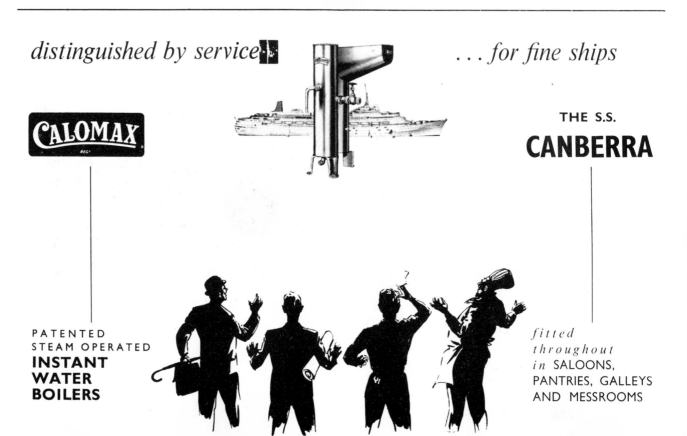

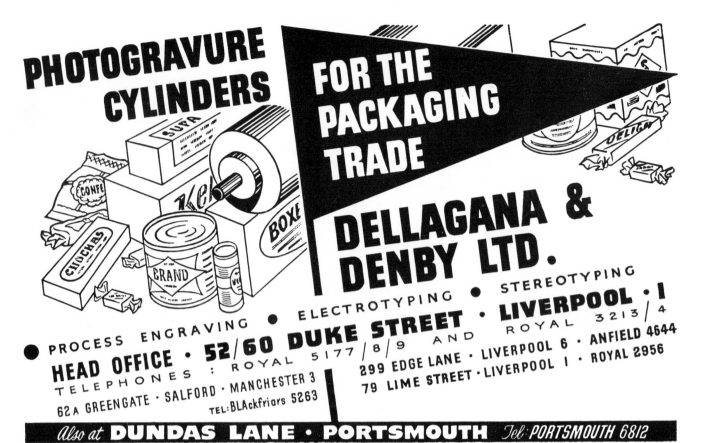

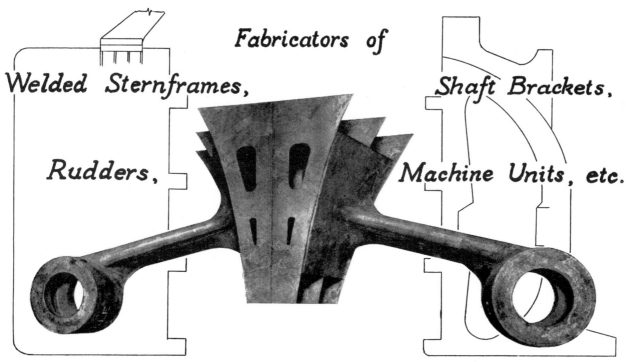

Fabricators of

Welded Sternframes,

Shaft Brackets,

Rudders,

Machine Units, etc.

Colville Constructional Co. Ltd.
GLENGARNOCK, AYRSHIRE.

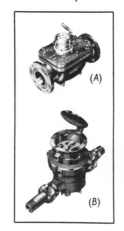

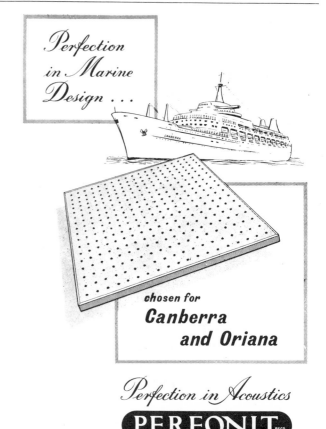

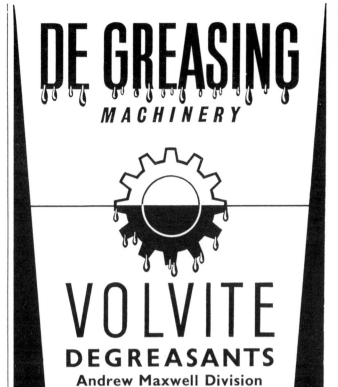

Q

INDEX TO ADVERTISERS

Published by the Shipbuilder Press, Ltd., at 39, Victoria Street, Westminster, London, S.W.1, and Townsville House, Newcastle upon Tyne, 6.
Made and Printed in England by Thomas Reed and Company Limited, Sunderland and London.
Registered for transmission by Canadian Magazine Post.

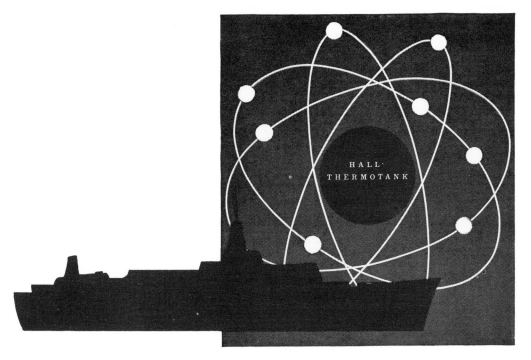

THE HALL-THERMOTANK organisation provides a comprehensive range of highly specialised services. These include air conditioning systems, refrigeration plant, lifts and escalators, ventilating fans and equipment, lighting installations, acoustic research and sound control, modern plastics products.

Structure of a Comprehensive Service

Nine specialist companies make up the complete structure of the Hall-Thermotank Group. They are ready to serve, together or individually.

J. and E. Hall Limited; **Thermotank Limited**; **Vent-Axia Limited**; **Axia Fans Limited**; **Lumenated Ceilings Limited**; **Sound Control Limited**; **Arnoplast Limited**; **Thermotank Plastic Engineering Ltd**; **Acoustical Investigation and Research Organisation Ltd.**

FOR THE P & O LINER 'CANBERRA'—
the world's most modern passenger vessel

The following contracts have been carried out by Hall-Thermotank companies.

- Refrigerating machinery (installed horse power 3,260 B.H.P.) and 17 lifts—**J. and E. HALL LTD.**
- Air conditioning system (22,000,000 B.t.u's)—**THERMOTANK LTD.**
- Fans for provision rooms, cargo holds and general services—**AXIA FANS LTD.**
- Sound-reducing doors and bulkheads—**SOUND CONTROL LTD.**

REFRIGERATION, AIR CONDITIONING, VENTILATION, LIFTS, LUMENATED CEILINGS, ACOUSTIC CONTROL, REINFORCED PLASTICS

HALL-THERMOTANK Limited, Regina House, 1-5 Queen St. London EC4

T30

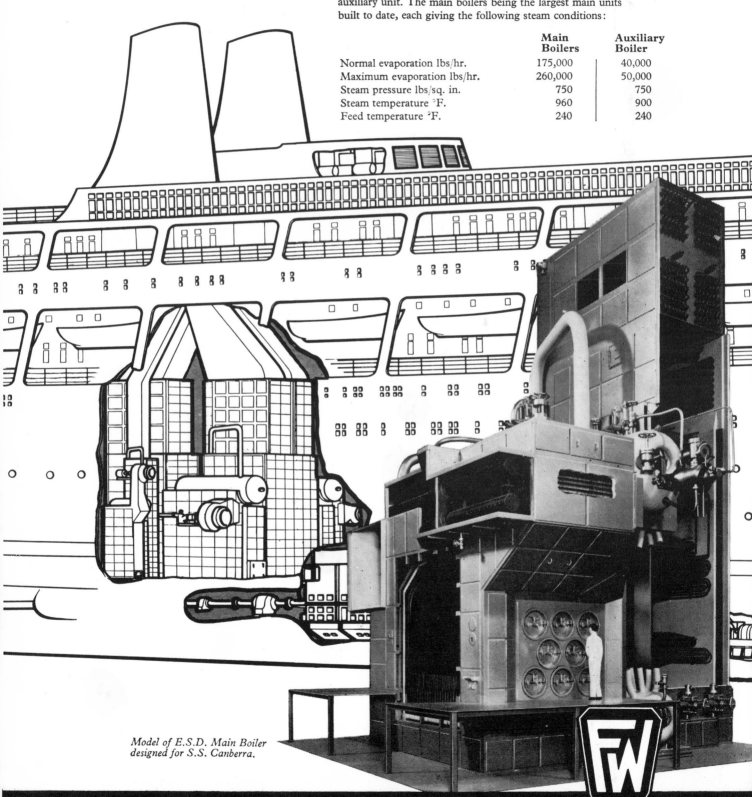